WORK AND MENTAL ILLNESS
Eight Case Studies

The Mental Patient Comes Home
by Howard E. Freeman and Ozzie G. Simmons

WORK AND MENTAL ILLNESS

Eight Case Studies

OZZIE G. SIMMONS
UNIVERSITY OF COLORADO

With the Collaboration of
HELEN MacGILL HUGHES

John Wiley & Sons, Inc. New York   London   Sydney

To Charlotte, Gregor, Lauren, and Paula

FOREWORD

Modern concepts of care of the mentally ill owe much to social science research. The application of knowledge derived from studies of small group reactions, family interaction, and hospital milieu has resulted in major reformulations of ideas about the functions of mental hospitals and methods of administration. It has been shown that the organization of all levels of personnel into a ward team has important therapeutic or antitherapeutic effects upon patients; that is, the system of interrelationships among his professional caretakers (doctors, nurses, aides, occupational therapists, etc.) has a profound influence upon the patient's disturbance—in no instance is the ward milieu neutral.

Interpretation of data varies; some scientists prefer to consider mental illness as a social maladaptation rather than an illness. Viewing patients from both orientations has been fruitful—it seems unnecessary (and may be quite limiting) to "choose" either approach to the exclusion of the other. Destructive behavior (i.e., damaging to the individual and/or society) stemming from a rejecting mother or deviant family pattern may be constructively seen as a form of social maladaptation. Nonetheless it is also useful to take into account the unique reactions of each individual to existing social pressures, since such reactions are influenced by his genetically "given" capacities to adapt to stressful situations, his mental (conscious and unconscious) equipment, and his particular life experiences throughout the phases of his development, all of which determine to a great extent what events he will interpret as stressful, as manageable, or as desirable among the varieties of human experience.

Many subjects of social science investigation have been rather global, as have interpretations of the data. The study of a hospital, a ward, or even of the total behavior of a "schizophrenic" (including his family, his friends, and his work) is quite complex. So many variables exist that exact duplication of the study becomes improbable, if not impossible. An analogous situation would occur if a chemist analyzed "dirt" with some expectation of exactly repeating the findings of a colleague working on "dirt" in another country.

This study by Ozzie G. Simmons attempts with considerable success to focus on that significant aspect of human behavior called *work*. The aim is "to reveal how patients live and act in the world of work, a world that may or may not be a part of their illness." (Chapter 10, pp. 231–232). This choice of subject is important for a number of reasons. As the term is used by the author, work is a reasonably specific sphere of activity, and thus the same activity can be studied by others with substantial assurance that they are studying the same thing in their attempts to verify or add to the author's concepts.

The detailed study of these eight cases, each illustrative of a pattern of employment and the effect (or lack of it) of mental illness on that pattern, provides information not previously available. The persistence of patterns of work during and after major mental illness suggests a restudy of our methods of vocational rehabilitation. It seems unlikely that a Victor Norton (Chapter 2) and an Albert Rossini (Chapter 9) will be helped by the same program; perhaps we must individualize our approach to rehabilitation as much according to differences in work pattern as we do with regard to differences in the type and severity of the mental illness.

Difficulty in obtaining and holding a job is one of the major bottlenecks in rehabilitating our mental patients, and this fact strongly suggests that we must consider many aspects of the patient in addition to the mental illness itself. In fact the mental illness may prove to be one of the least relevant factors in the patient's employability.

This book raises some important questions and provides some basic data from which further studies may proceed. Hopefully it will inspire more studies of specific and significant aspects of human behavior, so that our global interpretations can be based on increasing amounts of hard data.

Jack R. Ewalt, M.D.

Bullard Professor of Psychiatry Harvard Medical School
and
Superintendent, Massachusetts Mental Health Center

ACKNOWLEDGMENTS

The Community Health Project, of which the research reported in this book is a part, was initiated in 1953. It has been entirely supported by special and regular grants from the National Institute of Mental Health, mainly by grants M-1627, 3M-9167, and MH-9182. The Project, under my direction, was sponsored until 1962 by the Social Science Program at the Harvard School of Public Health. Benjamin D. Paul, then director of the Program, facilitated the conduct of the research. When I moved to the University of Colorado in 1961, it was convenient to transfer the Project to the Florence Heller Graduate School for Advanced Studies in Social Welfare, Brandeis University, where I hold a visiting appointment.

I am particularly grateful to Richard H. Williams of the National Institute of Mental Health, whose advice, interest, and personal support, all along, have been most helpful. The longitudinal case study program was directed by Katherine Spencer from its inception until 1956; Mark Zborowski was study director from 1956 to 1957. The field data on which these case studies are based were collected by Leota L. Janke, Edward Kohn, Dorothy M. Mathews, Herbert Naboisek, and Suzanne Vogel. I am most grateful to them and to the study directors for making this book possible. Stanley H. Cath and James A. Davis participated in an early phase of the study and Howard E. Freeman also participated for a time. From 1957 to 1959, Dorothy M. Mathews carried much of the responsibility for coordination of the field work and later contributed substantially to the processing of the data and to the development of a focus in analysis of the cases.

Portions of the manuscript were read by Robert C. Hanson, Richard Jessor, Lyle Saunders, and Richard H. Williams. The entire manuscript was read by Howard E. Freeman, who made many valuable suggestions and was extremely helpful in other ways. I owe a special debt of gratitude to Helen MacGill Hughes for her creative collaboration in the writing of this book. Her editorial and sociological acumen were of inestimable value. Special thanks are due to Jo Anne Withington for secretarial assistance in typing all drafts of the manuscript.

Jack R. Ewalt, former Commissioner of Mental Health for the State of Massachusetts, and Walter E. Barton and Harry C. Solomon, who were then superintendents of the two hospitals that collaborated in this research, generously helped and cooperated.

Ozzie G. Simmons

Boulder, Colorado
January 1965

CONTENTS

PART 1 INTRODUCTION

1 THE EFFECTS OF MENTAL
ILLNESS AND HOSPITALIZATION
ON OCCUPATIONAL CAREER

Most of the noteworthy research on the posthospital experience of mental patients depends on surveys for data. The best studies have yielded important and valid generalizations about relationships between sociocultural characteristics and posthospital performance, but the descriptions they provide of posthospital experience, of necessity broadly quantitative, are cross-sectional and not developmental pictures of events and outcomes.[1] In this they parallel the "treatment" of mental patients by hospital psychiatrists and other mental health practitioners who, if they reach the patient at all, usually gain little more than glimpses of his situation at a particular point in time.

In the presentation of a small number of individual case studies there can be no question of obtaining the sort of representativeness that is possible in surveys of large cohorts or samples; indeed, the cases analyzed here were selected for their variety rather than their typicality. They illustrate a number of ways in which the occupational careers of single and married males have withstood or succumbed to their mental illness and hospitalization. Moreover, these cases in all likelihood do not exhaust even the major variations in stability or change in the working life, under the stress of mental illness and hospitalization. But in such longitudinal case materials questions of a kind ruled out by the limitations of survey data can be posed. The answers may yield insight both fruitful and suggestive in understanding the processes and outcomes of posthospital occupational performance and in the planning

3

of further systematic research and of programs for psychiatric rehabilitation.

The proposition that the selection of an occupation and his performance in it are a crucial dimension of the male patient's world needs no elaborate justification here. A premise common in the sociological literature is that work is the purposeful activity most consistently expected of adult males in our society, and that a man's occupation exerts a compelling influence on his interpersonal and social behavior, both on and off the job: ". . . the job in our society exerts an influence which pervades the whole of the human life-span." [2] As Weiss and Riesman have pointed out, work is of central concern in our American society; a man's situation is described by his relationship to the single activity of work, whether he continues to work or has removed himself from it, and the great majority of American men look to work as the area within which to validate themselves.[3] The cultural evaluation of work in our society is reflected in the definitions in the medical dictionaries of rehabilitation, physical and psychiatric, which place the principal emphasis on occupational restoration.[4]

The interviews for these cases were collected at the end of the patient's hospital stay and during the posthospital period, so that they are in part retrospective and in part contemporaneous. They cover the prehospital, hospital, and posthospital periods, and thus tell something about the temporal pattern of a crucial aspect of the patient's life and the circumstances under which it took shape. The practitioner focuses on the patient's psychopathology, and ordinarily views his occupational history, if it is disjointed or in any way adverse, as in large part a function of his illness. But the patterning of any occupational career is subject to many vicissitudes quite apart from mental illness, as the literature on the sociology of work repeatedly proves. Also the case materials permit the view, in the first instance at least, that the development of the patient's work career can be understood in the same way as that of any other member of society. It may be profitable to distinguish two components of the career: the part that can be understood without positing cultural or psychological deviance, and the part that cannot. The tactics here then in considering the pattern of an occupational career will be to assume the individual's normality, and then to identify the ways in which the career is broken into by his illness and hospitalization.

The focal point in these individual case studies is always the former patient as a social being and, more particularly, those aspects and events of his social life, including his illness and hospitalization, that are directly relevant to the patterning of his occupational career. Although the main concern is the personal aspects of career, that is, the relevant behavior, attitudes, and changes that pertain to the patient himself, in the analysis of them the social system in which he lives, namely his family and community, are taken into account. Similarly, selected aspects of the patient's hospital experience and his encounters with hospital personnel must be considered in estimating the effect of illness and hospitalization on the maintenance of his occupational career. But this study is focused on the patient and his career. The family, the community, and the hospital will be considered only as potential sources of contingencies, both in his past and present, which can be shown to have a bearing upon his career.

In regard to the posthospital outcome, the etiological relationship between occupational career and rehospitalization will be only incidentally considered. Of the sixteen males in the original group from which the cases in this volume were drawn, all but one were hospitalized several times, although many worked continuously during their stays in the community; nine were hospitalized both prior and subsequent to the hospitalization during which they entered the study, four subsequently, and two were hospitalized prior to it. (See the Appendix for a description of the study group.)

An entry into the labor market and the establishment of a career is highly problematic even for large numbers of young people who may never become mentally ill; it depends substantially on the job opportunities available and on the appropriate occupational assets and orientation.[5] These, in part, depend on how the individual was socialized by his family, peers, and teachers and what he has internalized in the process. Some correspondence, therefore, can be assumed between what the patient has to offer the world of work and the part played by his relatives and other socializing agents in providing the necessary support and interest, both in the past and in the present. Members of his family, whether parents or spouses, thus constitute potential contingencies in the patient's occupational career. The influence of illness and hospitalization on the pattern of his career will depend on, in the first instance, how the patient has come to terms with the occupational world; *if* he has. But the state of the labor market at the time of entry or re-entry, the attitudes and behavior of his significant others, the severity of his illness, and his hospital experience may adversely affect his career, although he may, in fact, before his illness have possessed the personal characteristics necessary for initiating and establishing adequacy at work.

Although these cases are selected for their variety, they each tell something about the interrelations between career pattern and illness and hospitalization that is common to all. To identify such common factors amid the individual variations, it is necessary to view them from some common conceptual perspective. Consistent with the notion that the experiences of former mental patients can be studied on the basis of the assumptions ordinarily applied in the study of normal populations, the concepts developed by students of the sociology of work will be drawn on, rather than those of psychiatry and social psychiatry, focusing, as they do, on the individual and his pathology. It is hoped that ultimately the sociological approach can be integrated with those of psychology and psychiatry.

A CONCEPTUAL OUTLINE

The occupational career can be defined as the sequence of movements into and out of jobs, including both the vertical and the horizontal; the related behavior, namely, job-seeking, working, and job-relinquishing; and the attempts to facilitate the movements, such as training, education, and on-the-job acquisition of skills. Crucially related are the occupational assets and the orientation to his career which the individual brings to the world of work.

For the purposes of this study, the career pattern will be described in three main stages. The first, the prehospital stage, begins either with preparation for the career or actual entry into the market for jobs and terminates with the study hospitalization. The second, the inpatient stage, begins with the study hospitalization and ends with the patient's release to the community. The third, the posthospital stage, begins when the second ends and terminates with the close of the individual case study, that is, when information about posthospital experience was no longer forthcoming.

Employability and Career Pattern

The concept of employability, as used in this study, refers to the individual's ability to maintain, posthospital, the direction of his career and the pattern characteristic of it prior to his illness and hospitalization, that is, if that pattern represented successful performance. Employability also implies resilience and flexibility and refers to the ability to effect change so as to insure the persistence of the career when it is threatened. For changes in the career pattern which enable the individual to surmount the strain of illness and hospitalization on his ability at work will result not in reduction but in renewal and reinforcement, even if it be at a cost of modifying distinctive characteristics of the original pattern.

This concept of employability is, of course, frankly evaluative. Maintaining employability calls for realistic perception of one's own assets and liabilities, capacity to overcome failure and to perform under stress, some modicum of interpersonal competence, autonomy, independence, ability to make stable decisions and to implement them effectively—in short, the possession of the whole range of attributes and properties which are identified with mental health and, conversely, whose absence are identified with mental illness.[6] The assessment of the former patient's employability will require judgments based on these values as their reference points, and they will be the criteria of successful occupational adjustment.

Components of the Occupational Career

The central component of an occupational career pattern is, of course, the job itself. To hold a job means to be engaged in gainful employment, whether full or part time, and to be remunerated by salary or wages. Behavior at work may be described with regard to its continuity, stability, and the quality of performance: whether the individual has worked continuously since he entered the labor market and how to account for periods when he was available but did not work; the extent to which he attempts to stabilize job situations in which he appears to have an investment; and whether he is adequate in performance on the job, an obvious essential if continuity and stability are to be maintained.

A second component of the career pattern is job-seeking, which includes the individual's way of looking for employment, if he seeks a job because of pressure exerted by others, and if he begins to hunt immediately upon becoming employable, whether this is after absence from the job market or when he has terminated a previous job. His means of obtaining jobs are also relevant, whether through his own efforts or those of friends or relatives or an employment or social service agency. Normally characteristic is the finding of jobs through one's own efforts or those of friends or relatives; only a minority ever obtain work through more formal means.[7]

A third component is occupational mobility, the process by which individuals move from one position to another in the occupational hierarchy. It may be vertical, as assessed by specific hierarchical values, or horizontal, that is, from one position to another on the same level.[8] As Gross has pointed out, mobility in any given case depends on the definition, that is, on the number of occupational categories and the subtlety of the distinctions between them; the more detailed the occupational breakdown, the greater the mobility.[9] In this study, the concern is with both vertical and horizontal mobility. Vertical mobility occurs when there are raises and promotions within one job, or when the individual changes from one job or occupation to another which is either higher or lower in the occupational hierarchy than his previous job. Horizontal mobility refers simply to job-changing where no gain or loss in status in the occupational hierarchy is involved. For the purposes of this study, the position held by the individual when he entered the labor market is compared with the position held at the time of case termination; in addition, comparisons are made of his situation at various time points within this period. The amount of movement and variation in position that occurs during the individual's career will be assessed in accordance with the distinctions made above.

A tremendous amount of job-changing is characteristic of American workers.[10] Miller and Form reveal two important unstable work patterns: the initial work period, meaning jobs held before the completion of formal education, and the trial period, which refers to jobs held less than three years, which of course may turn up many times in the life of a worker.[11] A high rate of horizontal mobility is particularly characteristic of this period among unskilled and semiskilled workers, who as Caplow says, find it almost impossible to acquire a vested interest in remaining where they are and for substantial reasons are predisposed to change jobs on the slightest provocation or none at all.[12]

In the light of these considerations, it is interesting to note that some students of former mental patients take the position that frequent changing of jobs indicates emotional instability.[13] But the use of the number of jobs as an index of successful or unsuccessful work adjustment can be very misleading, since job-changing may in fact attest to the individual's exploration and testing in the occupational world to find for himself the best fit among the opportunities the world of work has to offer.[14] In any case, it seems clear that frequent job-changing is common among the unskilled and semiskilled, whether or not the individual is afflicted with mental illness. Perhaps the most useful procedure to follow in assessing the meaning of occupational mobility in a given case is to look at the *sequence* of jobs rather than at each job and at each change in itself (as well as the reasons for change, of course, if these are known), a procedure which should reveal whether or not the pattern indicates discontinuity and instability or attempts at continuity and stability.

Qualifications for the Labor Market

It is evident that an individual seeking to enter the labor market, whether a former mental patient or not, will have a wide range of opportunities in periods when employment levels are high, while under adverse conditions standards for employment are more stringent and he must face strenuous competition for jobs. Moreover, high employment facilitates casting about for the most attractive job and, particularly to the advantage of the former patient, reduces the attention paid to past history, especially at the unskilled and semiskilled levels.[15]

A second contingency is that of financial need: the individual may be forced to take any job he can find, regardless of his orientation and preferences, because of a financial crisis, his own or his family's, that can only be alleviated by his earnings. A third contingency is the alternatives to regular employment in the labor market, such as military service, further schooling or vocational training, or various substitutes for jobs, that is, marginal work provided by friends or relatives. The social and economic position of the individual's family determines the circumstances under which he enters the labor market for the first time: whether he enters the labor market earlier or later, why he left school when he did, and how he chooses his first job.[16]

The assets and liabilities the individual has to offer the labor market are considerably important. First there are his marketable job qualifications—such as skills, training, and/or experience.[17] Then his work habits: are they appropriate to acceptable job performance, such as punctuality, regular attendance, and the meeting of standards of productivity? His education is in itself considerably important both intrinsically and symbolically; as many studies show, there is a substantial relationship between educational and vocational achievement.[18] Thus Weiss and Riesman maintain that "the point at which a boy leaves the educational escalator is crucial in determining his future occupational opportunities." [19] Moreover, the experience gained in the school system is a primary source of motivation and orientation to goals in the world of work, since the school system is a microcosm of the occupational world.[20] Even for individuals of lower income who do not contemplate careers involving a long period of formal preparation there are still decisions about type and extent of secondary schooling and the objectives to be accomplished through work by leaving school.[21]

These occupational assets are only part of what is needed, however, to facilitate entry into the labor market in the most optimal way. To make the most of his potentialities, the individual should be able to select the appropriate channels of job-seeking or have access to persons or resources in the community that can either obtain a job for him or facilitate opportunities for jobs; to maximize his own assets and minimize his liabilities; and to evaluate the conditions and rewards attached to various kinds of work. Only those who have had some exposure to the world of work or who have been fortunate enough to learn about it from relatives or friends can acquire the information necessary for making the best choices. Apparently what is most common, however, is for the crucial decisions to be made on very vague and tenuous knowledge.[22]

Career Orientation

Career orientation is defined here as the perspective from which the individual sees his occupational career—his choices and preferences, his rewards and satisfaction, his values, and commitment to work as a means of attaining them. The career orientation is coterminous with one's self-concept as a worker; it is the perspective from which one interprets the meaning of his occupational attributes, behavior, decisions, and the events (including the actions of others) which he perceives as relevant.[23] Career orientation may be focused on the present, on maintaining the existing state of affairs; or on the future, on changing the existing state of affairs. In the first case, the individual may view his present situation as the best he can attain to, either because he believes that he has satisfied his desires or that he is permanently blocked from a higher level; in the second case, he may see his present situation as a stepping stone and set higher goals for the future. In both instances, the orientation has direction, either to perpetuation of the present into the future or to a move upward. But there is still another type, the nondirectional, where no levels are set for either present or future, because the orientation is diffuse or there is none at all.

The present interest is primarily in the former patient's public world rather than in his private world when considering the attitudinal and motivational components of his career orientation. Interpretation and inference are kept as close as possible to his actual performance in the world of work. In moving from behavior to orientation to a career, the focus is the former patient *as he presents himself to the world*. It does not matter essentially what the patient may feel privately; what does matter is what he *says* he feels and what he *does* about it. Nevertheless, the aspects of career orientation to be considered here include not only those relatively apparent to the patient's associates and readily communicated to them by him but also those which require considerable inference. When considering occupational choice, job satisfaction, and desired rewards, it is relatively safe to take what the patient says at face value. But the other aspects, namely, personal values and commitment to work, call for a good deal of inference on the part of the investigator. To begin with, these data can seldom be documented with the kind of information available, and even when such information is at hand, one cannot know whether the patient would have given it freely to anyone as part of his public presentation of self, or whether it was elicited or probed for by the interviewer, and would otherwise have remained part of the patient's private world.

Thus the information at hand about the former patients' private thoughts on the world of work will be brought in only as it facilitates interpretations of their *performance* in the world of work. Concepts such as personal values and commitment to work are included in the formulation in order to sensitize the reader to the case materials and provide useful guidelines for their analyses—but no more. Commitment and perhaps the type of commitment may be discussed in the case of those who work, and lack of commitment in the case of those who do not work when opportunities for work are available or potentially so, but it is very difficult to attempt to distinguish *degrees* of commitment.

An indication of the complexity of the problem of occupational choice is the three major categories and eight subcategories in the theory formulated by Ginzberg and his associates.[24] Sociologists are still a long way from an adequate theory of occupational choice, but they have made many attempts at conceptualization.[25] To summarize the work of Ginzberg and his associates: occupational choice is a developmental process involving a series of decisions made over a period of from seven to ten years or more. It is largely irreversible since the later decisions are limited by the previous ones, and in any case it ends in a compromise since it ultimately compels renunciation of some preferences, expectations, and satisfaction in the reaching of a stable decision.

Occupational choice is made by the making, changing, and reconciling of decisions, and it must be examined in the context of the alternatives open to the individual and his knowledge of them, and access to them.[26] But as noted earlier, the knowledge to inform realistic choices is meager among young people, particularly among sons of the working class, many of whom can choose their work only haphazardly, with no calculation and little thought of alternatives.[27] A vast amount of floundering and chance plays a prominent part in choices.[28]

Unfavorable economic circumstances, lack of education, absence of personal "contacts," lack of planning, and failure to explore fully the available job opportunities which characterize the working-class family are handed down from generation to generation.[29]

Kahl's study of "common man" boys showed that the majority have very modest educational and occupational aspirations; the few oriented to "getting ahead" were those whose fathers stimulated and pushed them.[30] And, as reported by Gross, 40 per cent of all working-class boys (N = 118) on graduating from high school had no occupational choice, but they said they merely intended to look for a job, without specifying any particular kind; another 20 per cent intended to learn a skilled trade, to apply for some manual job which did not require any training, or to enlist in the armed services.[31] With their low level of training and orientation, working-class boys are in most cases forced to take what they can get.

Ginzberg and his associates, discussing occupational choice, advance the hypothesis that the true and pseudocrystallized groups must be treated as substantially different behavioral entities, but that even "true" crystallized choices are not always final and may be reconsidered.[32] Actually, the process of crystallization, that is, the synthesis of many forces and considerations which produces a specific commitment to an occupational choice with full emotional acceptance, is always susceptible to unanticipated pressures and circumstances which may reopen the whole issue. Nevertheless, relatively speaking, crystallization of choice is a substantial occupational commitment, characterized by a resolute, unswerving attitude; pseudocrystallization is a decision characterized by unawareness of the elements involved in the choice and by incomplete acceptance. In the nature of the case, Ginzberg and his associates find it difficult to say when crystallization is likely to occur but state it is usually between the ages of 19 and 21, but may be earlier or much later.

A sociological focus will be maintained in this study, but the bearing of personality on occupational choice cannot be ignored. Unfortunately, no useful data on personality were collected in the present study. Actually Ginzberg and his associates took personality into account and concluded that although no psychological theory can adequately explain the process of occupational choice, emotional factors are inherent in it. Since relatively little is known about this fundamental relation, they strongly recommend further research.[33] Although there has been some good psychological research in this area, much of the pertinent literature is based on Freudian and neo-Freudian notions and not only is it oriented to intrapsychic mechanisms but also it essentially ignores the social and cultural. Thus "oral" personalities select verbal occupations such as law and teaching; "anal" personalities are primarily interested in acquisition and so select business; and so on.[34]

In any case, it is clear that the dilemma of occupational choice confronts the individual precisely at the time in his life when he must also engage in other intellectual and emotional conflicts. The adolescent is beset by problems of sexual identification, of gratifying immediate needs, of achieving emotional independence from parents, and so on. In short, in the adolescent period, say, from the age of 14 to 19, when the individual must make a number of decisions relevant to occupational choice which are decisive, in all likelihood, throughout his entire life, his knowledge of himself and of the facts of life are hardly adequate, unfortunately, to the task. Some of the most sensitive observations on these issues are made by the psychoanalyst, Erik H.

Erikson, who carefully explores the process of the formation of identity as one which neither begins nor ends with adolescence but continues lifelong, largely unrealized by the individual and his society.[35] Erikson weaves psychological and sociocultural variables together in an enlightening way in analyzing problems of the crises and diffusion of identity which become manifest at the very time when young persons are exposed to a variety of experiences demanding simultaneous but usually incompatible decisions.[36]

Given the emotional turbulence commonly believed usual in the adolescent period, it follows that the distinction between "normal" and "abnormal" disturbance is likely to be blurred. Ginzberg and his associates assert that it is still a challenge to investigators to establish the presence of "truly pathological elements" in the occupational choice of certain adolescents and that further research is necessary to set up effective criteria of normal and abnormal choice.[37]

The literature cites a long list of rewards that the individual may seek from a job, which are not mutually exclusive. Among them are self-expression (where the job becomes an end in itself), earnings and other material rewards (which the job becomes a means of obtaining), recognition, opportunities for the exercise of competence, for interpersonal gratification, promotion and prestige, and the enjoyment of particular physical settings and working conditions. A recent study discusses the "satisfiers" as those aspects which focus primarily on the job itself, and the conditions surrounding the doing of the job as having little relationship to job satisfaction.[38]

At least for the working class, high wages and security are the essential preoccupations in return for which the worker tolerates the job with quiet (or noisy) desperation.[39] Argyris has observed that the worker is paid for his dissatisfaction while at work and his wages are given to him to gain satisfaction outside of it.[40] In an early study, Bell states:

By what they [a sample of youth] voluntarily choose to say about themselves, it is evident that they don't like their jobs. With the single exception of those working on professional or technical jobs, more than half the youth in every occupational field expressed a preference for some other kind of work. In the semi-skilled group, which incidentally is one of the largest, about one in ten felt that what he was doing was exactly what he wanted.[41]

Among the automobile workers, Guest found that the dominant sat-isfaction in the job was the income and security it brought.[42] Similarly, Friedmann and Havighurst, in their study of work and retirement, found that for 34 per cent of their sample work had no meaning other than that of earning a living.[43]

Nevertheless, many workers find more intangible satisfaction in work, even if only, as Friedmann and Havighurst assert, because the routine stabilizes one's personal life. This is corroborated by a study of a representative sample of American men, 80 per cent of whom, when asked, "If by some chance you inherited enough money to live comfortably without working, do you think you would work anyway or not?" said they would work anyway, although they were not altogether clear as to why.[44] Also it has been dramatically demon-strated that during the depression unemployment per se could be one of the most tragic events for both individual and family.[45] In view of the central place that work occupies in the life of the individual, it must play a strategic part in helping him to establish his identity, and it becomes highly charged as a symbol of meaningful life.

Ginzberg and his associates point to the direct connection between crystallization of occupational choice and job satisfaction: the in-dividual who cannot make a choice does not know what he wants from a job, and thus is not likely to derive any satisfaction from it.[46] Rosenberg and his associates distinguish between workers who empha-size the satisfaction they will get *from* the work itself, the work itself being a goal, and those concerned with the rewards they hope to be given *for* the work they do, to whom work is instrumental.[47]

Given the limits of this study, there can be no concern with the whole spectrum of the individual's personal values but only with the criteria that influence his occupational interests and goals. From the elusive data from which values must be inferred it is difficult to isolate those relevant to occupation from those which are not. Rosenberg and his associates distinguish between (1) "people-oriented" values, (2) "self-expressive" values, and (3) "extrinsic-reward" values.[48] Those who emphasize the first kind view work largely as an opportunity for interpersonal relationships. Those who stress the second, the self-expressive values, regard work as an end in itself, permitting expression to their particular talents and creative potentialities. And, finally, those oriented to extrinsic values seek the rewards obtained *for* work rather than the gratifications obtained *from* it. Thus social workers are people-oriented, artists are self-expressive, and businessmen are oriented to extrinsic values. But the rewards that working-class people expect from their jobs show that their values are, more simply, earning a living, supporting a family, and acquiring whatever they can of the material goods so ubiquitously available in our society.

Finally, commitment to work may become a means of implementing one's values, whether one has reached the point where work is in itself emotionally important or has separated his self from work, engaging in it primarily because it is paid for and is the way of obtaining material rewards. These are the polar extremes of a continuum along which it is likely that individuals vary considerably. The extreme types include those who have some sort of commitment to the world of work. But there are others who presumably do not fit along the continuum at all: some may be alienated from the world of work, or at least may have no commitment to occupational mobility, having selected other alternatives; and, indeed, to them, commitment to a job and advancement in it may seem incompatible with realizing their particular values, which may be familism, health, personal freedom, or just peace of mind.[49] Other individuals (examples of them will be found in the case studies which follow) may fall outside the continuum either because they do not perceive work as a means to achieving their ends, or because they are simply incapable of coping with work's minimal demands.

These four aspects of career orientation—occupational choice, rewards and satisfaction, values, and commitment to work—clearly are mutually dependent. As mentioned earlier, the individual who cannot crystallize his occupational choice may be dissatisfied with his job because he does not know what type of job he wants; or may not perceive his personal values as compatible with the demands of work; or he may be unclear about his values in the first place. Conceivably, an individual may be highly committed to his work for the emotional or material rewards it brings, yet at the same time he may be dissatisfied with the job itself and seek satisfaction elsewhere. On the other hand, some who have a low degree of commitment to work may derive considerable satisfaction merely from having a job as a means of relating and contributing to society and of legitimizing their status in it.[50]

Hospitalization and Career Contingencies

Hospitalization (as well as the illness process itself, of course) is a disruption of and interference with the patient's career. To some former patients, it may bring in its wake new problems relating to the resumption of their careers at a later date. For one thing, although hospitalization in itself may adversely alter the pattern of a career, the mental hospital is not geared to compensate for the unfavorable effects nor is its personnel prepared to direct the hospital experience specifically so as to help with the problem. For example, Sampson and his associates report: "Hospital personnel had very little communication with either parents or relatives, obtained little information on which specific planning could have been based, and tended to operate with limited interest and insight about the social network of the patients." [51] For the most part, it seems hospital personnel has influence as an agent in the patient's career, an agent being one who poses career contingencies to the patient by participating in his life "fatefully." [52] As will be explained in some of the case studies, the point at which hospital personnel may be most likely to enter in is when insisting that the patient find a job as a condition for release, although knowing little or nothing about his particular situation. Olshansky and his associates maintain that readiness for release and for work are not one and the same thing, so that even this minimal attention paid to the patient may be a doubtful blessing.[53]

While separation from the world in consequence of hospitalization can adversely affect the patient's career, it sometimes spells a personal and social moratorium on an intolerable plight and brings him an opportunity to resolve his occupational dilemmas while insulated from the stress of the situation itself—again quite apart from whether the hospital experience offers any appropriate therapeutic intervention. Thus Erikson writes of the hospital as providing an institutionalized moratorium in which the young person can find his way free of the pressures that bind him in family and community.[54] To be sure, Erikson is assuming that the hospital will provide a therapeutic milieu, but, as will be seen in several of the cases that follow, the insulation brought about by the moratorium can be exploited by the patient even if he does not have any specific therapy. Similar observations have been made by others. Goffman observes that the moratorium on family living provided by hospitalization "has no doubt been of great help to some patients"; and Sampson and his associates found that for many married female patients hospitalization provided a protected milieu wherein marital problems could be "reinterpreted, isolated, and forgotten by the patient and her intimates; and critical relationships may be negotiated, modified and resumed under conditions of limited contact and experimental tentativeness." [55]

In any case, the hospital as treatment seems to have little impact on patients: two recent large-scale studies report no significant bearing of any type of therapy received in the hospital on posthospital success or failure in staying in the community or on levels of occupational performance.[56] Even the hospital which provides a work program is unlikely to hold out the normal incentives, such as pay, profit, or prestige, and in fact these may be incompatible with the work program. Indeed, as Goffman observes, the incompatibilities between the attitudes and incentives that prevail in work on the inside and work on the outside may demoralize the work-oriented person.[57] Olshansky and Unterberger comment on the ironic fact that in a culture in which everyone is expected to work, opportunities for hospital inpatients to work are neither common nor well planned.[58] As explanations of the paradox, they point to the historical acceptance of unemployment, the middle-class prejudice against menial work, the psychiatric bias in defining recovery in terms of insight following therapy rather than in the ego-preserving functions of work, and the widespread image of the sick person as disabled and therefore not expected to work during illness and hospitalization.

The Family and Career Contingencies

The attitudes and behavior of members of the patient's family in the world of work are of substantial historical significance to him as the source, presumably, of powerful influences on the course of his own career. But their attitudes and expectations may be also of considerable current significance to the extent that they are communicated to him and that he continues to be responsive to them. Moreover, as Bell and Vogel state:

The family of orientation must have provided the individual with a certain minimum of basic skills before he can enter the labor market . . . [he] must have a certain degree of emotional integration and control sufficient to allow him to operate adequately, and . . . certain basic information about, and attitudes toward, work that are essential to the performance of his tasks in the economy.[59]

It was stated earlier that in considerable measure an individual's job horizon is set for him by his family. There is also, of course, the influence of peers and school but, as Kahl concluded, the parental influence is pre-eminent, and "the boys learned to an extraordinary degree to view the occupational system from their parents' perspective. They took over their parents' view of the opportunities available, the desirability and possibility of change of status, the techniques to be used if change was desired, and the appropriate goals for boys who performed as they did in school." [60]

Role models for occupational orientation are provided by parents and older siblings. The individual may have followed the orientation of an older sibling and rejected that of his father; or *vice-versa*. Moreover, according to Ginzberg and his associates, he acts selectively and seldom, if ever, adopts all the values of his chosen model.[61] It may not, however, be so much a matter of internalizing the aspirations of fathers or brothers as of responding to their actual occupational positions. This is the conclusion of a study which showed manual workers as tending to use male members of their families and peer groups as social reference points in evaluating their own situation. If these significant others occupy positions higher than his in the occupational hierarchy, the worker feels less satisfied with his own, but if they are at the same or lower levels, he feels relatively more content.[62]

In addition to providing its members with role models, basic motivation, and basic skills, the family performs a "maintenance" or regulatory function for them in adulthood.[63] Bell and Vogel state that "Even the most mature adult personalities require some support and recognition if they are to preserve the proper orientations to work and maintain the appropriate flow of motivational energy." [64] There is, indeed, evidence that the posthospital performance of mental patients conforms to the demands and expectations of their families. Thus male patients who have the best work histories after release from the hospital are those whose relatives report that they not only expect the patient to go to work within three months after release, but also would insist on his living up to their expectations.[65]

The single male, a son living in the household of his parents, may be under relatively less pressure than a married male, particularly if there are other breadwinners in the household.[66] Nevertheless, in the case of lower-income families, economic resources may be so limited that even parental family members will intervene if the patient shows signs of faltering or of quitting his job; and this would be even more true of wives. In the American nuclear family, the primary responsibility for economic support rests on the husband-father, and his occupational role is thus considered crucial. Moreover, the family's status in the community is determined more by the job the head of it holds and by the income he earns than by any other single circumstance.[67] Any disruption then of the husband's career is likely to dispose the wife to intensify her demands on him, or to intervene actively in attempting to have him resume work, or even to take over the breadwinner role herself. Any of these courses is likely to influence the pattern of the husband's occupational career, and when it is broken into by mental illness and hospitalization, a variety of dilemmas and problems of managing may ensue; presumably much will depend on the relatives' attitudes toward the source of the disruption. This issue will be considered again in the next section.

MENTAL ILLNESS, HOSPITALIZATION, AND CAREER PATTERN

Of the eight case studies that follow, four are about single males, and each constitutes a distinctive variant of the patterning of occupational career as affected by illness and hospitalization. With the focus on persistence and change in career pattern from pre- to posthospital life, the four cases have been labeled "before" and "after" as follows: "Worker to Worker"; "Nonworker to Nonworker"; "Worker to Nonworker"; and "Student to Worker." Among the married males in the original study group there are no cases of nonworkers; all worked before illness and hospitalization. The variations in these patterns of career, however, are distinctive enough one from another to warrant presentation. Two, labeled "Worker to Worker," have been included because one illustrates basic consistency of career pattern from the pre- to posthospital period, while the other suffered vicissitudes before returning to the essential pattern of his prehospital career. The other two cases of married males illustrate significant changes, posthospital, and both have been labeled "Worker to Marginal Worker." There were no cases in the study group, among either single or married men, that exemplified a pattern of nonworker to worker.

An essential element in the situation is the individual's resistance to the stress of illness and hospitalization. Resistance might be manifested by the persistence, posthospital, of his prehospital career when the latter is adequate, or by change, if necessary, such as will maintain his adequacy. If the former patient can continue to be a worker, it does not necessarily mean that he has emerged unscarred or untouched, but that he has been able to overcome the threat of his affliction and resume, or assume, the expected level of performance. The patient who, after hospitalization, continues to be a worker, or the student who becomes a worker, had probably already acquired work experience, occupational assets, and appropriate orientation, and his behavior and orientation may measure up to his family's expectations.

The plight of the nonworker both before and after illness and hospitalization is different: he may possess none of the characteristics essential to initiating and maintaining a productive career and familial expectations may ask no more of him. But where there is discernible posthospital change in the pattern of the patient's career, there must be a particular configuration of conditions and events linked to his illness and hospitalization which call for identification.

In assessing the effects of illness and hospitalization on the pattern of the patient's career, his own and his relatives' conceptions of and attitudes toward mental illness and toward the hospital must first be known, since in all likelihood they influence substantially the reactions of both. In other research, significant relationships were found between attitudes of relatives toward mental illness and the posthospital performance of patients.[68] As found in several studies, the public is quite ignorant as to what mental illness is and consequently is unable to distinguish between mental illness and health as sharply as it can distinguish between physical illness and health.[69] Etiological associations of work with mental illness and ideas as to whether mental illness is curable may conceivably enter into the individual's conception of himself as a worker by modifying his idea of his occupational assets and liabilities and his evaluation of them; and this may in turn reopen the issues of his choice of career and even affect his decision to re-enter the world of work at all. On the other hand, work may seem to him the principal means of warding off relapse just by keeping him busy and thus freeing his mind of "disturbing thoughts."

Although hospitalization itself will have established the patient's status as one who is "mentally ill," there still will be the question, when he gets out, as to whether he and his relatives will seal off and conceal the experience or continue to accord him the sick role at some points, perhaps, and not at others. Hospitalization may bring feelings of shame and disgrace.[70] Olshansky and his associates found that about three-fourths of their sample of former mental patients did not identify themselves as such when entering the labor market, and they simply accepted concealment as a prudent act. About one-fifth of those employed obtained work despite their disclosure of hospitalization, and others reported that the issue did not even arise, for they either sought work from small employers who did not ask about mental illness or at a level where few if any questions at all are asked about past history.[71]

The effects wrought by mental illness on the pattern of the patient's career must depend in part, of course, on the extent of actual psychic impairment. The illness may be local, affecting only one particular area of life, and it seems reasonable to assume that the disruption will be less serious if it is other than the occupational, and if, too, the stresses of illness are felt elsewhere than in work. Yet studies show that many psychotics can carry on at work even when still ill.[72]

Unlike, say, death, which brings its appropriate and special expectations regarding behavior, there are no standardized conventional reactions to help the family to cope with their feelings and needs, and no prescriptions to guide them in the public roles they must assume as relatives of a former mental patient.[73] And among themselves, a redefinition of roles may have ensued, as the patient's economic responsibilities are taken over by others of the family who may seek to retain them because they wish it, or because they view the patient as incapable of resuming them.

The case studies which follow present a considerable range of variation in the developments of the occupational career which occur after the advent of mental illness and hospitalization.

NOTES

1. For examples, see Howard E. Freeman and Ozzie G. Simmons, *The Mental Patient Comes Home*, New York: John Wiley and Sons, 1963; Shirley Angrist, Simon Dinitz, Mark Lefton, and Benjamin Pasamanick, "Rehospitalization of Former Mental Patients: Social and Psychological Factors," *Archives of General Psychiatry*, 4 (April 1961), 363–370; Simon Dinitz, Shirley Angrist, Mark Lefton, and

Benjamin Pasamanick, "The Posthospital Psychological Functioning of Former Mental Hospital Patients," *Mental Hygiene*, 45 (October 1961), 579–588; Mark Lefton, Shirley Angrist, Simon Dinitz, and Benjamin Pasamanick, "Social Class, Expectations and Performance of Mental Patients," *The American Journal of Sociology*, 68 (July 1962), 79–87; and George W. Brown, "Experiences of Discharged Chronic Schizophrenic Patients in Various Types of Living Group," *The Milbank Memorial Fund Quarterly*, 37 (April 1959), 105–131.

2. Eugene A. Friedmann and Robert J. Havighurst, *The Meaning of Work and Retirement*, Chicago: University of Chicago Press, 1954, 3. See also Nancy C. Morse and Robert S. Weiss, "The Function and Meaning of Work and the Job," *American Sociological Review*, 20 (April 1955), 191–198; Raymond J. Murphy and Richard T. Morris, "Occupational Situs, Subjective Class Identification, and Political Affiliation," *American Sociological Review*, 26 (June 1961), 383–392; and Morris Rosenberg, Edward A. Suchman, and Rose K. Goldsen, *Occupations and Values*, Glencoe, Ill.: The Free Press, 1957.

3. Robert S. Weiss and David Riesman, "Social Problems and Disorganization in the World of Work," in Robert K. Merton and Robert A. Nisbet (editors), *Contemporary Social Problems*, New York: Harcourt, Brace and World, 1961. Also see Paul N. Geisel, "The Meaning of Work and Mental Illness," in Arthur B. Shostak and William Gomberg (editors), *Blue-Collar World: Studies of the American Worker*, Englewood Cliffs, N.J.: Prentice-Hall, 1964, 391–396.

4. Benjamin Simon, "I. General Problems," in Milton Greenblatt and Benjamin Simon (editors), *Rehabilitation of the Mentally Ill*, Washington D.C.: American Association for the Advancement of Science, 1959, 1–2.

5. See Delbert C. Miller and William H. Form, *Industrial Sociology: The Sociology of Work Organizations*, New York: Harper & Brothers, 1964; and Seymour M. Lipset, Reinhard Bendix, and F. Theodore Malm, "Job Plans and Entry into the Labor Market," in Sigmund Nosow and William H. Form (editors), *Man, Work, and Society*, New York: Basic Books, 1962, 297–305.

6. Compare Nelson N. Foote and Leonard S. Cottrell, Jr., *Identity and Interpersonal Competence*, Chicago: University of Chicago Press, 1955; Marie Jahoda, *Current Concepts of Positive Mental Health*, New York: Basic Books, 1958; and M. Brewster Smith, "Research Strategies toward a Conception of Positive Mental Health," *American Psychologist*, 14 (November 1959), 673–681. See also Charlton R. Price and Harry Levinson, "Work and Mental Health," in Arthur B. Shostak and William Gomberg (editors), *op. cit.*, 397–405.

7. Lipset, Bendix, and Malm, *op. cit.*

8. See, for example, the hierarchy developed in Seymour M. Lipset and Reinhard Bendix, *Social Mobility in Industrial Society*, Berkeley: University of California Press, 1959.

9. Edward Gross, *Work and Society*, New York: The Thomas Y. Crowell Co., 1958.

10. *Ibid.*

11. See Miller and Form, *op. cit.*

12. Theodore Caplow, *The Sociology of Work*, Minneapolis: University of Minnesota Press, 1954.

13. See Simon Olshansky, Samuel Grob, and Miriam Ekdahl, "Survey of Employment Experiences of Patients Discharged from Three State Mental Hospitals during Period 1951–1953," *Mental Hygiene*, 44 (October 1960), 510–521.

14. See Marjorie P. Linder and David Landy, "Post-Discharge Experience and Vocational Rehabilitation Needs of Psychiatric Patients," *Mental Hygiene,* **42** (January 1958), 29–44.

15. Simon Olshansky and Hilma Unterberger, "The Meaning of Work and its Implications for the Ex-Mental Hospital Patient," *Mental Hygiene,* **47** (January 1963), 139–149.

16. Lipset, Bendix, and Malm, *op. cit.*

17. In the case of skilled workers, as Moore points out, the notion of a "labor market" may be an abstraction of little meaning for the fates of those working because there is a different market for each occupation or group of closely related and somewhat interchangeable skills. See Wilbert Moore, *Man, Time, and Society,* New York: John Wiley and Sons, 1963.

18. See, for example, Bernard C. Rosen, "The Achievement Syndrome: A Psychocultural Dimension of Social Stratification," *American Sociological Review,* **21** (April 1956), 203–211.

19. Robert S. Weiss and David Riesman, *op. cit.,* 478. See also Moore, *op. cit.*

20. Talcott Parsons, *The Social System,* Glencoe, Ill.: The Free Press, 1951.

21. See Eli Ginzberg, Sol Ginsburg, Sidney Axelrad, and John Herma, *Occupational Choice,* New York: Columbia University Press, 1951.

22. Rosenberg, Suchman, and Goldsen, *op. cit.*

23. Compare Everett C. Hughes, "Institutional Office and the Person," *The American Journal of Sociology,* **43** (November 1937), 404–413.

24. Ginzberg *et al., op. cit.*

25. See Olav Skardal, *Toward a Theory of Occupational Orientation,* Oslo: Agricultural College of Norway, 1963; and Peter M. Blau *et al.,* "Occupational Choice: A Conceptual Framework," in N. J. Smelser and W. T. Smelser (editors), *Personality and Social Systems,* New York: John Wiley and Sons, 1963, 559–570.

26. Rosenberg, Suchman, and Goldsen, *op. cit.*

27. Weiss and Riesman, *op. cit.*

28. Miller and Form, *op. cit.*

29. Lipset, Bendix, and Malm, *op. cit.,* 303–304.

30. Joseph A. Kahl, "Educational and Occupational Aspirations of 'Common Man' Boys," *Harvard Educational Review,* **23** (Summer 1953), 186–203.

31. Gross, *op. cit.*

32. Ginzberg *et al., op. cit.*

33. *Ibid.*

34. Rosenberg, Suchman, and Goldsen, *op. cit.* For good discussions of occupation and personality, see Sol Levine, "Occupation and Personality: Relationship between the Social Factors of the Job and Human Orientation," *Personnel and Guidance Journal* (March 1963), 602–605; and Peter M. Blau *et al., op. cit.*

35. Erik H. Erikson, "Identity and the Life Cycle," *Psychological Issues,* New York: International Universities Press, 1959, Vol. 1, Monograph 1.

36. For an opposing view, see Frederick Elkin and William A. Westley, "The Myth of Adolescent Culture," *American Sociological Review,* **20** (December 1955), 680–684, who maintain that storm and stress is not a distinctive characteristic of the adolescent period.

37. Ginzberg, *et al., op. cit.*

38. Frederick Herzberg, Bernard Mausner, and Barbara Block Snyderman, *The Motivation to Work,* New York: John Wiley and Sons, 1959.

39. Compare Harvey Swados, "The Myth of the Happy Worker," in Maurice Stein, Arthur J. Vidich, and David Manning White (editors), *Identity and Anxiety*, Glencoe, Ill.: The Free Press, 1960, 198–204.

40. Chris Argyris, *Personality and Organization*, New York: Harper & Brothers, 1957.

41. Howard Bell, *Youth Tell their Story*, Washington, D.C.: American Council on Education, 1938, 132.

42. Robert H. Guest, "Work Careers and Aspirations of Automobile Workers," in Herman D. Stein and Richard A. Cloward (editors), *Social Perspectives on Behavior*, Glencoe, Ill.: The Free Press, 1958, 210–220.

43. Friedmann and Havighurst, *op. cit.*

44. Morse and Weiss, *op. cit.*

45. E. Wight Bakke, *Citizens without Work*, New Haven: Yale University Press, 1940.

46. Ginzberg *et al.*, *op. cit.*

47. Rosenberg, Suchman, and Goldsen, *op. cit.*

48. *Ibid.*

49. Compare the findings in Arthur G. Neal and Salomon Rettig, "Dimensions of Alienation among Manual and Non-Manual Workers," *American Sociological Review*, 28 (August 1963), 599–608. Incidentally, as Neal and Rettig point out, commitment to these alternatives to the value of job advancement is socially acceptable and not a form of alienation.

50. See Eugene B. Gallagher, "An Approach to the Study of Occupational Motivation," June 1960, unpublished manuscript.

51. Harold Sampson *et al.*, "The Mental Hospital and Marital Family Ties," *Social Problems*, 9 (Fall 1961), 143.

52. For the concept of career agent, see Erving Goffman, "The Moral Career of the Mental Patient," *Psychiatry*, 22 (May 1959), 123–142.

53. Olshansky, Grob, and Ekdahl, *op. cit.*

54. Erikson, *op. cit.*

55. Erving Goffman, *Asylums*, Chicago: Aldine Publishing Co., 1961, 383; and Sampson *et al.*, *op. cit.*, 155. See also Harold Sampson, Sheldon L. Messinger, and Robert D. Towne, *Schizophrenic Women: Studies in Marital Crisis*, New York: Atherton Press, 1964.

56. Freeman and Simmons, *op. cit.*; and Simon Dinitz, Mark Lefton, Shirley Angrist, and Benjamin Pasamanick, "Psychiatric and Social Attributes as Predictors of Case Outcome in Mental Hospitalization," *Social Problems*, 8 (Spring 1961), 322–328. In the last-named survey, the study group was from a private, heavily staffed hospital where it may be presumed that the opportunities for receiving therapy were much greater than in the state hospitals from which patients were drawn for the first-named survey and the present study. See also Joseph Zubin, *et al.*, "Epidemiological Aspects of Prognosis in Mental Illness," in Benjamin Pasamanick (editor), *Epidemiology of Mental Disorder*, Washington, D.C.: American Association for the Advancement of Science, 1959, 119–142.

57. Goffman, *Asylums*, *op. cit.*

58. Olshansky and Unterberger, *op. cit.*

59. Norman W. Bell and Ezra F. Vogel, "Toward a Framework for Functional Analysis of Family Behavior," in N. W. Bell and E. F. Vogel (editors), *A Modern Introduction to the Family*, Glencoe, Ill.: The Free Press, 1960, 9.

60. Kahl, *op. cit.*, 202. See also Ernest Becker, "Socialization, Command of Performance, and Mental Illness," *American Sociological Review*, **67** (March 1962), 494–501.

61. Ginzberg *et al.*, *op. cit.*

62. William H. Form and James A. Geschwender, "Social Reference Basis of Job Satisfaction: The Case of Manuel Workers," *American Sociological Review*, **27** (April 1962), 228–237.

63. Compare Talcott Parsons and Renée Fox, "Illness, Therapy and the Modern Urban American Family," *The Journal of Social Issues*, **8** (1952), 31–44.

64. Bell and Vogel, *op. cit.*, 31.

65. Freeman and Simmons, *op. cit.* See also Ozzie G. Simmons and Howard E. Freeman, "Familial Expectations and Posthospital Performance of Mental Patients," *Human Relations*, **12** (August 1959), 233–243.

66. *Ibid.*

67. Compare Talcott Parsons and Robert F. Bales, *Family, Socialization and Interaction Process*, Glencoe, Ill.: The Free Press, 1955.

68. Howard E. Freeman, "Attitudes toward Mental Illness among Relatives of Former Patients," *American Sociological Review*, **26** (February 1961), 59–66; and Freeman and Simmons, *op. cit.*

69. As examples, see Julian L. Woodward, "Changing Ideas on Mental Illness and its Treatment," *American Sociological Review*, **16** (August 1951), 443–454; Gerald Gurin, Joseph Veroff, and Sheila Feld, *Americans View their Mental Health*, New York: Basic Books, 1960; August B. Hollingshead and Frederick C. Redlich, *Social Class and Mental Illness*, New York: John Wiley and Sons, 1958; and Jerome K. Myers and Bertram H. Roberts, *Family and Class Dynamics in Mental Illness*, New York: John Wiley and Sons, 1959.

70. See Marian R. Yarrow, John A. Clausen, and Paul R. Robbins, "The Social Meaning of Mental Illness," *The Journal of Social Issues*, **11** (1955), 33–48; and Charlotte Green Schwartz, "The Stigma of Mental Illness," *Journal of Rehabilitation*, **4** (July–August 1956), 7–10. Also Howard E. Freeman and Ozzie G. Simmons, "Feelings of Stigma among Relatives of Former Mental Patients," *Social Problems*, **8** (Spring 1961), 312–321.

71. Olshansky, Grob, and Ekdahl, *op. cit.*

72. See, for example, George W. Brown, G. Morris Carstairs, and Gillian Topping, "Posthospital Adjustment of Chronic Mental Patients," *The Lancet* (September 1958), 685–689; and Brown, *op. cit.*

73. See Yarrow, Clausen, and Robbins, *op. cit.;* and Edmund H. Volkart and Stanley T. Michael, "Bereavement and Mental Health," in Alexander H. Leighton, John A. Clausen, and Robert N. Wilson (editors), *Explorations in Social Psychiatry*, New York: Basic Books, 1957, 281–307.

PART 2 SINGLE MEN

2 WORKER TO WORKER: VICTOR NORTON

Victor Norton was first interviewed in this study at the time of his release from the state hospital in December 1958. Although then only 20 years old, he already had behind him about three years of experience as a worker in a steel plant, a short term of service in the Air Force, and a hospital stay of eleven months.

The interviews with Victor and his mother took place within a span of seven months. The first, a joint interview with him and his mother, was followed by three with him alone and four with her. As in all the cases, information was also obtained from his hospital record and from interviews with hospital personnel which carried his story up to April 1961.[1]

THE SETTING: PAST AND PRESENT

Victor was born in Boston in 1938, the seventh in order of birth of nine living children and three more who died in infancy. The family had always lived in Boston at one residence for many years. Two years before this study, the Nortons had made an unsuccessful attempt to establish themselves in their own home, financing a mortgage by means of the veterans' benefits paid to Leo, one of the older sons. Mrs. Norton described the place wistfully as "a nice house with a big yard." But the expenses were too much for them and they soon sold the place "to avoid spoiling Leo's credit with the government." They then moved to where they were first seen by the interviewer, who described it as a small apartment in an old wooden tenement in a slum. Their top (third) floor apartment, reached by a very narrow, dirty staircase, was carved up into tiny rooms separated by flimsy partitions. The apartment was neat and orderly, the windows and linoleum floors clean, and the furniture well kept.

Mrs. Norton's parents came to the United States from Denmark about the turn of the century, although she was born in a suburb of Boston. Mr. Norton's family was "mostly Scotch" in origin; but he and his father were born in Boston. Protestants, the Nortons of late years had not been church-goers. Mr. and Mrs. Norton were 60 and 53 years old, respectively, at the time of the study.

When Victor entered the hospital in January 1958, the household consisted of his father, mother, four brothers and sisters in addition to himself, and the 2-year-old son of one of the sisters. His four siblings then at home were a widowed sister, Jane, who was the small child's mother, and his senior by five years, a brother, John, one year older than he, and Betty and Raymond, his juniors by three and seven years, respectively. John was drafted into the army during Victor's hospitalization and was stationed in Germany when Victor came home. Betty, although only 17, married a sailor during Victor's absence, and had moved to a place of her own nearby. Thus the household to which he returned consisted of his parents, his 25-year-old sister, Jane, who worked as a welder, her little boy, and the 13-year-old brother, Raymond, who was still in school.

The elder brother, Richard, fourteen years Victor's senior, was a waiter who lived in New York. He had studied literature at Columbia University and became an ASTP student at Johns Hopkins University during World War II. According to Mrs. Norton, he had literary ambitions and was writing a book while supporting himself as a waiter. Helen, thirteen years older than Victor, was married to a railroad worker and lived in Minnesota. Marian, eleven years older than Victor, was single and had an apartment of her own in Boston. Finally, there was Leo, seven years older than he, who was married and living in the suburbs. Leo left school at the age of 16 to work for a steel company. Like Leo, Victor and his brother John left school before they were 16 and went to work for the same steel company as he had.

The father had been a truck driver for twenty-five years, after which he spent fifteen years working in various capacities at a boys' club in Boston. According to Victor, his father left the boys' club because he refused to be manager when he was offered the post. Victor's mother's account differed: he did whatever jobs the club manager asked, including that of locker room attendant, in which capacity he sometimes let boys who lacked the necessary two cents take showers free. A new manager did not agree with this practice, and finally Mr. Norton quit the job. After a period of unemployment, he obtained the same sort of work at the YMCA for a time. At the time of the study, he was a dishwasher at a local hospital, a fact which both Victor and his mother were reluctant to admit. Mrs. Norton, who regarded her husband's post at the boys' club as one of considerably higher status than his present job, reported that his pride had been badly hurt, that he had worked hard all his life and now at the age of 60, while doing as well as he could, was not earning much.

Mrs. Norton worked shortly before and after her marriage as a "private waitress in homes." She worked again in a factory for several years around 1938, at a time when her husband was unemployed and the family was on relief.

Mr. Norton worked for fifteen years from 2 to 10 p.m.; that and the hours he spent on his other jobs kept him from being at home when the children were about, so that they "grew up strangers to their father," as Mrs. Norton put it. Discipline was administered by her, but she was not much of a disciplinarian, she said, her only measures being threats and deprivation. Yet when the children were small, she managed to keep down their noise and quarreling, making sure that as a working-man and the breadwinner their father's rights were protected, for he was "out in the conflict, getting money for them." Victor's relations with his father were not close, but then, she added, none of the children were close to him, with the possible exception of Leo.

Mr. Norton, although a small man, had been a great baseball player in his youth, and, according to Victor, had "almost made the Red Sox." He helped Leo to become proficient in a number of sports and taught Victor to box, but the boy, although he won a Golden Gloves competition in the 60-pound division, was never as interested in sports as was Leo.

Leo took a job in outside construction with a steel company at the age of 16, and he was still working for the company ten years later, at the time of the study. He spent two years in the Navy where he obtained further training in his trade, sheet metal work. Leo and his wife both worked and built a large house for themselves in the suburbs which they were busily furnishing with "nice things," and now had begun to be very active in town affairs. Although he had risen to become a "boss" for the steel company, Leo still longed for more education, convinced that he could earn twice as much if he studied algebra and learned how to be a draftsman.

During the years when he lived at home, Leo was always urging his younger brothers and sisters to study while they had a chance, "especially things like their algebra." Richard and Leo, as the oldest, had a hand in raising the others but their tactics were not similar. According to their mother, Richard, the intelligent one, worked on the others by persuasion and was clever and persistent. Leo was "rough": if one would not do as he was told, Leo would "just knock him into a corner."

Victor viewed his parents as "too easy-going" and regretted they had not been stricter. He liked Betty best and fought with John, but admitted, "I like to fight a lot." Leo was closest to him. Victor described Leo as "a rugged man who works hard," and said he wanted to be like him, "to marry and have kids like everyone wants to have." The children made a close-knit little society, warm, zestful, and affectionate, often forming a united front in opposition to their parents.

Each of the children had to work and pay board until married and living away from home. There were always one or two children contributing to the family support, sometimes more; the family's prosperity depended directly on how many were working and living at home at the time. There were good years which the mother recalled with pleasure, ending ruefully. "Of course, we have about run out of children, and therefore there are slim days ahead."

At the beginning of the first interview, conducted jointly with Victor and his mother the day after his release from the hospital, Mrs. Norton volunteered the information that she herself had been a patient in "this kind of" hospital once, about twenty-five years ago, after the birth of her fourth child. She was in the hospital a month; it was something she "would never forget."

A chronological summary of the principal events of Victor's career at work and his hospitalization is as follows:

1953–1954: Victor entered the labor market at the age of 15. He left high school during his second year, unknown to his family, and was signed out of school by his mother three months later so that he might take a job while still under the legal age of 16.

1954–1957: He worked for a steel company as a machine operator for almost three years.

1957: He left his job at the steel company in April to enlist in the

Air Force. On being discharged from the Air Force two months later, he returned immediately to his job at the steel company where he worked another six months until December, when he suffered an injury to his foot while on the job. He was admitted to a general hospital.

1958: He was transferred from the general hospital to a state hospital at the age of 19 in January, about a month after his accident and the termination of his job. He was hospitalized eleven months, until December.

He obtained a job with a photography company as a picture developer one month before his release from the hospital, and was laid off, seasonally, after Christmas, having worked at it seven weeks.

1959: At the end of January, three weeks after the loss of his previous job, Victor got a part-time job as an usher in a movie theater, and held it for two weeks.

In February, he obtained a job as assistant shipper in a small shoe factory and was later promoted to regular shipper. By the middle of July, he was still working at this job.

In mid-August, he was rehospitalized, having held his job as shipper for either five and a half or six and a half months.

1960: He was released from the hospital in May after a stay of nine months. He found a job as a construction worker in a second steel company one month before his formal release from the hospital.

1961: By April, he was still working for the steel company.

Of the eight years between the ages of 15 and 23, Victor spent one year and eight months in the hospital. During the remaining six years and four months, he worked continuously, holding five different jobs, with the exception of two months in the Air Force and a three-week period of unemployment during his first posthospital stay in the community.

THE PREHOSPITAL CAREER

Victor's mother said that he had been stubborn as a child. When threats were of no avail, she would enlist his sister's help; it always worked. It was no use hitting him, for repeated blows only made him sick.

Victor described himself as working since the age of 11. He "always wanted to keep busy; just had to keep busy." He sold newspapers, shined shoes, and made the rounds of the neighborhood stores looking for errands to run. Around home he was always busy, cleaning the basement, chopping wood, fetching coal, and so on. When asked if he needed the money, he replied, "No, I just had to be busy." Mrs. Norton concurred in this, saying that there had been no need for him to go to work that early but that he wanted to and had bought most of his own clothes. She pictured him as "too steady—he always had the attitude of needing something to do."

When Victor was 8, on his teacher's recommendation his mother took him to a psychiatrist once a week for about six weeks. She was told that Victor was all right; it was just that he was acting out some of the scenes from comic books that he was reading at the time.

He attended grade school in Boston and after he entered high school transferred from his district to one in another part of the city because he wanted the sheet metal training offered there. He left high school during the second year, in 1953–1954; after all, he pointed out, his younger brother, John, who had quit school before him, was already working. His mother referred to the circumstances of his leaving school so early as a strange story: a teacher insisted that he owed fifty cents for his locker, and Victor maintained that the payment was not yet due. The teacher, noticing that Victor had a shirt-pocket full of cigarettes, confiscated them. Victor then pulled out a half a dollar, threw it on the floor in front of the teacher, and walked out, retorting, "You're getting your cigarettes cheap!" He never went back. Mrs. Norton went on to say that for the next three months he would leave the house as though going to school, taking his lunch with him but spending the day in Boston, and no one knew it. Finally, he could not stand it any more and divulged his predicament to his sister, Jane, asking her what he should do. She advised him to tell his mother and he went into a panic, but she then did it for him although against his will. Mrs. Norton said that Victor was much concerned, since he was not 16 yet he could not find work in Boston. Deeply upset at the thought of how worried and distraught he must have been during those three months, she went to the school and signed him out.

Soon after, he found a job at a steel company through Leo, who had worked there for years. It was inside work operating drills, lathes, and other machines, and he learned how to do it on the job. Both he and his brother were small men yet they learned how to handle heavy work. He stayed with the steel company for almost three years, from 1954 to April 1957, when he left to enlist in the Air Force.

Victor and a friend enlisted together. After just two months, however, he was given a "general" discharge, while his friend stayed on in the service. He described his general discharge as the "next thing to honorable." He said that he could not meet the standards and would fall asleep in his classes, a failing which he blamed on the hard schedule of marching and training, combined with studying and attending classes.

Returning home in June 1957, he immediately resumed his old job at the steel company. Six months later, in December, a piece of steel weighing two tons fell by his foot while he was at work. The load was being hoisted on a chain, and Victor warned the boy who was working with him but failed himself to get out of the way when the chain broke. He was taken to the city hospital, treated for a minor crush injury, and sent home because no fracture was found. He was home for about two weeks toward the end of which he refused to eat anything, cried and laughed inappropriately, and put pressure on his foot to cause himself pain. Finally, Leo and his wife came to visit him and told Mrs. Norton she should put him somewhere, preferably in a mental hospital.

The next day they took him to a large private general hospital where, according to his mother, before they would treat his foot they insisted that she sign a form permitting them to transfer him to a mental hospital if this were indicated. Mrs. Norton was very reluctant to do so, and argued with Leo that it is much easier to get into "one of those places" than it is to get out. But she signed the form, and after that, she said, the matter was out of her hands. After two weeks at the general hospital, where they found that he had a fracture, after all, Victor became disturbed and was transferred directly to the state hospital by ambulance on January 7, 1958.

Victor's presenting symptoms, as described at the state hospital, pictured him as "seclusive, withdrawn, retarded, and reveals paranoid delusions and auditory hallucinations [manifesting] negativism, delusions of persecution and reference, inappropriate laughter, and bizzare grimacing." Several of these symptoms antedated his accident at the steel company by a week or more. He was diagnosed as suffering a schizophrenic reaction of the acute paranoid type. Victor told the interviewer later that he could not remember what his worries were when he was in the hospital but later he explained: "I was trying to get what I could out of life, some enjoyment. I played solitaire into the small hours and worried a lot . . . about girls . . . and about not keeping things separated, like things that belonged to playing cards, for example, from things belonging to working."

He was 19 years old. This, his first stay in a mental hospital, lasted eleven months.

THE HOSPITAL PERIOD

Victor never had many friends, according to his parents, particularly since they moved to the new neighborhood several years before; he dated rarely and was shy with girls. The hospital record described his state in a way that corroborated them: "thought content is concerned with auditory hallucinations which relate to fears of homosexuality and castration . . . The patient is confused about his own sexual identification."

Victor did not want to stay in the hospital at all but ran away at every opportunity and fought with the attendants when caught trying to escape. His first successful escape was in February, a month after admission, but he was brought back by his family the next day. In March and April he escaped four or five times; each time he was brought back by some member of his family, usually by his mother or his sister Jane. The main reason for running away, he said, was his rage at being behind locked doors: "It was not fair . . . it was like being in prison." He voiced his scorn of the attendants who were brutal, declaring he "had no use for a hospital that employs that kind of people." On another occasion, however, he said that those in the hospital who really know anything about the patients were the attendants, and he expressed the greatest respect for a Negro attendant on the night shift who, in his estimation, really understood him better than anyone else did. Asked by the interviewer if the hospital was not a place where he could talk over his troubles with someone, he replied, "No, out there they are just animals, and you can do nothing constructive."

During the first month of his stay he was visited by a number of friends but only two continued to go to see him. His family visited him regularly, his mother came weekly, and his father, brother Leo, and older sisters once or twice a month. Some time in May he began going home on visits every weekend.

Victor said that all he did while locked up was watch television.

There were times after he was moved from a locked to an open ward when it took daily coercion to get him to go to occupational therapy, and the therapist reported that he repeatedly demanded to know when he could go home—"He did not initiate or respond to any verbal contact other than this." But it did not last. After a few months, Victor said that it was difficult for him in the hospital because there was nothing he could do. By August he was begging to be allowed to work, and finally to his great gratification he was assigned to the laundry.

In late October apparently on his own initiative Victor began job-seeking outside the hospital and in November, one month before his release, he obtained a job with a photography company. He had apparently engaged in considerable job-hunting before, since his administrative psychiatrist reported a week before his release that he claimed to have lost three jobs before obtaining this one because of the hospital's insistence that he come back early each day for psychotherapy. While working at the photography company, Victor returned to the hospital each night at 10 p.m. A week before his formal release from the hospital, his administrative psychiatrist made it clear that by virtue of finding a regular job, he had set the conditions for his own release.

Victor first attempted to get back his job with the steel company, but he was unsuccessful. A letter from the hospital apparently written in reply to an inquiry from the steel company, dated April 1958, states that "the patient has a severe emotional illness which we do not feel will clear rapidly and requires long hospitalization." He and his mother both said that the company would have taken him back when he applied, but the insurance people would not allow it because he had been a mental patient. So he remained with the photography firm. He had got that job through a referral from a worker at the state division of rehabilitation, who sent him to a man at the state employment office in charge of a "special section for people with special problems," and he accepted it because there was not much else available. He was still working there when he was formally released from the hospital on trial visit on December 5, 1958 for a year.

THE POSTHOSPITAL CAREER

When asked, Victor said that he had not told his employer at the photography company about his hospitalization, and that people did not

understand and "are afraid—they think you might be violent." When
he was sent to see a man in the special section at the state employment
office, he was told that it "would go against him" to be identified as a
former patient and was advised just to forget about it and fill out a
regular, not a special, application. He followed this advice in applying
for his first job, and when he returned to the state employment office to
look for another in late December he made out another regular application not mentioning his hospitalization at all. Mrs. Norton, as though
to condone the lack of candor, pointed out that he "can't afford not to
work, especially now that his father is 60."

When asked if his hospitalization made any difference in the way he
did his work at the photographer's, Victor replied in the affirmative
and said that he "watched himself." Yet he asserted that his family gave
him no special attention except that his mother did not like him to go
out walking at night.

At an early point in the study, Mrs. Norton objected to the interviewer's visits because they would call attention to Victor's hospitalization. "My opinion, frankly," she said, "is that the best thing is to forget
the whole thing." She referred again to her own mental illness and
hospitalization with distaste: she had been locked up in a "stall" where
her food was brought to her. Her relatives, she recalled, came to visit
when she returned home and it always seemed to her that they came
"just to look at her." So she knew what it was like for Victor—the self-
consciousness when first coming home from a mental hospital, and the
fear of people bringing it up in conversation. But she had conquered
it—"You go through phases of fear and retreat, you resolve to face it,
and you go out among the people, which is the solution."

Victor's job was to develop pictures. He said that he liked it; in fact
he "liked work, period." But he knew when he took the job that it
was seasonal work and he expected to be laid off after the Christmas
rush, since he was one of the newest employees. Yet when he had
been on the job only a month, he announced that he had received a
"sort of" promotion, for when a more experienced worker had quit,
he had been given his job, which was more exacting work at better
pay. He worked a five-day week at an hourly rate of $1.25, and often
worked overtime. When asked if he got along with his boss, he replied
that he "always does."

Victor paid his mother $20 a week out of his earnings for board.

While he was in the hospital the family income consisted of the slim wages of Mr. Norton and $25 a week from Jane, who gave half her paycheck. Anticipating the termination of his photography job, Mrs. Norton said that it was too bad Victor would be laid off, since "he has to work," and "he likes what he is now doing."

In a discussion of work during the first interview, Victor expressed the view that people are divided into two types: the construction worker and the salesman. He said that it was no use if you were of one type in trying to do work that suited the other type, and he himself was a construction worker. When asked what he would like to do if he lost his present job, he said definitely that he would like to be in shipping: warehouse work, receiving, packing, and sending. There would not be too many people in this sort of job, and working with too many people tended to confuse him. Moreover, he would have only one boss. One or two bosses is all that he could take; too many would bother him. To get a job in shipping, he stated quite confidently, "I would go to all the warehouses in turn, ask and see if they have something."

Soon after his release, Victor claimed that he had had many friends and that he was still seeing some of them. He said that his hospitalization had made no difference to some, but it did to others "because of fear." He went on to say, "But it makes a big difference with girls. They won't come near me. I don' mind it so much now, but it's the future I'm thinking of, and that's where it hurts." Mrs. Norton explained that his "real" friends were all in the old neighborhood, and although at first he would go to see them, he eventually gave this up. He had not made any friends on this new street, although they had lived there for a year before his hospitalization. According to Mrs. Norton, he had been set on once by a gang hanging about the neighborhood lunchroom and beaten up.

Since Victor worked into the evenings his free time was largely limited to weekends which he spent mainly playing cards and going bowling with the entire family, or alone to the movies and on occasional solitary walks.

As he had expected, Victor was laid off by the photography company after Christmas. He had worked there seven weeks, the first four weeks while still in the hospital. He was unemployed for three weeks, and then obtained a job as an usher in a movie theater, where he worked from 5 to 10 p.m., five evenings a week. This job, which he found through the state employment office, paid only 90 cents an hour but he took it because nothing else was available, and he continued to look for another during the day, visiting employment agencies and watching the newspapers.

While working as an usher Victor said that he was looking for something in which he could use his experience; "otherwise I don't care." He summarized his experience as the training he received in electrical work and printing during high school and the skills in machine operation acquired while he was working for the steel company and referred to construction work as unfortunately closed to him because of the matter of insurance. When asked why he was in such a hurry to get a job since, after all, he had been out of work for only three weeks, he explained, "I *have* to work. I don't know why. I'm not happy unless I'm doing something constructive . . . I just want a job; I don't mind if it is twelve hours a day."

As noted earlier, Victor was released from the hospital on a trial visit. In Massachusetts the formal procedure of the trial visit is that the patient return to the hospital once a month for an interview; the formal discharge, if his condition warrants it, is ordinarily granted one year from the date of release. Mrs. Norton said that he missed going back for an interview once and received a letter from the hospital that upset him. "He is afraid of being made to go back and he doesn't know which is worse—going there for a check-up or staying away. He goes."

Victor left his job as an usher after two weeks—during which he searched persistently—and got work as an assistant shipper in a small shoe factory, a full-time job found in early February 1959, through either the state or a private employment service. In early March there was some possibility that he would be laid off for seasonal reasons, but the shipper to whom he was an assistant recommended him as a very good worker and he was kept on. He liked this place because they left him alone. By mid-April, Mrs. Norton reported that Victor was "doing very well, likes it, and the people like him." Victor himself announced after two months on the job that he was now the regular shipper and earning a "living wage," the other shipper having left. When he had held the job for five months, his mother reported that the family "know he likes the job because he is always talking about it—so much so that they stop their ears, or kid him." At this time he was planning a week's vacation to visit his brother, Richard, in New York. He was disappointed that the company was not going to pay him for the week off, but Mrs. Norton said that she urged him not to give up the job because of it and he agreed that was only fair since, after all, he had not yet worked a year there. She said that it was too good a job to throw away and the principal thing she wanted to avoid was his "quickness," that is, that he would get "riled" and say or do something reckless.

In the last interview with Victor, held at the end of April 1959, he said that his main goal was to have a family and that this was the "object of work." He added that a husband should help at home by doing the heavy work, such as washing floors and also that he would like to live in a better neighborhood like the one he lived in before, or in the suburbs, like his brother, Leo. Of his present neighborhood, he said, "Here the people just hang around the corners. They have no ambition."

In the last interview with Mrs. Norton, conducted at the end of June 1959, she said that Victor was paying $20 a week for board, which was the same amount as he had paid when he held the job in photography. His sister, Jane, was still contributing to the support of the family, as was his father, although the latter's health was failing and he did not earn very much. Although very dedicated to his work, Victor often went to a local amusement area on weekends, now that it was summer, for he liked to gamble and was free with his money—particularly for the slot machines. Yet he meticulously paid his weekly board before he spent anything on pleasure, a practice for which his mother was openly grateful. With regard to the matter of taking a vacation without pay, his mother had told him "that was the whole reason for living at home. I knew how to take the bad with the good—no wage, then no board payment."

Victor was quite interested in girls, but he did not know how to go about meeting them and this, according to his mother, was his "main problem." About this time, however, Victor remarked that he was finally getting to know the boys in the neighborhood and played pool and went bowling with them. But he no longer saw his old friends; they did not want to see him because of his hospitalization.

In early March, Mrs. Norton could not provide any details about

Victor's new job as shipper because he did not tell her. "He is less confiding than the other children—each has his little story to tell; but he stays in a corner." She went on to say, however, that "the hospital has done one thing for him—he talks more than he used to." She always had been careful not to ask about his plans and activities because she did not want him to feel watched, which he would resent very much; but she did not think this was an issue any longer. The subject of girls, however, was still too touchy, and she would not mention it to him.

In the last interview with Victor, he said he felt in every way the same as he did before hospitalization except that he now tried to get enough sleep, which had not been the case before. He still wanted to make a living and looked forward to the future. He said that the illness might recur, that he would know this if he began "mixing things," but that he could cope with it by getting more sleep. He was still working as a shipper at the shoe factory when interviewing ended on June 30, 1959, and stayed at this job until at least mid-July. But there is no information as to whether he was still working up to the time of his admission to the hospital for the second time, six weeks later on August 18 where, as it proved, he remained for nine months, until May 1960.

Although there was no further interviewing in Victor's case after June 1959, some information about the subsequent course of events was obtained from his hospital record and from a telephone conversation with his therapist after his release from this second hospitalization at the end of nine months. On admission, he was described as "agitated, depressed, confused, and deluded." The sequence this time seems very similar to that in his first hospitalization: during the first six months, he showed little change; then he began to improve and after eight months he asked permission to return to work, and began to work one week later. He was still working at his job three weeks later when he was released, "cheerful and cooperative and very happy at his job." Returning to live with his family, he was formally discharged eight months after his release, in January 1961.

The job he took in April 1960, while still hospitalized, was at a steel plant, although not the one in which he worked prior to his first hospitalization. He was reported to be still working there as of April 1961, and thus held the job continuously for over a year. His father was no longer working but he himself was earning $90 a week and was supporting his family. Although a number of workers had been laid off, he was kept on, for he had a good record with his employers.

DISCUSSION

The case of Victor Norton exemplifies a variant in the pattern of occupational careers of single males who are former mental patients, in that he continued to be employable, both before and after hospitalization, and even during it. The discussion of his case and of the seven others will follow the conceptual outline presented in Chapter 1.

Career Pattern

Victor's career, both before and after hospitalization, was patterned by a high degree of continuity and stability at work, and his performance was apparently adequate to meet whatever standards were imposed. From the age of 11 until his entry into the job market, full time, he was either working or seeking work whenever he was not in school. Once he left school, he was continuously employed up to the time when information about him came to an end, except for his sojourns in the hospital and a three-week interval between his first and second posthospital jobs. Even during hospitalizations, he began to work regularly at least a full month before his actual release, and he suffered no interval of unemployment either before or subsequent to his term in the Air Force. He moved directly from the second into the third of his posthospital jobs and held the third one almost until the time of rehospitalization.

In addition to the remarkable continuity of his career at work it is clear that Victor consistently attempted to stabilize his situation. He not only remained with the same steel company almost up to the time of his first hospitalization but also he attempted to return there after release. Once he held a job, he was not disposed to leave it for another and the only time he left of his own volition was when he was a part-time usher, that being a stopgap until he could find a full-time situation.

Victor never failed to seek a job when he needed one, including the times of entry and re-entry into the labor market. The time before his release from the hospital and the three weeks of unemployment at one point after his release were taken up with persistent job-seeking. Although his brother, Leo, was instrumental in getting him his first job, Victor looked for his own work thereafter. Through all of this, he maintained his independence and effectively made use of all available resources. He took advantage of whatever leads were given him by the agency and obtained all of his posthospital work without anyone's intercession. Similar to Frank Monaco, he had the advantage of a kind of natural at-homeness in the world of work that set him apart from the diffident and ineffectual Harold Lang or the tongue-tied Albert Rossini; he knew how to "sell" himself.[2]

Adequacy of performance was clearly never an issue in the several jobs that Victor held: all available reports show he was regarded as a good worker. The length of time he held his first job as a steel worker in itself attests to it, and this was not questioned when the steel company refused to take him back after hospitalization. Termination of all three of his posthospital jobs was for reasons that had nothing to do with the quality of his work, and it should be noted that he received promotions in the two full-time jobs he held after release.

The direction of Victor's career, both pre- and posthospital, was essentially upward. He began his first job as an unskilled worker, acquired skills on the job, and eventually became a skilled worker. There was considerable horizontal mobility during the posthospital period when he held three different jobs in the eight months but the sequence of movement is important rather than the number of positions. He left the first place by reason of seasonal layoff and the second when he had opportunity to obtain a better job. There was also some vertical mobility in his first and third posthospital jobs. From the perspective of his entire occupational career Victor suffered loss of status in the occupational hierarchy after hospitalization, in passing from skilled to unskilled worker, but he made substantial progress, posthospital, up to skilled worker again and returned at least to the prehospital level of skilled work subsequent to his second hospitalization.

In working, job-seeking, and occupational mobility, Victor's posthospital career does not differ essentially from the pattern he had established, prehospital. Although his career *line* was affected, in that he had to abandon his principal occupation for a time, there was no appreciable change in *functioning* at any point, and no discernible effect upon his employability.

Qualifications for the Labor Market

Although he was only 19 when hospitalized, Victor was already relatively well established in the world of work. In over three years of experience in steel construction he had become proficient in machine operation. He would undoubtedly have had no difficulty in using these skills had he been able to return to the steel company, and indeed he did ultimately return to steel work after his second hospitalization and had been at it continuously for over a year at the time of last contact. Victor had left high school in his second year—which, of course, is generally regarded as auguring ill—but he could count among his assets the electrical work and printing he had learned there. These assets and his knowledge of machine operation were the repertory he had to offer employers at the time of his release from the hospital. When none of it turned out to be actually marketable at the time, he readily undertook to learn photo-developing in order to obtain a job and was promoted to "more exacting" work after he had been at it only a month.

Victor thus had very specific ideas about his qualifications, and although he clearly preferred work in which he could use his experience, he was flexible enough to adjust desires and abilities to reality if necessary. Besides a realistic awareness of his own assets and liabilities, he also had decided notions about the setting and conditions in which he could work best. He knew that he wanted to work where he would not have to contend with "too many people" or "too many bosses": the first situation "confused" him and the second "bothered" him. He had specific ideas about what constituted a "real" job, namely, one that was full-time, that would enable him to do work that he could consider "constructive," and that would provide a living wage. In summary, he appears to have had little difficulty in appraising his situation at all times and in making appropriate decisions and choices.

Career Orientation

Victor's preference was steel construction work and he not only attempted to return to his old job in it as his first choice after hospitalization, but also he was ultimately successful in obtaining just such work after his second hospitalization. He unambiguously typed himself as a construction worker, and thought there was no point in aspiring to any work not "natural" to that type. This choice was specified and crystallized at an early point in his career, and he held to it with remarkable consistency. Since he maintained so steadfast an attitude toward his choice, it can be said, in Ginzberg's terms, that it constituted a "true" and not a "pseudo-" crystallization.[3] He was also definite and specific about his secondary or alternative choice, namely, shipping work, and was to all appearances familiar with what it would involve. Despite the consistency of his choice and of his desire to use his particular qualifications, however, he was far from rigid when opportunities were at variance with his choice and his qualifications: "I just want a job. I don't mind if it is twelve hours a day!"

All the evidence points out that Victor viewed work primarily as a satisfaction of personal need. He "liked work, period," and both he and his mother projected his liking for work back to when he was 11 years old, yet there was no financial need for him to work at that early age. He said that it was his need to keep busy that made life hard to bear in the hospital, since he "couldn't do anything." He eagerly accepted work in the hospital laundry, and there is no indication that he saw anything to be gained from it beyond the opportunity, itself, to work.

Victor's opinions of his several jobs reflect both his liking for work and his satisfaction in doing it well. As Mrs. Norton said, "the family knows he likes his job because he is always talking about it." His primary satisfaction, then, was intrinsically in work itself; the adequate performance of it was apparently of great emotional significance to him. Devotion to work is hardly surprising in Arthur Jackson or Peter Field, the one a physicist, the other a musician, for their callings were of a kind expected to bring its own rewards in personal satisfaction and in social status. But Victor was, after all, a factory worker: the reward to him was the immediate activity for its own sake. And although not of foremost concern, financial rewards were important both because of his obligations at home and because he liked to have money to spend on himself. Although he wanted a "living wage," the size of his earnings did not seem to be a critical matter; he enjoyed work only secondarily as a means to material rewards. It also seems clear that conditions of work and the gratification of sociability were of little concern to him. His profound liking for work and close identification of work with constructive activity dominated every situation in which he found himself.

Victor's statements about his personal values were as explicit and unambiguous as those about his occupational choice. He wanted to get married and have children "like everybody wants to have," and he wanted to live in a better neighborhood, ultimately in the suburbs, away from his present neighborhood. Moreover, although preoccupied with the immediate satisfaction of working, he also defined work as the only acceptable means of gaining immediate rewards and long-term goals. Obtaining a job as soon as possible was the only course he would consider, once he knew he was to be free of the hospital.

There was, in summary, great compatibility between Victor's occupational choice, his satisfaction and desired rewards on the job, and his personal values, on the one hand, and his assets and qualifications, on the other hand. He knew what he wanted to do, what he wanted from a job, what he would like to have out of life, and how to get what he wanted. There was not only a good fit between what he wanted and what he could do, were the opportunity at hand, but a remarkable persistence in pursuing what he wanted and a demonstrated flexibility in adjusting his desires and his abilities to the realities of the labor market. In all these things he stands alone among the cases. In particular, Frank Monaco, the would-be physician, Peter Stone, the musician, and David Field, the cabby, exhibit lack of fit between aspiration and capacity.

Career Contingencies: The Hospital

Hospitalization, of course, interrupted Victor's career, since he had already been continuously employed for a number of years. Symptomatic behavior occurred so immediately before his hospitalization that it apparently had no significant effect on his behavior at work except during a brief period culminating in his accident on the job. Hospitalization did not result, however, in any substantial disruption; indeed, he returned to active employment even before his formal release. His sustained employability and immediate resumption of work must in large part be attributed to the fact that illness and hospitalization set in *after* his occupational pattern had become so strongly established that upon release he entertained no alternative to working, and the relatively extended hospital stay, eleven months, was no deterrent.

To Victor, his hospital stay meant, in the main, enforced idleness and, once he was relatively symptom-free, he pressed persistently for an opportunity to work. True, he resisted occupational therapy while in the hospital but he himself took the initiative in seeking work in hospital industry, presumably because occupational therapy was, to him, no substitute—an opinion to be found in Peter Stone and David Field as well. Hospital industry, too, never represented "real" work in his mind, and he was bent on returning to the outside world as soon as possible.

Apparently, the hospital personnel did not play a significant role as agents of his career during his hospital stay. Whatever may have been the goals set for him in individual and group psychotherapy, functioning at work was not, it seems, an issue. Also work was not an issue in determining his readiness for release from the hospital, for during his hospital stay and the release procedure he took the initiative in resuming work, and the hospital's role was essentially that of onlooker, in large part because he was so obviously ready to return to the world of work.

Career Contingencies: The Family

Victor exceeded his family's expectations by seeking work at so early an age that financial obligations had not yet been imposed on him. Moreover, he left school to work of his own accord and not because of pressure from home. Characteristically, Mrs. Norton supported his decision once she learned of it and signed him out of school. Then Leo lent a hand by obtaining a job for him at the steel company.

It was clear that the model of Victor's career in pattern and in orientation was his brother, Leo, and not his father. His working hard and holding on to a job, his occupational choice and its crystallization, his modest aspirations, and his particular personal values all markedly resemble characteristics attributed to Leo, and this was confirmed by Victor's expressions of respect and admiration for Leo, which were in contrast to his denigration of his father. If anything, Mr. Norton's career was one of downward mobility, from truck driver to boys' club attendant to dishwasher, and there were signs that Victor was ashamed of his father's low status, at least at the time of the study.

Mrs. Norton was the one family member who advanced Victor's posthospital career. She concurred in his decision not to disclose his hospitalization to prospective employers and offered the justification that he could not afford to remain unemployed in view of his father's slender earnings. She apparently appreciated Victor's eagerness to return to work as soon as possible, but there are no indications that she put any pressure on him; indeed, it is obvious that Victor needed none. Whatever action she did take was presumably in the interest of making it easy for Victor to work and stay on the job. There was, then, substantial congruence between the son's behavior and attitudes and his mother's. Although Mr. Norton remains nebulous as an agent of

Victor's career, there is no indication that his attitudes were at variance with those of Mrs. Norton, if, indeed, he expressed them at all or ever attempted to intervene. These circumstances of his career set Victor poles apart from Carl Duncan, whose more bourgeois and sophisticated family gave him but token encouragement and no financial asistance at all.

Pattern of Career as Affected by Illness and Hospitalization

Victor clearly knew that he had been mentally ill and believed that he could ward off a recurrence by not worrying and by getting enough sleep. He did not regard these preventive measures as infallible, however, and characteristically thought that it was strictly up to him to cope with his problem and that in large measure he could do so, but always accepting the possibility that things might get out of hand and that he would become ill again. In his confident and pragmatic view of his illness, Victor stands unique among these cases.

He carried over into the posthospital period the profoundly unfavorable attitude toward the hospital and toward therapy that he manifested during his hospital stay and maintained the minimal contact of monthly visits only because of fear of being returned to the hospital if he did not. According to the therapist who reported on his second hospitalization, however, Victor's attitude toward group therapy, at least, was somewhat more positive at that time.

Both as a worker and as a person, Victor affirmed that he saw himself as not being any different after illness and hospitalization from what he was before, except that he had to "watch" himself on the job. At the same time, he was quite positive that his hospitalization had made a considerable difference in how others, his friends and prospective employers, saw him and treated him. But the biggest difference he saw was in his relationships with girls. Whatever relationships with girls he had before his illness and hospitalization—and they appeared to have been neither extensive nor profound—he reported as ended. He observed that he did not mind this too much in the present, but that it "hurt" when he thought of the future. The focus of his difficulties, then, was other than work, namely, peer and cross-sex relationships, on which hospitalization undoubtedly had an unfavorable effect.

To Victor, work was not an area of life to be critically affected by illness and hospitalization. He did not jump at any etiological associations between particular kinds of work or environments and recurrence of mental illness. Indeed, his strongest preference was for returning to the job he held before hospitalization, and he was quite flexible about taking on other kinds of work when it proved unavailable. In stark contrast to the case of the more talented and sophisticated Arthur Jackson, whose illness was totally overwhelming, in Victor the whole issue of illness and hospitalization was essentially sealed off from his life at work, and no significant changes in orientation and functioning can be discerned when his posthospital career is compared with what his life was before.

NOTES

1. See the Appendix for a description of the method employed in collecting data for these case studies.
2. The references here and subsequently are to the other men whose stories are told in this book.
3. Eli Ginzberg, Sol Ginsburg, Sidney Axelrad, and John Herma, *Occupational Choice,* New York: Columbia University Press, 1951.

3 NONWORKER TO NONWORKER: HAROLD LANG

When he was 16 years old and in the eleventh grade, Harold Lang left school for good. In the seven years between the time he left school and the conclusion of this study, he had been hospitalized three times, totaling just over three years and ten months. He had served a year in the Air Force, and had held a variety of unskilled, ill-paid jobs for a total of three years and six months. His longest continuous stay in the community between the ages of 16 and 23 was two years and one month.

Information about him was collected during extensive interviewing between 1957 and 1961. In that time, the patient himself was seen ten times, his mother nine times by herself and twice in the company of his father. A woman florist who employed him briefly was also consulted, and there was a score of talks about him with hospital personnel.

THE SETTING: PAST AND PRESENT

When he was first interviewed in the summer of 1957, Harold was a good-looking young man of 20, slender, with dark wavy hair and brown eyes. He was the fourth of eight children in a Catholic Boston family. Among his brothers and sisters the one closest to him was the eldest, Kevin, 29 years old, married, and the father of one child. There was a baby who lived "just long enough to be baptized"; then came two girls, aged 27 and 22, both married and living elsewhere in New England. Harold was the next, followed by Donald and Derick who were still in high school and two little girls, 12 and 7. The last four children lived at home, as did Harold when he was not in the hospital.

The father of the Lang family was Boston-born and of Italian parentage. He replied, "ship's mechanic" when asked his occupation, but this is so highly seasonal and sporadic that for about ten months of the year he had to turn to other work, as, for example, when he worked for a short time as a plumber's helper and in a box factory which failed soon after he started work. For long periods he drew unemployment compensation, which brought him about as much as he could earn, while his wife resorted to public relief and, sometimes, private support from the church. Harold's father was a friendly, outgoing individual, but rather given to self-pitying descriptions of his financial straits and the scarcity of work for such as he. There are hints that he was a hard disciplinarian of his children in the southern European manner, rough and clamorous, and that Harold from time to time intervened on behalf of the younger ones. On one such occasion the mother called the police because of the noise and the blows, and the father was shocked when he, and not the son, was the one escorted to the police station. Mr. Lang repeatedly made an issue of Harold's chronic joblessness—all too like his own—and once, when hospitalized, apparently dreading a scene, Harold asked his mother to visit him without his father, lest the latter "start to rave again."

Mrs. Lang was born in Italy but brought to this country at the age of 4. A small woman, she seemed perpetually driven and worried. The family lived in two nicely cared-for apartments during the study, in run-down buildings in neighborhoods which, while not distinctively Italian, did provide them with some neighbors of their own origin. There is little evidence, however, that they cultivated the friendship of those about them; their social occasions were spent strictly in the family circle, which, in addition to the two married daughters living away, included a grandfather, three uncles, and several cousins in the suburbs. The apartment they occupied during the latter part of the study had no telephone, and when Harold came home he had to share the boys' bedroom just off the kitchen which was the center of family life and bathe down the street in a public bathhouse.

The Langs were painfully poor. At one point, for instance, Mrs. Lang reported that she was four months behind in the gas bill and was permitted to pay it off a month each week. She had two more such payments to make, however, and meanwhile the new bill was looming, as was the light bill. They bought oil for heating from the landlord who seemed to have been patient in money matters. More than once Mrs. Lang confessed that she feared she could not afford to feed Harold as well as he should be fed while recovering from his illness, if he were to be released.

Throughout the whole time of the study, the small intermittent earnings of Mr. Lang were the family's primary source of support, to which were added from time to time a share of the wages of any child who chanced to be working. When the father was out of work, his unemployment compensation was one thing they could be sure of— sure, too, of an agonizing wait before the checks started coming. This was their plight for most of the time under consideration. When he was earning, Mr. Lang gave his wife whatever he felt like giving, in the belief that he needed money for himself and had a right to it: "He seems," she said, "to begrudge whatever he gives the family." Thus even when times were good for the family, the mother could never count on any definite amount for household expenses.

A year after Harold was discharged from the Air Force, Donald enlisted in the Army, from which he parted seven months later on failing to pass a test. The boy then got work as an inspector for an optical company and contributed weekly to the upkeep of the household, but after eighteen months he resigned to go west, and although his letters spoke of good intentions, he no longer bore a share.

Derick was expelled from school soon after the study began. He was then 16, and in the tenth grade. Eventually he found a job washing dishes on Sunday forenoons in a bar for $3. This was followed by a ten-months' stretch of work as a restaurant bus boy.

Kevin had left high school in his sophomore year to join the Marines and during four years of service learned to be an electrician. He suffered at least one period of unemployment during the time of this study, and when he got work at last he installed burglar alarms, on his own, an enterprise into which he took on Harold as his unpaid helper. Kevin gave him a dollar, however, "whenever they met" and in other ways helped out, when, for example, he paid Donald's carfare to an employment office to make inquiries on Harold's behalf and gave Harold carfare to call on a prospective employer.

When Harold had jobs he regularly gave his mother a share which he spoke of as half his earnings, but at one time it turned out the half was $40 out of $60. Harold clearly expected to assume a "proper" share of the burden—in one interview he and his mother discussed what part of his money a son living at home *should* give—and, indeed, when he first left school he gave as a reason the fact that his mother needed money so badly that he thought he ought to find work.

Mrs. Lang was the most insistent about Harold's earning money. Driven by bitter appreciation of what it cost to feed an extra mouth when he was home, she tried to bargain with the hospital that he should be released only after a job had been found for him. She repeatedly referred the responsibility for placing him in a job to the hospital. She herself once through a worker in her church found him a job making wigs in the Catholic Charities' workshops but by the time Harold presented himself the place had been filled.

His father said that "naturally," whatever the job was, it would have to be something that Harold liked—"how can a person be expected to keep on working and stay well if they must work at a job they don't like?"—a stipulation in which Harold tacitly concurred; he left jobs repeatedly because of "heat," "dust," "noise," or "press." The father declared that Harold would like to be a draftsman for he had been good at art work, chiefly at copying cartoons, in high school and in the Army. But Harold himself met the suggestion with subdued enthusiasm and his doctor, although he spoke of bringing the possibility to the attention of the occupational therapist, appears to have done nothing further.

Although for a year Mrs. Lang attended meetings called at the hospital for the close relatives of patients, she never seemed to conceive of Harold as a sick man who needed understanding, intelligent treatment, and moral support if he were ever to be well. Her view of him was of a boy whose spells of irrational behavior were a possible menace to life and limb and whose recurrent interludes of unemployment were a great financial burden. At first she implied that if only he could get the right kind of work he would recover. Later she grew less hopeful and reached the conclusion that a fair degree of recovery had to come first.

A chronological summary of the principal events of Harold's work career and the dates of his hospitalizations is as follows:

> 1953: Harold left school at the age of 16 soon after he started his
> third year of high school. There is no indication that he held
> any sort of job before that time.

1953–1954: Between September 1953 and July 1954 he held three or four jobs, one of which was an assembly-line factory job that he held for one month during the spring of 1954. The last of these jobs was packing spectacles for an optical company, which he held until shortly before his first hospitalization.

1954: He was admitted to the state hospital on July 31 at the age of 17 and was hospitalized for more than two months until October 8.

1954–1955: From October 1954 to November 1955 there is no information about his working other than a reference to a stockboy job at a large grocery, dates and duration unknown.

1955–1956: Harold enlisted in the Air Force in November 1955 and was discharged in November 1956, after becoming "disturbed."

1956–1957: He was admitted to the state hospital at age 19½ on November 19, 1956, and hospitalized for thirteen months until December 16, 1957. From September until November of 1957, while living in the hospital, he worked for a nearby florist. It was during this hospitalization that he began to participate in the study.

1957–1958: From December 1957 to July 1958 he made a few attempts now and then to seek a job, but held none. He did obtain a job in April 1958 but never reported for work. During May 1958 he occasionally helped his older brother, Kevin, install burglar alarms, but without remuneration.

1958–1961: He was admitted to the state hospital on July 7, 1958 at age 21, where he remained two years and seven months, until February 10, 1961. During October 1958, he held a job for a few weeks at a rubber factory and left this to take a job as a dipper of metals and errand boy at a chemical plant, which he held for two-and-a-half weeks. There is no further reference to jobs sought or held during this hospitalization, although for a very short time he worked in the hospital greenhouse and then on a food truck. Released on February 10, 1961, he was readmitted to the hospital a month later on March 11.

Of the eight years between the ages of 16 and 24, Harold spent a total of almost four years in the hospital and one year in the Air Force. During the other three years he worked only occasionally, on jobs of short duration.

THE PREHOSPITAL CAREER

At the age of 16, when in the eleventh grade, Harold left school because "it didn't seem to be worth it." Moreover, he realized how welcome a share of his wages would be to his mother, were he to find work. He never thought of continuing in night classes, but some time later said that if he had it to do over again he would try to finish high school. He played basketball but was not on the school team. He volunteered the information that his two older sisters were the only ones in the family who got on the honor roll and that he himself came closest to it once when he had only 2 C's and had "tried like anything" to reach the goal. He liked drawing and copied cartoons because he "could not think them up by myself."

In the twelve months after he left school (1953–1954), Harold held three or four small badly paid jobs. By the time the year was up, he had been hospitalized. He was then 17 years old. It is not clear from the records that this was the first time he had been a mental patient; his mother spoke of a "first time," when they borrowed $400 from the paternal grandfather and when, after electric shock treatments from "that Dr. Green," he came home "entirely well." But these statements were never substantiated. She may have been talking of a time before his admission to the hospital in July 1954; on the other hand, she may have been confusing it with the hospital experience itself. There is, then, at least the possibility that he had received medical attention for mental disturbance before he was 17.

One of his first jobs lasted just a month; he left it because "the press" made him "nervous." The last one was packing spectacles for an optical company. That job ended soon when he was suddenly picked up by the police, wandering naked on the street. His mother explained this by assuming he had been swimming (it was the end of July) and had either been robbed of his clothes or forgotten where he put them. The record said that at the police station "hospitalization was advised" but it did not say by whom. He was admitted thereupon to the state mental hospital. On admission, Harold was diagnosed as "schizophrenic reaction, chronic, undifferentiated type, severe." He was withdrawn and confused, made no spontaneous remarks or movements, and spoke in monosyllables. He was released, unimproved, for trial visit to his brother, Kevin, after a stay of two months.

Details of his career for the next year are not fully known. He held a job as a stock boy in a large grocery concern for a time. In November 1955 he enlisted in the Air Force. With animation uncommon in him, he said he "loved" the Air Force, but could not be prevailed on to say why. His assignment was to ground maintenance, "chopping down little trees" at a base just outside San Francisco. This lasted just one year. It was recorded by a hospital resident, later on, that he had "exposed himself before a WAC officer." He was diagnosed as disturbed, sent to the base hospital, and eventually discharged and sent home. That was in November 1956. Almost immediately he entered the same mental hospital in which he had spent a short time two years before. It was after this hospitalization, which lasted thirteen months, that Harold was first interviewed in this research.

Harold was now 19. His mother, who described him as always having been "a good baby," revealed that he grew up a shy boy with few friends and always in need of encouragement and support. By the time he was 19 she had never known him to ask a girl out on a date, and the only evidence of interest in the opposite sex brought about his discharge from the Air Force. There is, too, an enigmatic reference by his mother to two or three incidents in his high school days when, according to Harold, some neighborhood boys "spoiled him," an experience that brought him shame. When pressed for details his mother looked embarrassed and said she supposed he had meant by that that they "asked him to do things he shouldn't do."

Harold's second admission to the hospital, the study hospitalization, was instigated by his family. He frightened them all by prowling at night indoors and out, unclothed, and by an odd habit of kneeling and blessing himself. When his father caught him moodily fingering the gas jets, then snatching up a kitchen knife and running out, they found it too much and had him hospitalized.

THE HOSPITAL PERIOD

On examination at the hospital, Harold was described as "anxious, cooperative, alternately laughing and serious, confused and troubled, complaining of headaches." He denied having hallucinations. Following electric shock treatment, he showed marked improvement and was eventually permitted weekend visits at home.

He "did well" in occupational therapy that winter and by spring, in March 1957, although depressed and seclusive, he was assigned to work in an industrial detail in the institution. He never liked it and had to be prodded each day to report in the proper department.

At the end of a month, Harold was taken out of industrial work and two months later he was making a success of mimeographing. Now he began to show interest in what he was doing and no longer voiced the daily complaint that he did not want to go to work. It was at this time that Harold himself spoke to the therapist about going out to look for work, having drafting in mind. The doctor pointed out that he ought to be given more training, as his only experience had been during high school; but this never appeared to have been done. Meanwhile, the interviewer had suggested that he follow up his liking for mimeographing by finding work at it on the outside. Harold, it appeared, had never connected his intramural occupation with "real" work. When he went to the State Employment Service, however, he learned that factories were closing down and that there were no calls for workers. Thereafter he looked for work in a supermarket and following a tip given to him by someone in the hospital, he looked into a printing place; but in vain.

By the end of the summer he was making half-hearted attempts to find a job, but soon gave up even going out to look. The ward notes describe him as a "very fragile" personality, one not to be pushed, as of yet, to independent endeavor. In September he was found a job at a florist's near the hospital; the employer was a woman who volunteered to take on patients, apparently from a sense of civic duty. There he did "token" work for $5 a day, so slowly as to be of quite limited value, sifting loam and watering and feeding plants, running errands, wiring pine cones for wreaths, and the like. It was undemanding to an uncommon degree: he was usually there, he said, at about 8 a.m. but was told to come "when he could" and stay until 4:30, at which time he returned to the hospital, and on a day when there was little to do he was given his money and told he could leave for the day. The florist remarked that "he was a very nice boy. You tell him to do something and he does it." He contributed nothing of these earnings to his family.

At this time the ward notes describe the patient as "quiet and cooperative, free, apparently, of hallucinations and delusions and no longer engaging in bizarre behavior." He is reported as taking little interest in his fellow patients. No friends of his age visited Harold in the hospital: his only callers were his mother and his brother, Kevin, and, rarely, his father and an uncle. (Two years before, during his first stay in the hospital, an unidentified man had come to see him—his only visitor outside of his immediate family.) For much of the time of this study, there would have been no money for Harold to spend on pleasure with young friends. He spent hours of his weekend visits at home sitting by himself before the television set, unshaven, preoccupied, and unresponsive. And when the family's set went out of order, he passed the evenings watching the programs at Kevin's.

Although Harold was interviewed from time to time during this sojourn in the hospital, it was almost impossible to come to a conclusion as to how he felt about his life there. He made no voluntary comments, met leading questions with monosyllabic answers, rarely looked directly at his interlocutor, and frequently appeared bored or uninvolved in the conversation—a state of affairs brightened by very occasional flashes of interest and warmth, although with little increase in communicativeness. The content of his hallucinations or what he thought when he had been prowling naked and tinkering with the gas taps remained inaccessible; indeed, he said he had no hallucinations.

Midway through this hospital stay the therapist reported he was making good progress. Whereas he had behaved compulsively in the early months, walking up and down, for instance, turning the ward lights on and off, and more than once pushing his hand through the window panes, he was now working with interest in the mimeographing room, handling quite complicated processes with fair competence. Moreover, he was more sociable; he even played Ping-pong with regressed patients.

The hospital attributed the change to individual therapy and drugs and released him. The therapist had been planning to have Harold work on the outside, returning at night to the hospital, for the institution could see to it that he was up and off to work in the mornings. Eventually when the job was found at the florist's he was given it with the understanding that if he "did well and held it" he could get out and go home any time, for he was now considered "much, much better." But Harold conveyed to the interviewer the fact that he did not know just what was asked for as to performance and length of time in these conditions. As the job lasted only two months, however, the questions soon became academic.

Now the therapist expressed the opinion that it was best for Harold to do one thing at a time: first, hold a job "for a period of time," then undertake life at home in the family; or, home and *then*, after he had been able to adjust there for a sufficient time, a job. Release was to hang upon his finding and holding a job. Nonetheless, he was released jobless on trial visit, "to remain home with his family and to continue looking for work on the outside." He was described as "moderately improved," having made some gains in contact, following electric shock treatments. He had been in the hospital thirteen months.

THE POSTHOSPITAL CAREER

It was now ten days before Christmas 1957. At home the father had been jobless again because the box factory that employed him had just failed; but he secured new work. Kevin, who assumed the role of father to the younger children and protected them from Mr. Lang's surliness and the noisy outbreaks that followed his bouts of beer drinking, was not a part of the household, as he was married and on his own. Donald was now giving his mother $15 a week from his wages at the optical company and Derick, who washed dishes on Sunday mornings in a bar, contributed something from his weekly $3. Mrs. Lang seemed genuinely fond of Harold and was anxious to have him at home. She had found a good deal of gratification in the hospital's group sessions for patients' relatives, although she gave the impression that she regarded them as designed for sociability rather than as aids to helpful family attitudes.

Now 21 years old and, in his mother's opinion at least, "completely well," Harold lived at home for the next seven months. In that time he had no work at all. His mother, driven almost desperate by the mounting bills, insistently harped on his getting out of the house and hunting for work, and the interviewer resorted to meeting him in the hospital where, at least at first, he went weekly to report. (Later he often was remiss in meeting the appointments.) He made one call at a U.S. Employment Office, but to no avail, and thereafter for the next few months contented himself with following the classified advertisements: "There's lots of jobs listed"—but he never found one to his liking. To the exasperation of his mother he slept until noon, making no effort to get out to apply for work in the mornings before the agencies' listings were exhausted, or to leave in the evenings to avoid the inevitable unpleasant encounters with his father. To his therapist, Harold confessed having once at this time struck his father, who, rebuked by his wife for drinking on the job, had replied to her in a manner that the son found intolerable. At the same time, his mother discouraged what meager extramural social life Harold might have had. A maternal uncle in the suburbs invited him to spend a week with them, but Mrs. Lang declined on his behalf for she feared he might "grow violent" and "hurt the children." He had been slapping and scolding his little sisters and she declared the visit would have to be put off until his "nervousness" wore off.

Bad luck and caprice got between Harold and what job openings came his way. A friend of his mother's reported a job at wig-making at the Catholic Charities downtown, but when Harold went to apply for it, it had been filled. Another opening was found for him by Kevin: moving cartons at a coffee syrup factory. Kevin saw the advertisement and urged Harold to apply. Harold actually got the job, but decided it was too far to go and never reported for work. His mother said he considered rejoining the Air Force. It was never learned if this were possible in the light of his discharge, but in any case he took no steps to re-enter.

In May he filled out an application for a job as stock boy in a large grocery store nearby. He had to make call after call to see if a job were open for him, grew discouraged, and finally stopped going. At about this time he was at least busy, if not earning, for Kevin took him on as an unpaid helper installing burglar alarms, a job which Kevin had made for himself. Kevin, as a matter of fact, was now in the habit of giving him a dollar when they met and carfare for going to the employment office.

In June he reported just too late to secure a job in a bubble gum factory. Then he looked for work at the airport, but they kept telling him to return and it came to nothing.

At the end of six and a half months on the outside, Harold was returned to the hospital in July 1958. He had had no work at all since his job at the florist's, six months before. This time he was to stay in the hospital for two and a half years.

This, Harold's third hospitalization, began on a day when his mother called Kevin to come to the house, saying he was "worse and should be in the hospital." She thought they could deceive him by saying the doctor had telephoned to change a pending appointment to that day. Although he made it clear that he saw through the ruse, and showed no surprise when Kevin observed that he might have to stay on after the appointment, Harold went along peaceably. His own explanation was that he "had been acting up at home"; his mother spoke of it as his "nervousness." He used to nag the younger children about cleanliness —he himself had some months before had an interval of not shaving or keeping clean—and once slapped his sister's face when she insisted she had washed. The children were afraid of him. (When he was well this was not so.) He would stay in bed until mid-afternoon. The family found him impossible to talk to: he would sit and stare and questions would have to be put to him repeatedly before he would answer. The most convincing symptom to his mother, however, was his exaggerated slowness in getting anything done. His desultory job-hunting was made difficult by growing confusion about directions and his failure to cope with transportation. He grew critical of food, the house, and the neighborhood. He would wash himself over and over as though unaware of the repeated motions. On the day his mother decided to call Kevin, he was breaking household objects, the last being the taps of the gas stove which he decided had to be changed. She interpreted all this as manifestations of returning mental disturbance.

The landlady meantime had served an eviction notice and the family moved in August 1958, a month after Harold's readmission. She had complained that Harold used too much water; and, indeed, Mrs. Lang specified as one symptom of returning illness that he would run the bath faucets interminably. Mrs. Lang was sure that was the real ground for the landlady wanting to get rid of them, although the ostensible ground was that she needed the apartment for a relative. Luckily, this came in one of the very short periods when the family was doing relatively well financially. They moved, the two parents and the five younger children, into a six-room house.

After Harold had been back in the hospital for several months, Mrs. Lang became preoccupied with the notion that it was up to the hospital staff to obtain a job for Harold before he was released again. She felt that if only the hospital people would get him started at a job, this would enable him to seek perhaps a better job with the possibility that he could get one. But if he were to be released jobless and just out of a mental hospital, this "was a strike against him." Mrs. Lang never communicated these thoughts to anyone at the hospital, however.

When he had been in the hospital for three months, Harold declared that he would like to go to the institution's school for attendants and become a hospital attendant himself. He planned, he said, to speak to the doctor about it. Meanwhile, his father told him he had found factory jobs for them both, to which Harold replied that he preferred an attendant's work; but he neither accepted the first nor entered training for the second.

Soon after this, in October, he applied at an employment agency and found work making rubber soles. He was put on the night shift, worked then from 3 until 11 p.m., and earned $70 a week. After work, he would go home for dinner at his family's, and then return to the hospital after midnight. This lasted only a few weeks; he found it too unhealthful and unpleasant: ". . . no job is worth getting sick for again," he said, in one of his very infrequent references to his own condition. Spurred on by his mother's assertion that the hospital would not let him come home unless he was sufficiently "improved" to hold a position, he went back to the agency on the day he left his job and through it got work dipping metals and moving cartons in a factory producing polishing compounds. But this he found was "too heavy" and "too dusty" and he left it in less than three weeks. Thereafter there is no record of jobs sought or held. He was kept on occupational therapy for a year and was never moved into hospital industry.

Mr. Lang was working, making $85 a week, when Harold had re-entered the hospital; but three months later, by October 1958 he was unemployed and drawing $45 a week in unemployment compensation. In the whole of the first year of Harold's hospitalization he held jobs as a plumber's assistant and occasionally at ship cleaning. He was working in July 1959 but lost his seniority when his wife's illness kept him at home. Then his company went out on strike and he became ineligible for unemployment compensation.

Donald, who had been giving his mother $15 a week, left his job to go west eight months after Harold was readmitted. From Texas he wrote he was employed on a dude ranch and hoped to be sending money home soon. Derick had been helping with the household expenses, but he was laid off that July. Mrs. Lang said she hoped Harold would come home "if he could be well and have a job." Otherwise she feared she could not afford to feed him as well as an ill person should be fed; moreover, coming home when he was unemployed seemed not to help him at all, for he lacked both interests and occupation.

In the short interludes when he had work, Harold gave his mother money out of each pay check, the amount depending on what he had left after purchases for himself. He lived at the hospital but was home always for weekends and at times for dinner, and he gave his mother to understand that he would contribute about half his earnings when he rejoined the family circle. For a short time he became entangled with a girl in the hospital, bought new clothes with his earnings at the chemical plant, and began paying $10 a week toward the purchase, for $50, of his brother-in-law's old car. He enrolled in night school in order to finish high school. His mother hoped he would help with payments on a second-hand television set with which the family hoped to replace their old one. By the end of October 1958 she was "sure he would not get sick again" and was most anxious to have him home—provided, always, that he had a job, a stipulation which she reiterated at each interview.

Elspeth, Harold's girl friend, apparently his first, was a 20-year-old who had run away from a stepmother and an unhappy home. She was charged with being "stubborn." She planned to enter the hospital's school for nurses at a time when Harold talked of training as an attendant. But she was transferred to another institution and when Harold called there to see her he was refused; moreover, a long letter he wrote her was returned to him, undelivered, with the advice that he give up trying to get in touch with her. By this time, so he said, he had found another girl friend.

Harold's state had its downs as well as its ups. In July 1959 at the end of his first year in the hospital, he was eating paper, cutting himself and, in general, acting irrationally. He once knocked out a fellow patient and on several occasions managed to escape. By this time his mother who had insisted all along that a suitable job would be Harold's salvation, now came to look upon his working solely as a convenient and longed-for source of money to help her run the household, rather than as a therapeutic measure.

In January 1960 Harold held a low-grade job in a department store restaurant for a month, being laid off not for personal reasons but in in the course of a general reduction of staff. He was then out of work, made no effort to find a job, missed therapy sessions, and sat about in the hospital, unshaven. For a little while he worked in the hospital greenhouse, but he soon after became a management problem, "acting out" with the nurses, and "in need of firm control," as recorded in the hospital history. He ran away with increasing frequency and would be found walking the streets naked. Eventually he was moved into a closed ward. In full view of attendants and patients he on one occasion picked up pieces of glass from a broken light bulb and chewed and swallowed them. He got to the point of eating his own feces, grew threatening and destructive, and frequently had to be kept in seclusion for his own protection and the safety of others. Yet, by the beginning of 1961, after months of individual therapy and many vicissitudes, he requested work in the hospital, occupational training, and weekend visits at home. He was assigned to work on the food truck and discharged early in February. Then in March his behavior again became bizarre and provocative and he was readmitted to the hospital.

At this point, contact with the case was terminated.

DISCUSSION

Harold Lang is of theoretical interest as a man who *never* found a real place for himself in the world of work. In this he is unique among the cases. Of the eight years subsequent to leaving school, he had been hospitalized about half the time, had worked for far less than half and at half-a-dozen occupations.

His story points to a state of unemployment-proneness: he either could not, would not, or did not take jobs when they were available. There is no evidence that his illness made him unemployable; as a matter of fact, all his jobs were obtained when he was actually a patient. His career might be shown as two curves, concurrent but independent. One is his state of health—often he was ill, sometimes he was well. The other is his status as to employment—occasionally he had work, most of the time he had none. Now and then his employment might coincide with his good health but, and this was probably the more common, at other times it overlapped a season of ill health. In the same way, a stretch of unemployment might find him well or ill. But it was coincidence, not cause and effect. He might be defined as *an unemployable youth who sometimes suffered psychotic interludes.*

Career Pattern

Symptom-free or not, Harold never held any job for long. His career is characterized by lengthy periods of unaggressive and sporadic job-hunting and even longer periods during which, like David Field—whom he resembled in this but otherwise not at all—he simply did not look for work at all. In most instances places were found for him by others. Moreover, Harold pronounced conditions at work as unendurable and left after a very short try at it. In the eight years of his working life for which there is information, he was successively: an assembly-line factory operator, a packer of spectacles for an optical company, a stock boy in a large grocery store, an enlisted Air Force serviceman assigned to grounds maintenance, a florist's helper, an operator in a factory making rubber heels and soles, and an errand boy and assembly-line worker in a plant that produced polishing compounds.

He left high school at 16, he had no job waiting for him, and no skills to sell. His first hospital sojourn began within the year, a year in which he held three or four jobs of manual work calling for quite unrelated abilities. He never became established in any occupation for thereafter his hospital stays were frequent and prolonged, removing him from the labor market at the very time when he should have been accustoming himself to its demands and expectations. None of the first positions he filled required or inculcated any special skill, and he never stayed in any one of them long enough to acquire competence. Thus he never secured a place thanks to any knowledge or habits of work gained on a preceding job, each being purely episodic and discontinuous with the one before. There is neither stability nor continuity in his working life. Moreover, he grew less able to hold a full-time position as the years passed. The twelve months of military service appear as his longest stint in one situation—perhaps the only one where he was judged by standards of the ordinary man.

With his disposition to quit after a few weeks, Harold was never in a position to be judged as a worker. The florist reported him as "a very good boy" (but he was then 20) who "did what he was told" but who was so slow as to be almost useless; she appeared to regard the employment of him as a good deed rather than a business transaction and what he did as token work. One can only conclude that he was never a thoroughly adequate performer at anything.

There were times when Harold followed the classified advertisements and presented himself at employment agencies. But just as his mother persisted in thinking that the hospital, even the interviewer, should find work for him, so Harold never put himself forward forcefully or made a good case for himself as a prospective hireling. His mother heard of a job which he missed by being too late; his brother took all the first steps to get him a job advertised by a coffee syrup factory; his father landed factory jobs for them both; but it all came to nothing. Even when he was told where to go to seek an opening, given the carfare, and sent on his way, it was to no purpose. In other longer periods, Harold took no steps at all to find work. It is as though he never saw job-hunting and job-holding as the rational means to realize his readily acknowledged wish to help his harried mother and bear his share in the family. Nor did he ever specify any life goals which might make even a distasteful occupation bearable, except for the one remark that he would like to be able to go out in the evenings and take girls on dates "like the other boys do."

All Harold's jobs were so low-grade, so unskilled, that it is impossible to speak of any direction of movement in his working career. He was mobile in being in and out of work but his jobs were basically always of about the same quality so he neither advanced nor dropped back, occupationally speaking, but was only horizontally mobile.

He left jobs for reasons of his own in all but the case of the Air Force, where he had no choice, and the florist, whose work was seasonal. Thus the rubber factory was "too hot"; work at the plant making polishing compounds was "too heavy"; before even reporting for work on the first morning he had already decided that the coffee syrup plant was "too far away." His career at work continued intermittently even before he was first hospitalized and always at a low level; it is hard to see that it was much or at all affected by his medical history. One conjectures that he still would never grow into an effective worker and a valued employee, whether his fate were to spend the rest of his days as a hospital patient or to be discharged eventually for good.

Qualifications for the Labor Market

Hospitalized as he was at 17, a high school drop-out facing the labor market with no skills, Harold was and he remained unqualified, inexperienced, a readily replaceable cipher in any job. The only desideratum for him with regard to a job was whether or not he liked it. He appeared to have no conception of work as building a career but went from job to job, where offered, with no carry-over or exploiting of acquired skill or experience. By working he could make money. At first he spoke of wanting money to help his harassed mother. Later on he wanted a car, clothes, and the wherewithal for hypothetical dates— at which point, like his father, he began to forget about his contribution to family expenses. But there is no evidence that he ever voiced an opinion about his pay, or complained of it or asked for a raise; no sign, in short, that he ever faced the question of his own worth as an employee. And during the summer of 1957, when jobs were scarce and factories were shutting, Harold, although badgered by his mother, could hardly be argued into reporting early in the forenoon at the employment agencies before the listings were all gone.

Disparaging comments were almost Harold's only assessments of his jobs; he was not inclined to gaze inward to evaluate his stock of assets and handicaps as a worker or to seek employment deliberately in fields where he might have at least some shadow of advantage. Although attracted to the mimeographing he was learning in occupational therapy, he did not project it in his mind as a possible pursuit on the outside. When, on being prodded by his father, he named drafting as a skill he might offer to an employer, it was an unrealistic gesture since his only experience had been in a high school art class.

Career Orientation

Laconic by habit, Harold rarely voiced any opinion of work beyond saying it was "all right"—except, of course, in the instances in which he made specific complaints. He once said he thought he would like to re-enter the Air Force: he "loved" it. But he could not be drawn out to recount just what he liked and, as far as is known, he never actually took steps to rejoin. Later on he thought he would like to go to the hospital's school for attendants and learn to be one. But again he did nothing about it. Moreover, by that time, he was going through recurrent phases of violence and unmanageability. The projections his therapists occasionally made for him never reached even a beginning of materializing.

Never having made any vocational choice whatsoever, Harold could not achieve a crystallized choice. Nor, as he filled the succession of little jobs, could he ever be said to have arrived at pseudocrystallization. Indeed, work seems never to have appeared to him as a definitive aspect of a man's life.

A sympathetic and affectionate son, Harold was sharply aware of the family's poverty and his mother's heart-breaking struggle to make ends meet in a household where the men seemed prone to unemployment. (It is only fair to recall that the study period included the recession of the late 1950's.) Yet he did no more than follow his mother's lead in setting up conditions under which he would work: it must not be "too dusty," "too far away" . . . "He will take whatever they have, if he likes it," she said. And he agreed with his father that "you can't be expected to take a job and hold it if you don't like it." Neither he nor his parents believed that one must be prepared to put up with discomfort for the sake of money and the things it would make possible, and all three spoke of the conditions of work as decisive. This is to imply that the job itself was its own end and pleasant circumstances the reward, while the worker never sees any further than that, never arrives at an instrumental conception of working.

As a rule, Harold shared his earnings with his mother. He spoke once of giving her "half" but was actually giving her $40 out of his weekly $60. But when the interviewer observed that it is hard to say just what is the proper fraction of the household burden of expense for a son to assume, Harold responded with a rarely sympathetic and appreciative look. When this and other scraps of evidence are considered, one may conclude that, although too fussy about conditions of work to stay at it for long, he *occasionally* recognized that a job was a means to get money and, as noted earlier, he once mentioned a car, clothes, and dates as things he wanted money for. In extenuation, it should be admitted that jobs on the level of his are, as a rule, routinized, monotonous, unchallenging and—but for his work at the florist's—disagreeable. Yet twice he asked for something to do in the hospital and was placed first as a helper in the greenhouse and then was assigned to the food truck. He gave expression to shy pride when his mother boasted that he had got word of a job through an agency, found the place filled but returned to the agency and secured a second job in the same forenoon, and this at wages of $70 a week—while it lasted. His mother insisted on regarding a job as the price of his release from the hospital and his job-hunting, haphazard and luke-warm as it was, may have been motivated by what she represented to him as her bargain with the hospital, for there is no doubt he enjoyed being with his family.

Career Contingencies: The Hospital

Since Harold never had anything like the promise of a permanent job which could be the foundation of a career, hospitalization can have had no effect upon it. Rather, on the three occasions of admission to the mental hospital considered in this study, he was jobless. Apart from sometimes finding conditions of work unbearable, he seems to have seen little significance in work and so a token job on the outside or a light, undemanding assignment on the inside may have been about equal in his mind.

His therapists from time to time speculated on possible avenues of outside employment for Harold, such as typing or mimeographing, but in each instance, for unstated reasons, never went on to make the necessary arrangements. On the other hand, it was through the hospital—and, Harold added, himself—that he got his month-long job at the florist's, token work created for a mental patient by a public-spirited boss whose establishment was close by. It seems clear that the hospital physician, during the study hospitalization, took the position that Harold's release was contingent on demonstrating that he could find and hold a job, and assumed the obligation to facilitate this goal by finding him the job with the florist. But when Harold failed to "demonstrate" that he could hold a job, even such a protected job as this, the doctor withdrew this condition for release, and Harold was released "to continue looking for work on the outside."

There was some talk about the effect of hospitalization, were it known, upon Harold's chances of being hired. Mrs. Lang once observed that he said nothing about it when applying for work, but his haphazard job-hunting could not have been a real test.

But hospitalization entered decisively into his social life by keeping him for months at a time out of the world. In all his years in the institution, he seems to have had only one visitor who was not identified as a relative. Nor did his family, except for his mother, often go to see him. Mrs. Lang always went on Sundays when Kevin could drive her there and usually on Wednesdays. Mr. Lang went rarely, and once "made a scene" there over Harold's joblessness, and to the relief of all, stayed away thereafter. Kevin sometimes went. Harold's girl friend, herself a patient, was easy for him to find in the day rooms and on the grounds, until the time when she was transferred. All in all, his social encounters were uncommonly restricted and his social repertory must have been meager indeed. His inexperience in dealing with others may have handicapped him as a job-applicant. In a rare burst of confidence, Harold claimed that if he had money he would go out in the evenings on dates; but it might have been lack of assurance as much as lack of money that kept him from companions.

Career Contingencies: The Family

In the Lang family no one—neither Harold's brothers nor his father—had occupations for which they had been prepared and trained and at which they were working steadily. Here, again, Harold's plight is unmatched among the eight cases. Mr. Lang was described as a ship's mechanic but this work never took up more than two months of the year, and he was often on unemployment compensation. He once worked as an untrained plumber's helper and spoke of possibly becoming a plumber but he never took the actual steps. He once found a factory job for himself and one for Harold—which Harold, at least, never took. Kevin, said to be the real father in the family, had learned to be an electrician when in the Marines and did draw upon this skill in civilian life but not consistently. Kevin read the classified advertisements for Harold, went himself to the employment agencies, and did everything but actually apply for the jobs, including often giving Harold carfare and small sums. And Mrs. Lang, who nagged him interminably about not working, did find one job for him through a friend; but he was too late.

For one member of the family after another, work was just whatever job happened to be available at the moment. Kevin's work was employment he made for himself. (He had his own family to support.) Donald, at a time when he was the sole source of steady money, gave $15 a week toward the household expenses, but soon was contributing less and less and when the study ended was in Texas on a dude ranch, promising money but sending none. Derick, expelled from school, never got anything much better than a job washing glasses in a bar on Sunday forenoons. And the father, even when he was earning, "begrudged it to his family," according to Mrs. Lang, and took unto himself the right to spend his wages as he wished. Harold's income was negligible or nonexistent. As a unit, the family was downwardly mobile beginning at a low level and despite a few signs of cooperation, threatened constantly by its members' individualistic conception of it. There are no models in it of ambition, protracted effort, continued preparation, deferred gratification, advancement, and increasing rewards.

Mrs. Lang expressed repeatedly throughout the study period her concern with Harold's joblessness. In part, this concern clearly stemmed from the desperate financial need of the family, but it is also clear that she tied her hopes for Harold to his getting and holding a job. If he were working, he could buy whatever things he might want, he would make friends, and he would be out of the house, in addition to helping the family financially. But Mrs. Lang did not believe that Harold could get and keep a job if left to himself, and except on the rare occasions when her hopes were fired by a short burst of work activity on Harold's part, as when he held two successive jobs in October 1958, she did not believe that she could get Harold to become a worker. She and others in the family did make sporadic attempts to find a job for Harold or to spur him into action, but presumably the failure of all such efforts confirmed for her that this task was really the hospital's responsibility, which was the conclusion she ultimately came to as the study grew to a close.

Pattern of Career as Affected by Illness and Hospitalization

Harold's story offers the strongest contrast to Victor Norton's. Victor, aggressive from childhood in everything pertaining to work—preparation, the cultivation of skills, adaptation to new work, job-hunting, and so on—gave thought to his condition and how he should conduct himself so as to reassure employers and others and ward off illness. Of course, his articulateness provided access to his picture of the world but even without that, his performance tells its own tale: that he expected to handle himself and his affairs and to do so responsibly. He recognized illness and the hospitalization that confirmed it as presenting problems of employability, but surmountable problems.

But Harold, with his seclusiveness and his extreme passivity in the matter of working, was quite another problem to himself and others. There is no evidence that he speculated on his illness and its bearing on his working life. This is natural enough seeing that his jobs, tenuous and ephemeral as they were, were obtained through the efforts of others and in nearly all instances while he was still in the hospital. Harold offered a variety of reasons for why he left particular jobs or failed to begin work when a job was available, but on only one occasion did he justify leaving a job by saying that it was "unhealthful" and that "no job is worth getting sick for again." But for this one brief reference to hospitalization as a possible handicap to employment, he otherwise betrayed no awareness of his plight. In other words, it was as if in his mind illness and hospitalization were not a plight at all. And he was right, for, to repeat the formulation stated earlier, the conjunctures of his state of health and status of employment were apparently haphazard and purely coincidental. Thus one is led to deny the relevancy of illness and hospitalization to the career of this dubious participant in the working world; indeed, one questions if there was any impact at all.

Mrs. Lang anticipated stigma: she insisted the hospital should find her son a job to go to on release when his medical history would be a "strike against him"—but there is no indication that it ever actually was an obstacle to employment.

Harold's best record was his year as grounds maintenance man, "chopping down little trees" at an Air Force base. Was this because in so highly structured an environment as the military he found the unremitting support and the disciplining expectations he appeared to need? If so, the hospital, an equally authoritarian milieu, might have supplied him a favorable habitat. But on the two occasions when a therapist proposed intramural training which would eventually help him to get work on the outside and meanwhile keep him purposefully occupied on the inside, the plans aborted, for reasons unknown. It is as if the hospital, while attending to him as a patient, never took him seriously as a potential worker. The Air Force did; and when he was discharged, it was for exhibitionism: there were no complaints about goldbricking or failure on the job. If strong support were what Harold needed, it was something which neither the community nor his singularly ineffectual family was in a position to give.

4 WORKER TO NONWORKER: CARL DUNCAN

Carl Duncan was 30 years old when first interviewed in 1958 for this study. Thin, stiffly erect, slight, with a solemn fixed gaze, he was leaving the hospital at the conclusion of his sixth period of hospitalization. In the years since he had been of an age to work he had enjoyed one period of almost three years in the community and when contact with the case terminated in 1961, this proved to have been his longest span of time outside mental institutions, apart from his three years in the Coast Guard. Following his military service, of the eleven years of potential employability that ended in 1961 he had been hospitalized for nearly four years and employed for about the same length of time in a dozen short clerical jobs.

The story of his career which follows has been reconstructed from three interviews with the patient himself, one jointly with his mother, and eight with Mrs. Duncan alone in two of which his father briefly introduced himself. Two therapists were each seen twice.

THE SETTING: PAST AND PRESENT

The Duncans, in the eyes of the younger children at least, are an almost classic case of the family suffering from "fallen fortunes." As always, fate pressed harder on some of them than on others: of the seven children, the older three enjoyed advantages in childhood denied to the younger—or so the latter thought—of whom in particular the patient, Carl, the fourth son, saw himself the innocent victim of cruel circumstances.

Mr. Duncan, a man of 60 when the interviews began, graduated from a state teachers' college in Massachusetts, his native state. Following his service in the Medical Corps in World War I, he became a sales manager in the malt products division of a large brewing company. He did very well at his work which for seventeen years took him away from his family, often for weeks at a time. Consequently, Mrs. Duncan raised the children almost singlehanded, settling all questions of discipline herself, and in those early years, at least, the husband and father when at home was waited upon, fussed over, and idolized by the whole family. She used to feed her big brood in the kitchen; then, she related, the older little girl would set the table in the dining room for the parents, who would dine by themselves with some formality. When the departure of one of the older boys freed a bedroom, Mrs. Duncan converted it into a "den" for her husband. There were family jokes about "nothing being too good for father," about his unconvincing gestures to wait upon himself and his prompt yielding when his wife and children proffered help.

The Duncans lived in an old-fashioned but roomy and comfortable house on a quiet street of a Boston suburb. It was well kept and although the furniture was worn there lingered suggestions of departed elegance and affluence. The house was actually the property of Mrs. Duncan's family and that might have been why they had not been able to refuse her when an epileptic sister proposed to live with them. There were distressing episodes when she had seizures in sight of the children, and when Carl was 15 she died horribly in their midst "right in the living room fireplace." Mrs. Duncan believed this made a shocking impression on young Carl.

After seventeen years with the brewery, Mr. Duncan suddenly lost his position when the company went out of business. He had had bad luck before. He had been a valuable salesman for a yeast company which was sold to a rival concern and was dismissed from another firm as soon as he had built up a sales territory. "He seems," said his wife, "to have spent his whole life building up other people's business, instead of working for himself."

Fifty years old and jobless, Mr. Duncan on the advice of his sons proposed to enter a new field—selling life insurance. A newcomer, he did not make any money at all for two years. Eventually he transferred to health and accident insurance, but for years he made very little and the family lived on capital, for providentially, twice when things looked blackest, Mrs. Duncan had come into money. Her brothers sold the family's business for $3 million and her equity, paid in two installments, maintained the household. When our study began, the father was just getting on his feet again, but the house was mortgaged.

Mrs. Duncan appreciated her husband's struggles and stood up for him, knowing that as they grew up the children looked on their father as something of a failure; yet even she once remarked on "how awful" it was to use up capital on the daily necessities of life. She always had held it unthinkable for her husband to have entered into her family's business—"relatives don't mix well in business"—and was determined that, since unequal wealth destroyed family feeling, no one of the children should have more than any of the others. This, of course, proved no more than a pious hope for fate had already proven otherwise.

Mrs. Duncan, a Catholic New Englander like her husband, had worked as a secretary for five years before her marriage. An attractive, lively woman who gave a deceptive impression of being easy-going, she was apt to control her children by little schemes and artifices; yet was very affectionate. The children were deeply attached to both parents. Carl himself said he got on well with them all; "they are ordinary people: no peculiarities." "Ours is a peaceful house," said his mother.

Of the seven children, Peter, the oldest, born in 1923, had an M.A. from a good institution and was a mathematics teacher and athletics coach in a nearby suburban high school. He saw combat between 1942 and 1946 in the Air Force. Father of two children, he was described as good, patient, and fond of his work.

Yale, the second oldest son, seemed closest to the patient. He was born a year after Peter, had graduated in engineering from a first-class university, served four years as a radar control operator in the Air Force and then re-enlisted, serving again in 1951 and 1952. He had then been an engineer in Schenectady and eventually took a job in Boston as a designer of missiles. His wife had recovered very successfully from schizophrenia following three years in a mental hospital. They had one child. The family thought Yale was like their mother, quick and energetic.

The third son, Dick, was brusque, rough, and aggressive. Two years younger than Yale, he had served in the Seabees and was a field engineer for a California oil pipeline concern. He was said to have fine qualities. He offered to put Douglas, one of the younger boys, through college because their father could not finance it, and bought tickets to Los Angeles for his parents to come out to visit him and his family.

Peter, Yale, and Dick were the ones who "had it good": their school days were passed in the days of the family's prosperity. The patient, Carl, born in 1928 two years after Dick, was the first of the "have-nots," as the younger four seem to have defined themselves.

After Carl came Douglas who was born in 1931. At 28, when the interviewing in this case began, Douglas had seen a good deal of the world. He graduated from college in New England, worked in a milk plant, served in the Navy, and was stationed in Japan as an electronics mate. Finally he settled in an aircraft plant in California where he did research. He almost had finished the courses he was taking five nights a week toward another degree. As a matter of fact, Dick moved to California to help Douglas finish school; the latter was to go to classes by day while his wife taught school and Dick's wife took care of the children. Douglas had refused to let Dick pay outright for his schooling and had turned down a like offer from his father-in-law.

The Duncan's first daughter, Carol, was born in 1932. She was her mother's favorite, an executive secretary of great competence, and president at 25 of the local suburban women's club. During the study she and her parents were much distressed by a love affair she was having with a Protestant boy. Then she suddenly accepted a second admirer who, although a Protestant, too, went to the priest for instruction and consented to a Catholic upbringing for their children. Carol's wedding, managed entirely by the efficient bride, was one of the big events in the family's history. Carol was always conscious that in childhood she had gone without things the older children had but with her ability, attractiveness, and abounding self-confidence she set about getting what she wanted for herself. She was "good" with Carl, sharing more than once with Yale the painful task of returning him to the hospital.

Deprivation embittered Emmy Lou who was the baby of the family and four years Carl's junior. She was a legal secretary during the period of the study, in what her mother described as "a better job, making much more money than we ever imagined she would." A pretty girl, but not as popular as Carol, morbidly sorry for herself and resentful of the family's straits, she bought luxuries to embellish the small back room which was her bedroom until Carol married.

Thus when Carl returned home from the study hospitalization the family at home consisted of his parents, his two young sisters—Carol's wedding came later—and himself. Peter and Yale lived with their families in neighboring towns. Carl when at home was for the most part in the basement workshop or in his bedroom, a large unheated attic chamber—"that big beautiful bedroom"—which his mother allotted to him to accommodate his artistic endeavors. There he would occupy himself at drafting, indifferent, it seemed, to the extremes of New England's weather. This had been his only occupation in the year before he had entered upon the study hospitalization and when he came home he reverted to it.

A chronological summary of Carl's work history and hospitalizations is as follows:

1946: Carl finished high school at the age of 18 and spent one semester in normal art school but left, deciding he did not wish to teach.

1947–1950: He volunteered for duty in the Coast Guard, serving three years, first as a carpenter's helper and later as an office worker.

1950: He worked for one year as a porter in a supermarket, his first full-time job, while taking night classes in a museum school of art, after one term declaring he was done with art. He visited a monastery for one week.

1950–1952: He worked in a dairy in California and for three months in 1951 in a lumber camp in Arizona.

1953: In March he was found fasting and praying in the Arizona desert. He was brought home and admitted as schizophrenic to a state hospital where he spent three and a half months.

1953–1955: He remained two years and one month in the community. Some months after release he found a job as a bank clerk and was discharged as "too slow" after five months. He found a similar job, also for five months, which ended identically. Then he held several small jobs for brief periods, the last one lasting ten days and ending about five months before his second hospitalization. In March 1955, he attended a ten-day retreat with the Trappists where, despite his "calling," he found life "too hard."

1955–1956: He spent seven months in a second state hospital.

1956: In March, on release, he took a job as a filing and typing clerk, which lasted five weeks. He was unemployed during the rest of his community stay. After three months and three weeks in the community, he returned to the hospital for three months. At this time he decided to switch to architectural drafting in which employment and training were more available to him. Then he was in the community for two months, one week, of which he spent three weeks as a precision measurer in a photographic firm, after two weeks of job-hunting. When he lost the job he was unemployed for one month and then rehospitalized the day after Christmas 1956.

1957: He remained in the hospital for one month and eleven days, was released to the community for one month and twelve days, during which he did not work, and then came back to the hospital for one month and twelve days.

1957–1958: He was in the community for one year and two weeks. He stayed at home, and for some time spent several hours a day practicing drafting.

1958: He was readmitted to the hospital for one month, one week. This was the study hospitalization. After his release, he wrote five inquiries to employment agencies but took no job. Seventeen days after his release he was returned to the hospital.

1958–1960: He was hospitalized for two years and ten days. During the last six months of this long hospital stay, from January to June 1960, he was placed on an arrangement whereby he alternated two-week visits home with three-week stays in the hospital where he worked as a bookkeeper on the hospital farm. In June he was formally released on trial visit. He stayed in the community for four months, during which he held a job as a machinist for a time. He was readmitted to the hospital in October 1960, when the trial visit was brought to an end.

1961: He was still hospitalized when the case record ended in March.

Of the fourteen years in which Carl was potentially employable, from 1947 to 1961, he spent three years in the Coast Guard and three years and ten and a half months in the hospital. Of the seven years and one and a half months he spent in the community, he was employed for slightly less than four years in about a dozen jobs.

THE PREHOSPITAL CAREER

From the time he was 6 years old, in 1934, Carl Duncan seemed destined to be an artist. One of his teachers conveyed this conception of him to his mother, who had like tastes. He went to a WPA school when he was 7 and learned tap-dancing at which he became so proficient that he earned the nickname, "Rubber-legs." As he grew older he had isolating hobbies. His brothers all took up musical instruments and enjoyed sports but Carl showed no interest in joining them. He built a marionette theater in the basement and spent hours absorbed in his marionettes and his painting.

As a 9-year-old he sold papers and magazines. In high school he changed from the precollege to the business course in order to have more time for art and ended with four years of training in office work. He had no formal instruction in drawing or painting but planned to go to art school. As a high school senior he was chosen in lieu of a professional artist to illustrate a pictorial history of the town, an undertaking to which he devoted his spare time for a year. The family was enormously proud of it, particularly when an important city newspaper reproduced his art work in a full-page story. After school Carl worked in the neighborhood drugstore. Years later his mother recalled how old ladies would ask after "that nice boy who used to wait on us so considerately and courteously." He was a cheerful, normal youngster, pleasant, sociable, talkative, and well liked. He worked hard, did well at school, and in time occasionally dated one girl or another.

Carl graduated from high school in 1946 and then went on to normal art school. But at the end of one semester he left it because he found he did not want to *teach* art. He never told much of what he was thinking but he gave Dick to understand—and his later behavior bears it out —that he volunteered to serve in the Coast Guard at this point in order to use the money he would get under the G.I. Bill as well as his regular pay to go to professional art school later on. He chose the Coast Guard, he said, because it was "the smallest branch . . . more unique. And you get more attention. Besides it is the most active: you go wherever there is water." He occasionally painted portraits of his companions-in-arms, and even sold some.

There followed three years which included no combat experience, divided equally between Florida, Hawaii, and Missouri. There is no record available of his impressions beyond a remark written to his mother from St. Joseph, Missouri, that it was "the loneliest place in the world." At some time he had a few dates with a girl he met at the "Y." He worked as a carpenter's assistant in the maintenance division by his own choice but when in Florida he was assigned to office work. When he left the service at the end of three years, it was with a good record, no illnesses, and an honorable discharge. He had saved money and sent it home to his mother.

When he reached home in January 1950, he enrolled in art classes at night in the professional school of a museum with a world-wide reputation. By day he worked as a porter in a supermarket. He was a good student. But one infers this was a heart-breaking time for Carl, yet he took no one into his confidence except for once remarking to one of the brothers that it was discouraging to find he simply could not afford the many supplies which art instruction called for. It turned out that because of the timing of his service he was, after all, ineligible for G.I. assistance. Moreover, his mother had felt compelled to use his saved pay to pay household bills. So Carl, at 22, found himself with no professional training, no money of his own, and no hope of any from his parents. When he left art school at the end of his first term, he told them all that he did not want to be an artist. He never painted after that, except for one occasion, years later, in hospital therapy.

It was at this time that the family, recalling events eight years later, began noticing a great change in him which his mother in retrospect identified as the beginning of the illness that was to dominate his life thereafter. Formerly "full of fun," talkative at meals, and interested in the events and all the new things that the newspapers brought to his attention, he now was subdued and withdrawn. He began to refuse invitations and to neglect old friends.

He continued to work at the supermarket but two months after he left art school he declared that he had a "special calling," that he could not tell them about it and that there was "no room in his calling for art." In April 1950, he went to Kentucky to spend a week as the guest of a Trappist monastery. His mother was thrilled by his religious vocation and his father was proud of a son who was "willing to go all the way," to renounce the world utterly as a cloistered monk, vowed to silence, rather than to compromise with the world as a priest does. But on returning he announced that they had "asked too much" of him and that "it did not fit in with" his plan. The plan remained a secret.

Leaving his job at the supermarket late in the year, he set out on the way west and wrote from Ohio, "This is the last letter you will receive from me." He reached California where he found work in a dairy which lasted until some time in 1952, with a three-months' break in the summer of 1951 when he had worked in a lumber camp in Arizona. Then, a year after they had last heard from him, the Duncans suddenly received a letter from an engineer in Arizona who reported finding Carl, fasting and praying in the desert. This had been his mode of life for the preceding seven months. The letter was followed by one from a sheriff reporting that their son was mentally ill and would have to be taken home. Yale undertook it. He found Carl shockingly emaciated, his clothing dropping from him in rags, bearded and solemn with staring gaze. He could not be induced to talk of himself or reveal what had happened, beyond confiding to his father that he had become immortal and was engaged in a "mission, an abstract purpose." Three days after Yale brought him back they took him to a state hospital.

He was committed and diagnosed as schizophrenic. "I'm supernatural," he declared. "I have enough power in my little finger to destroy thousands." He was under the impression that his family had brought him to the hospital for a physical examination and he kept insisting that he should be allowed to go. After a course of shock treatments he was able to talk rationally about his days in the desert, only, however, to the extent of admitting that he had been surprised to find his money had not lasted as long as he had expected and that he had almost starved.

This was Carl's first time in the hospital. He entered on March 30, 1953, and remained there until July 13, when his mother, too impatient to wait, brought him home without an official discharge. After that he was in the community for two years, one and a half months ending on August 29, 1955. At least at first he seemed to be his old sociable self.

As soon as he was released, Carl hunted for work and found himself a position as a bookkeeper in a trust company. He held it for five months when he was let out because he "was not quick enough for them" and "they expected too much of me." His mother said that he enjoyed the work and was "very regular in his habits." He soon obtained a second post of the same kind, which came to the same end. There followed a succession of small office jobs, terminated in some instances by himself, in others by his employer, of which the last was a job of clerking in a bank; it lasted a week and a half. By now Carl had found he "did not care for that kind of work. Too trying." He told his mother he was going to make a ten-day retreat among the Trappists in Kentucky again. She felt this was his own decision and made no attempt to change his mind.

True to his promise, Carl was back in ten days. But he was uncommunicative, sitting about all day, talking to no one, listening to the radio, and day dreaming. He did look for a job, found one, kept it for one week, and lost it. That was in March 1955. He was described as failing rapidly; he flew into temper tantrums, broke dishes, accused his family of persecuting him, and otherwise refused to talk to anyone.

In August, after five months of idleness and irrational, violent behavior, he was taken to another state hospital. The diagnosis was "schizophrenic reaction, affective, suggestions of catatonia"; later on, "paranoid" was added. Throughout the whole seven months of his stay there he insisted it was all a mistake, that he did not belong there but should be at home where he "wanted to decide" upon what work he wished to do.

He was released at the end of March 1956, and almost at once found himself a place as a typing and filing clerk in an investment house. This lasted five weeks at the end of which he was discharged; as he put it, he "made a lot of mistakes and was fired." He seems to have had no other work between then and July when he was sent back to the hospital; the precipitating conditions were the same sort of behavior as had sent him there a year before. He would shout at members of the family, "What are you doing to me? Why are you persecuting me?" and he would hold bizarre poses and engage in odd repetitious rituals.

This time he was in the institution for three months and one week. As before, he insisted it was all a mistake and that he should be freed.

A Thematic Apperception Test revealed that he was a person who set himself impossibly high goals. He had to do better than others, to invent "new and superior methods." Sensing his failure to attain these heights, so ran the diagnosis, Carl suffered from a conviction of nothingness, of no status; he knew he had built his life badly and was filled with self-loathing. His therapist considered him incapable of planning for himself and noted on the record: "Goals will have to be limited for this 29-year-old, bright, talented, terribly anxious, sensitive, withdrawn man, who holds on to his impulses and forces a façade of extremely strained relationships with people, despite an underlying longing for affection." The therapist notwithstanding, Carl was *full* of plans: he wanted to get work when released which would exploit his talents, and hit upon drafting. If he found he was deficient, he would take correspondence courses. And he thought he would get a room and live alone as he was not getting on well with the family.

This is exactly what he did. Released in October 1956, "cheery and talkative," he spent two weeks at home. Then one day he failed to come home for dinner. He had got a job making precision measurements for a photographic firm and had rented himself a room. But this brave gesture could not be sustained: in three weeks he had lost the job, run out of money, and had no choice but to go home. Discussing it later, he observed it was work for which he was unprepared and in which he had no interest.

Two weeks later, Carl was showing alarming symptoms. Whenever anyone began to talk he would clear his throat so loudly and insistently as to drown out the speaker, most particularly if it were his father. This continued for a fortnight, until the Duncans found it intolerable and at his mother's request and with the help of the police he was taken back again to the hospital. He had been home for nine weeks.

He remained in the hospital for about forty days. Once again he proclaimed himself perfectly well, in no need of medical attention and, in fact, there only because of some error. But the therapist by now was raising the question of transferring him to an institution for chronic cases. He was released, but at the end of one month and twelve days he was back again and for an equal length of time. Then, at the end of April 1957, he was released and this time he lived in the community for one year and two weeks.

There is no evidence that he found or even sought work in all that time, nineteen months, since his last post, the three-week stint of precision-measuring. In the winter of 1958 he did ask one of his brothers to buy him a drafting book and then set himself up in the basement workshop, practicing with pen and pencil for hours. But Yale said it was nothing more than copy work. "Nevertheless," said his mother afterwards, "he was working hard. It may have been a strain."

In the spring of 1958 Carl again began, as his family put it, "to fail." To Mrs. Duncan's horror he began for the first time to swear, screaming to God to "make them stop persecuting" him. He broke plates in a rage, insisted on eating alone, took elaborate precautions against being brushed against when anyone passed by him, ran the shower loudly for an hour in the morning and again at night, and went in for all manner of compulsive rituals. In a very uncommon admission of disability he admitted to his mother, "I don't have all my faculties, as you do." Carol accompanied him when, finally, two plainclothes detectives took him away for his sixth hospitalization. This was the study hospitalization, and lasted five weeks. He was 30 years old.

THE HOSPITAL PERIOD

There is almost no information available about Carl as a patient. He did not seem to have engaged in any intramural occupation. But his mind was evidently busy with plans for he told the interviewer that he intended to look for work as soon as he was released so that he could pay for a correspondence course for a "specific" job, but he did not say what it was. He insisted that he would hunt for himself and not draw upon the resources of the hospital because he did not want to be known as an ex-patient. When asked if it had occurred to him to try to get work while still living in the hospital he admitted that he knew of such a possibility but gave no reason why he had not taken advantage of it. On visits home on weekends he helped with the dishes, called on the neighbors, and gave many signs of a return to normal. At the end of five weeks he was in the community again. But not for long.

THE POSTHOSPITAL CAREER

This time Carl was in the community for just seventeen days. In that interlude he wrote five letters to agencies soliciting jobs—"well and accurately typed," said his mother. He received one reply, enclosing a form to be filled and returned. This he kept putting off and in the end he never mailed it back. "Carl puts off everything," sighed Mrs. Duncan. He sought part-time evening work so that he would not be on the job when other people were around and yet could be out of the house for perhaps three hours. Mrs. Duncan confessed to the interviewer that he had not been able to make use of his letters of reference from previous employers (going back to his year-long job in California) because she had put them away one day while house-cleaning. This time he did not help with the household chores as he had done before, and there is no record of his returning to his drafting. Thus it is clear that the seventeen days of freedom came to very little. His mother was of the opinion that he had not had time enough to find anything to do and also argued in favor of some sort of manual labor which would entail "less strain on his mind, yet keep him busy, which is the thing."

The precipitating circumstances of his next rehospitalization were more painful than ever. Carol had been having a visitor, a boy friend from New York, and she was terrified lest Carl should begin screaming, "Why is she persecuting me?" as he had been doing. Moreover, in addition to the swearing, which greatly offended his mother, he had grown morbidly sensitive to every sound and charged the family with making excessive noise to annoy him. Mrs. Duncan, cowed, had taken to wearing soft slippers and they all gave him a wide berth. But he complained of noise even when the house was silent. Finally, on a day when he appeared downstairs for meals for the first time at 4 in the afternoon, his parents sent for Yale who brought two plainclothes men and took him this time to the state hospital where he had gone on his first admission. (All five subsequent hospitalizations had been at another hospital.) It was July of 1958, almost exactly five years since he had left that institution. He was now entering upon his seventh hospitalization.

The family was frankly relieved when he left and agreed that he would have to stay away until he was so much improved that there could be peace and order in the house when he returned, "even if it took two or three years."

As it always had, Carl's mood changed rapidly in the hospital. For the first time he discussed his hallucinations freely with his mother when she visited him and began to admit the noises which had so tormented him might have been imaginary. Another new and promising manifestation was his inclination to talk of himself to his therapist and to tell him "all the things that were not my fault, for which (the family) is to blame." To his mother he observed that if a patient does not talk to his therapist "you just sink down among the forgotten." His parents were able to visit him together on weekends. Until now Mr. Duncan had sat in the car for forty-five minutes while she was with Carl, joining her in only the last quarter-hour of the visit. But now he went straight in with her for the full time and rejoiced in the fact that Carl, who as a boy had idolized him, was able to talk easily with him again.

Carl was convinced that his stay at home had been too short to do any good. It was "unfair": he had had too little time to find a job and "show" what he could do, and so in planning for his next return he decided upon a clerical job at night while no others were about, and art work by day. What he had disliked about some of his jobs, he said, were "the trivialities," the "menial disadvantages," phrases which turned out to mean monotony.

This time he was quite busy in the hospital. He practiced typing which he did quickly and accurately and took an interest in occupational therapy. He gave a hand in the moving into a new building, "The Studio," where he set himself to the task of painting the portrait of one of the nurses—the first time he is reported to have painted since he renounced it, and the last. Whereas hitherto he had ignored the money his family brought, he now began to use it at the canteen. For the first time he discussed other patients as sick people when his parents came. Still, his therapist pronounced him not yet ready to go to work. He was at home for longer and longer intervals now and by Christmas time it had stretched to five days at a time. Mr. Duncan was on his feet at last, although he was in debt and the house was mortgaged. These were pleasant times for the whole family. It was a relief to Carol who welcomed his help when she redecorated her room, yet she was understandably apprehensive at the thought of her approaching wedding and how he might behave.

By April 1959, the family thought he was "his old friendly self again." He helped with chores and seemed reconciled to the household sounds, except for still taking umbrage at his father's voice and his slightest movement. Now, for the first time, the family began to wonder if Carl connected his plight with his father's financial failure and with their use of his military pay for their own needs. (His mother had winced when this was mentioned during an interview.) But Mrs. Duncan was, as always, firm in the belief that she would "know he was cured the day he walks out that front door to work."

By October Carl, mentally recasting his career, arrived, reported the therapist, at the point where he declared that his idea that his employers had not liked him was probably of his own imagining. And now, too, he began to refer to possible stigma and the difficulties it might make in his search for work. It was as if he had got outside of himself and his illness and taken a hard look. But insight was only fleeting; it did not last.

At the beginning of the new year, 1960, Carl was permitted to alternate two-week visits at home with three-week stays in the hospital. Spring found him working on the hospital farm again, attending to the bookkeeping. He did well at it and said he felt "good." In his free time he was taking lessons in typing and drafting. In mid-June, two years and ten days after he had re-entered the hospital, he was released on the customary year-long trial visit, with the understanding he was to report regularly to a neighborhood clinic. He had no job but he "intended to get one soon" and repudiated the suggestion that he had "problems." At the end of that summer he was still job-hunting in a passive way: he had sent in his name to several agencies.

Some time in September he found a job as a machinist, the nature and suitability of which is not disclosed on the record. He quit the job before mid-October, when a return of symptoms compelled him to go back to the hospital. In January 1961, he had to give up keeping the hospital's farm books which he had taken over again, because persistent hallucinations and compulsive gestures interfered. In March, as this account of him ends, he was working in the hospital kitchen. Nearly six months had already been added to his long history of hospitalization, and the end was not in sight.

DISCUSSION

The tragedy of Carl Duncan is that of a broken career and a broken man. Like Arthur Jackson and Frank Monaco, Carl chose his profession in childhood and pursued it with single-minded determination as long as he could. Arthur eventually drifted out of physics and into work of a level far below what his original capacity and education had fitted him for and, as long as he was not ill, did well at each occupation; Frank compromised on a second profession. But Carl, thwarted in his artistic ambitions, never excelled at any alternative. His career, eroded by disappointment, gave way to illness and he ended completely unemployable. He adds to these accounts the case of the man who was a worker, at least at first, but who never had a career.

Career Pattern

As a boy Carl devoted his leisure to puppets, drawing, and painting. In high school he changed from the precollegiate course to the business course in order to save time for art. Thus he acquired immediately saleable clerical skills. At normal art school it took him just one semester to realize he did not want to *teach* art. By volunteering in the Coast Guard at that juncture he, as he thought, could accumulate funds to pay for art education later. He worked well in those three years in the service, saved his money, and was honorably discharged.

Until now he had deferred professional training in his chosen field. Now at last he was ready to enter seriously into training for professional art—only to be faced with the chilling facts that he was not eligible for G.I. money for schooling, that his family had spent his military pay, and that his father had no money. So he took a full-time job as a porter, and studied art at night. Discouraged in his attempt to keep up with his classes when he had not enough money for supplies, he broke off dramatically and told his family he was finished with art.

In grief and frustration he tried to renounce the world, but failed again: he was not accepted as a monk and when he resorted to a hermit's life he was snatched from it by the sheriff, defined as mentally ill and hospitalized. Thereafter his life consisted of futile attempts to finance, by little clerical jobs, an alternative career as an architectural draftsman—a more marketable form of art. It never worked; recurrent illness now dominated his life.

The impasse in his art education seems to have ruined what promised to be a normal career in the labor force. Like many boys, Carl began to work early, selling newspapers and magazines at the age of 9 and when in high school working in the neighborhood drugstore. He was 22 when he found his first full-time job—a porter in a supermarket. His military service was done creditably for the full three years. He must have worked continuously from 1950 to 1952 in California. Then came the first psychotic episode. After that the longest jobs he had were two positions as bank clerk, each of which he held for five months.

Here, then, was a young man whose vocational choice crystallized when he was young, who clung doggedly, despite monstrous discouragement, to his ambition. One can attribute to him striking continuity of purpose. But as to continuity in employment: it is true that in his first years after leaving high school he worked persistently, consistently, first in the Coast Guard and then in the civilian labor market and from all reports did well, but when his artistic ambitions collapsed and jobs became a way to finance his alternative career in drafting, his record changed drastically. He did badly and could not hold a position; he never knew a promotion and no post was ever an advance over the one before it or drew upon skills acquired in experience. There was no longer any stability. Of course by that time he was ill.

In this later phase, that he was mobile meant only that occupationally he was a rolling stone. Footloose in the labor market, his many moves, like Harold Lang's, were random, unrelated, and lacking in direction.

Qualifications for the Labor Market

Carl was always conscious of his lack of professional education. At the same time, he talked of portrait-painting as "too competitive." "Many fellows who studied art for four years at college can't make a living now." He took rational account of this in compromising on architectural drafting—or, more exactly, planning to do so—an adjustment which would have kept him in art but an art that was in demand. He never reached the point of seeking employment in it, although one suspects he might have succeeded. One must go through the regular courses, earn the certificate and get qualified, he said, before one could hope to be hired. Thus, in the end, he entertained two sets of standards and ambitions: impossibly high in art, where he had gifts but no training; very low in clerical work in which he had the advantage of a high school course. But his high school training in itself was limited; he lacked shorthand and of automatic aids he could handle only the adding machine. That he gave no sign of ever thinking of himself as a clerk makes questions of choice, commitment, and orientation inappropriate. But in his aborted career as an artist choice, commitment and orientation were early, unequivocal realities.

All his job-seeking was for office work because, as he said, he could do it; he had been trained in it. Carl was, after all, the first of the brothers and sisters who had to struggle for advanced professional education, and he may have overestimated its importance. Nevertheless he was prompt in job-hunting after the first few hospitalizations, but the time came when he stayed at home and made no effort to get work although he continued to talk of office work at night with correspondence courses in drafting on the side. Fearful of stigma, which he experienced only in his imagination, he never enlisted the hospital's help. Equally dependent, Albert Rossini had the advantage of always being able to turn to the union for work following hospitalization: Carl had no such backing.

Career Orientation

Everyone—his parents, his teachers, the community—whose pictorial history he illustrated when still a high school boy, and he himself, thought of Carl Duncan as cut out for the life of an artist, probably a professional portrait-painter. Not only had he natural gifts but also his expectations for himself and his ambitions were unswervingly focused upon it. The choice crystallized when he was barely old enough to go to school and he consistently directed his steps toward that goal. Up to the point when he declared that he was finished with art as his occupational choice, his plans for professional training—although they were never to be realized—and his orientation were all in focus.

The self-expressive pursuit of art would have been its own reward, but Carl was never to enter it. With money he was always open-handed: his mother said he would give any he had to anyone who needed it. (Nevertheless, he seems never to have intended that *all* his military pay should go to the family.) In his office jobs, on the other hand, his gratification was extrinsic, in the remuneration—yet not in the money itself but as the means to get into art. He never mentioned rewarding circumstances like the friendship of work-mates or fun in the office or the praises of the boss. In today and gone tomorrow, he was never in any one post long enough to gain proficiency, approval, or friends. When he spoke of the satisfaction of "routine in a job," he might have meant job security, something which he himself never experienced. Or he might have had in mind the stability which routine lends to personal life (and which Friedmann and Havighurst so well appreciate.) [1]

Once, after the study hospitalization, he presented a quite different light on the meaning of work. He wanted, he said, a job which would take three hours a day so that he could "get out of the house for part of the time." This was when he was catatonic and always in trouble at home, a time, too, when he was decidedly unemployable.

Career Contingencies: The Hospital

In nearly four years in mental hospitals, Carl seems to have spent a very small fraction of the time in hospital work and occupational therapy, except toward the end when he took up painting during his seventh hospitalization. His intramural occupations were dishwashing, painting chores, and bookkeeping. He did bookkeeping with fair success, but it was, of course, in no sense competitive. The hospital seemed not to have insisted that he go out into the community with a job assured. By ill luck, just when he hit upon the alternative of drafting and might have established himself in it as a way to salvage what looked like a blasted career, the therapist entered on his record: "The patient has spent ten of the past sixteen months in hospital, unable to make any adjustment to the outside world, and may have to be transferred to an institution for the chronically ill." The doctor had once suggested that Carl study drafting systematically while in the hospital but the plan had to yield to the exigencies of his illness. When the record ends, Carl was helping in the hospital kitchen and there was no mention of painting or occupational therapy of any kind.

In short, hospitalization, as far as Carl's working life was concerned, was purely an interruption. He salvaged nothing from it, occupationally—and in this his experience is reminiscent of two of the married patients among the eight: Peter Stone and David Field.

Career Contingencies: The Family

If the hospital provided Carl a moratorium on the thwarted life on the outside, it also gave him a respite when life at home grew intolerable for himself, as well as his family. The Duncans thought of themselves as a peaceable, united family, yet it is clear there was seething resentment beneath the calm exterior. The younger children, Carl among them, were in the painful position of loving and pitying their father yet of resenting his ineffectual performance as a breadwinner and the deprivations they kept telling themselves it had cost them. Even so Carl, more reticent than the others, said of his father, "He has done a lot for me" and of his mother, "She's very wonderful and nice to me at all times."

Sympathetic as she was, Mrs. Duncan seems to have had no clear idea of what ailed her son; and as for his father, from guilt or from lack of imagination, he was curiously detached from his son's ruined life. But they were patient with his accusations and vagaries up to the point when, during his last hospitalization, Mrs. Duncan burst out "We've had enough!" and implied that this time Carl would stay institutionalized until they had the assurance of a quiet household when he returned. One feels sure the time would come when Carl's fate would be wholly a function of the family's tolerance: when they had "had enough" they would bundle him off to the hospital; when his behavior had moderated, they would welcome him home: and then it all would begin again.

No one in the family circle was a model for Carl. There is no hint of a surrogate to replace his father when he abdicated. The older boys were successful in their careers; the younger brother, Douglas, was particularly energetic and ambitious. But Carl, dedicated to art and later on inspired by a special calling to a secret mission, must always have thought of himself as "different" and apart. There are no hints, however, as to the content of his hallucinations beyond that with them came a sense of persecution.

Mrs. Duncan soon came to be of the opinion that a job would solve all of Carl's difficulties, even those at home: "The important thing is to work at a job. It's steady and keeps him occupied while he's convalescing." A labor job, she decided, would "place no strain on his mind." Like Mrs. Lang, she thought the hospital should have a place "where fellows like him could go to get jobs: something special for them." Yet she had no illusions as to Carl's worth as an office worker, and she knew he could never hold a job.

In marked contrast to the Langs, the successful and more sophisticated Duncans made little effort to help their disadvantaged member to find work. He had to fend for himself, and did so, but he gives the impression of an applicant who may not have had sound notions of where and what to seek, or of how to exploit *himself* when facing a prospective employer.

One wonders whether the boy's parents were not, in reality, opposed to the prospect of seeing their son become an artist. It is one thing to have a high school boy excel in drawing and painting—it being distinctly understood that this is an indulgence of his leisure hours while the serious business of school goes on uninterrupted. The praise of Carl's teachers and the townsfolk and the favorable notice of the newspaper may have trapped the Duncans into accepting the definition of their son as a budding artist; Mrs. Duncan, too, had an artistic bent. But these were people cast in conventional mold. Quite possibly they thought of art as play and artists as odd characters who were not really workers; and hoped "he'd get over it." Certainly they were pleased when he felt "called" to the monastery and also when he turned to architectural drafting. In any case they did not mobilize their forces to help him, although it was their act in diverting his military pay that blocked his road. Affectionate as they were, they may not have admitted their disapproval of his choice of life work; yet, in the end, prevent it is exactly what they *did* do. For one different in temperament and in situation might have solved Carl's dilemma, but he was a boy who may have needed the support his apathetic kin never gave him. Generous help was not the clan's habit: when there was no money at home, Mrs. Duncan's millionaire brothers did not come forward except for a single occasion when the children were quarantined with scarlet fever and a sister-in-law sent her chauffeur with a load of groceries. However, Dick, himself an engineer, did back Douglas, also an engineer, in managing a family and a professional education. Perhaps the matter resolves itself, for this family at least, to the question: what is work?

Pattern of Career as Affected by Illness and Hospitalization

In the first few years of his ailment, Carl insistently denied his own condition. It was not until his fourth hospitalization that the therapist noted "he knows he has problems and might recover with treatment." There is, however, little indication that he ever entered into his own therapy. Not until after he had undergone many months of hospitalization and many vicissitudes of employment did he remark that stigma might make it hard to get placed. Apart from that one admission, his hallucinations of his "calling" and other, unrevealed preoccupations were too pervasive and too deep-seated to penetrate, and hardly anything is known of what he felt about himself and his plight.

Carl was unlucky in the duration and in the timing of his illness and his hospital stays. His ailment prevented him from ever getting a start in drafting and as for office work, his heart was never in it, and his search for work during those short stays in the community was unenthusiastic and not very productive. Notwithstanding a dozen natural advantages in talent, education, and family over the hapless Harold Lang, and a promising beginning, Carl seemed headed for the same end: negligible as a working member of society, consigned to alienation, gone from view, and forgotten.

Carl's dilemma might be summarily stated as an unsuccessful search for identity. He had no career—and in American society identity is largely defined by career. Occupationally, he never found his niche. He could not be an artist. He could not be a monk. He could not be a clerk. Nor did he find himself as an adult male. Just as he was entering into man's estate he sank into the condition of an invalid child, never a lover and no longer responsible for the direction of his own life.

NOTE

1. Eugene A. Friedmann and Robert J. Havighurst, *The Meaning of Work and Retirement*, Chicago: University of Chicago Press, 1954.

5 STUDENT TO WORKER: FRANK MONACO

In 1952, when he was a 19-year-old premedical undergraduate, Frank Monaco spent a short but unspecified period in a private mental hospital. In the next nine years he was to pass over six months in mental institutions, this being a total of seven more visits, all short and one for as little as ten days. In that time, too, he gained his B.A.; spent four and a half academic terms first in medical school and then dental school; finished a six-month stint in the Army Signal Corps; and held four jobs, two of which were teaching in suburban high schools. This record of his history ends as he entered his eighth hospitalization, a 28-year-old teacher who had just received notice of suspension.

His story was told by himself in eight interviews, by his father in five, his mother in one, and with his mother and his father, in a second; in addition to which there were talks with his therapist three times and with a nurse and a hospital social worker each once.

THE SETTING: PAST AND PRESENT

When Frank Monaco entered the study he was 24 years old. Dark in complexion, brash and overactive, he was assertively careless in dress and gave the impression of one who, although when well he might have taken pride in keeping fit—indeed it turned out he had played basketball on two university teams—had for the time being grown careless and flabby. His bearing toward the nurses bespoke a confidence in himself as a virile and attractive male which, when he was in the "high" phase of his illness, became gross aggression. At those times he spoke of himself as "Jack-in-the-Beanstalk Kinsey." His enjoyment of people was obvious: he was extremely sociable and encounters with him at the hospital were constantly interrupted as he hailed friends passing down the corridors.

Frank was ending his first stay in a state hospital (his previous admissions were to private hospitals) and in going home was rejoining his parents and an unmarried aunt whom Mr. Monaco had brought over from Italy the year before. The other Monaco child, Frank's senior by five years, was Louis, a university-trained mechanical engineer who had left home years before and now lived in the suburbs with his wife and two small children.

Frank's father was a heavy-set, excitable Italian who had come to the United States in 1924 when he was 22 years old. He had been able to afford only two years of study at the University of Naples but at every opportunity would sneak into medical lectures, fascinated and regretting that he himself could never be a physician. He became a bank clerk in Italy and found similar work on arriving here. He married a compatriot and the first child, Louis, was an infant when the depression closed banks and Mr. Monaco lost his job. Since he failed to obtain WPA employment, he energetically scrounged for work and found it in a market where, he said, he did everything from meat cutting to clerking. After five years he became a salesman for one of the largest New England insurance companies and was still one twenty-five years later. Self-confident and gregarious, he found he preferred it to banking: "you meet people all the time." Undeterred by the heavy Italian accent which he never lost, he made a comfortable living. He read and studied, made himself *au courant* with pertinent legislation and current practices and was wont to pass on his hard-earned wisdom in saws and clichés such as, "you have to sell yourself first; then your product." He constantly treated his sons to the saga of his own rise from an immigrant boy without friends or influence who weathered the depression to a competent businessman with useful political connections. The reward for the pain of leaving his father and his homeland was, as he put it, that it "made a new man of him."

As a father, remarked the interviewer, Mr. Monaco did not know where he left off and his son began. Yet a fierce preoccupation with his family did not preclude a certain civic sense, for, although heavily burdened with debts for Frank's illness and education, he kept up as though superstitiously a variety of small charities. He read child psychology in order to assuage anxiety about the boy, but it was cold comfort to find that it is customary today for children to ignore their parents' authority. "I'd hate to bring up a child now," he admitted, "I wouldn't know how to do it." Yet he persisted. Characteristic of his fussy interest the father drew up a daily schedule for Frank which would allocate his studying and his leisure to the best advantage. He insisted, "We let him alone, to decide for himself," yet Frank complained he had no independence with a father who would ask, "Are your shoes shined?"—"Do you need money to go to the show?" And as his mother's habit was to anticipate his wants and silently fill them, he was denied even the privilege of asking for things. There was no common talk between them.

Frank's mother was a self-effacing person, too pained at first by Frank's breakdown to go with her husband on his almost daily visits to the hospital. If little is known of her as an individual, it is because her husband or her son usurped the interviewer while she, a background presence, fluttered in with coffee and cake. Yet on the two occasions when the interviewer deliberately sought her out, she proved surprisingly firm and thoughtful. She depicted her husband as having high ambitions for Frank, worrying himself sick with disappointment and oscillating between unbounded indulgence and despairing indignation; while she herself was resigned, grief having given way to fatalism: "I just don't mind." When Frank was hospitalized for the fourth time she took a political job to help with paying the debts, and Mr. Monaco began working at night.

The Monacos lived at the time of the study hospitalization in a four-room apartment, old-fashioned but immaculately kept, on the second story of a two-flat building in a working-class section of Boston. The large front living room was also the parents' bedroom. Frank slept in a narrow alcove off it, just exactly wide enough for a single bed. Of late years, of course, Frank had rarely been there, for he had lived on campus since he was a junior in college. The aunt slept in an attic room. She was Mr. Monaco's only relative in the United States but his wife had five brothers and innumerable kin, many of whom lived close at hand.

Obsessive love dominated the atmosphere of the household, with Frank's struggle for autonomy occasionally breaking to the surface. When Louis married at the end of his schooling, Frank accused him of evading his responsibility for "taking care of our parents." Louis appears to have resolved the unpleasantness by staying away: in the four years spanned by this case study he was never on the scene. The father's natural grief at Frank's repeated psychotic episodes was aggravated by the sense of loss, as he was ambitious for Frank's hoped-for profession as though having a son in medicine, or even in dentistry, would make up for the fact he could not be a physician himself. His pride in Frank was in contrast to his feeling for Louis. Always a good student, the elder boy was said to defer study until the last minute and yet he always excelled at school. But Mr. Monaco referred to his profession, engineering, with contempt: "Why would a college boy do that?" And Frank, a good but less facile student, even after he had been dropped from three first-class institutions himself, sneered at his brother's choice of a less expensive and less famous university. None of them was ever heard to remark that Louis's choice was more in keeping with the family's means, and all appeared to agree that nothing was too good for Frank. For his part, Frank was openly envious of Louis's good academic record.

According to his father, Frank, even as a boy, set himself exalted standards and could not bear to be bested. All through school he measured himself against his classmates. And he had to be in the best high school and the best university. He was a "sore" loser and would sulk for days if his team lost a basketball game. His father claimed that his own ambitions for Frank were more modest, a better and more secure life than he had had.

A chronological summary of Frank's work history and hospitalizations is as follows:

1950–1954: Frank was an undergraduate at one of the country's foremost universities, and was awarded the B.A. degree in 1954. He spent the summer before his junior year working as a doorman in a resort hotel. He fell in love with a girl of whom his parents disapproved, agreed not to see her anymore, and then slashed his wrist in an attempt at suicide. He was sent to a private psychiatric hospital for a short stay, where he was diagnosed as acutely psychotic. He was then 18 years old. He spent the other summers during his college years as a camp counsellor.

1954–1955: In the fall he entered the medical school of another famous university, but two weeks before the examinations in the spring of 1955, he was hospitalized for a total of three weeks, first for two weeks at the university's psychiatric clinic and hospital and then for a week at the private hospital in Boston where he had been admitted for his first hospital stay. In the fall of 1955 he went back to medical school to take the first year of work over again, having rested all summer.

1956: He remained at medical school until spring, when he again left, this time for good. He was then given private therapy at his father's insistence. In the fall he entered the dental school of still another university, again a leading institution. But in a little over a month he had to be taken home and hospitalized at the private institution where he had been admitted twice before. He stayed there for three weeks in November, was then at home for three weeks receiving private therapy, and was rehospitalized on Christmas Day, this time at another private hospital.

1957: Frank's stay at this hospital lasted forty days, and ended in early February, when he was transferred to a state hospital. He remained at the state hospital for two and a half months, until late April. This was the study hospitalization, and his release ended a series of sojourns in three different institutions during 1956–1957 totaling five and a half months. He began job-hunting soon after his return home and two months later found a place as a salesman for a wholesale drug firm. He held this job for seven months.

1958: Frank was discharged from his job as drug salesman in February. In that month the Monacos purchased a house and Frank helped with the moving, while again job-hunting. After a month he found a place in a federal tax office but left it after one month to enter the Army Signal Corps. His tour of active duty was for six months only, from April to September. After his discharge, he took a teaching position in a suburban school, but it is not clear whether he took the job in the fall or when the spring term began in February 1959.

1959: He taught school until summer, then took a three-week holiday in Los Angeles. At the end of the summer he became depressed but overcame it without hospitalization. That fall he moved to a high school in another suburb and taught tenth-grade physiology and biology.

1960: By spring he had gained his heart's desire, a red convertible. He continued teaching, and began dating a former girl friend who was now married. This affair ended when the girl returned to the city where she resided (she had been visiting in Boston), and Frank went to Europe for his summer vacation. There he suffered a slight concussion in a traffic accident. He began private therapy on his return to teaching school in the fall. That winter he was often out very late at night or out of town for weekends, his parents knowing nothing of where he was or what he was doing.

1961: During March and April he grew threatening and paranoid, losing interest in teaching and complaining that the students made fun of him. In mid-May he was suspended for inappropriate and violent behavior. He had been having an affair with an airline stewardess which ended at this time. He sought therapy at a Roman Catholic shrine, developed delusions of grandeur and finally grew so unmanageable that his parents had him taken back to the same state hospital by the police. He was hospitalized ten days, stayed in the community seventeen days and was rehospitalized at another state hospital in mid-June. He was still there in August when contact with the case was terminated.

Before the series of hospitalizations that began in the winter of 1956, Frank spent more than five years in three different universities. Between the winter of 1956 and the summer of 1961, he spent a total of almost six months in three different hospitals and at the end of this time was committed to a fourth hospital. He served six months in the Army and was employed for over three years in four jobs, as a drug salesman, in a tax office, and as a teacher in two high schools.

THE PREHOSPITAL CAREER

When Frank was a small boy he suffered a succession of illnesses and accidents which brought him for four or five weeks at a time into pleasurable association with hospitals, nurses, and doctors. And when he exclaimed to his doting father, "I love the doctors!" he was voicing an early predilection that gave direction years later to his ambitions for a career and was to have a fateful effect upon his adult life. Mr. Monaco needed no encouragement to keep the matter of a medical career to the fore. During one of Frank's illnesses, he pestered the doctor so often and at such unreasonable times that the latter in self-defense gave him medical books to read.

From babyhood, Frank had been a special child in his father's eyes. Louis had started school when a second son, a baby not quite two years old, died of pneumonia, a loss the father mourned so deeply that twenty-four years later he could not speak of it without tears. Born a year after this heavy blow, Frank became his comfort and joy.

It was something of an anomaly for Frank, the child of immigrants from the wrong side of the tracks, to get into one of the best of the city's public schools, in the fifth grade. It took him far out of his own neighborhood among boys he did not know. But he made a popular and successful student, became captain of the basketball team, and despite his accidents and ailments made creditable progress. The principal recommended him for a scholarship in a top-flight university, when it came time to leave the school, but he reduced it to a half-stipend when he caught him bouncing a ball in the corridors. Mr. Monaco used personal persuasion, including tears, but could not move him.

Entering one of the best universities in 1950 at the age of 18, Frank attained the B.A. degree four years later. He spent the summers as a camp counsellor, except for the summer at the end of his sophomore year, when he worked as doorman in a resort hotel. He was putting aside his earnings to realize a plan long entertained by his parents and himself—to leave home and move into a dormitory. But in the middle of what looked like a promising undergraduate career he fell in love with a girl he met while working at the hotel. Nothing is known of her except that his parents would not accept her; moreover, Mrs. Monaco induced Frank to promise to stop seeing her as they both had their schooling to finish.

Wallowing in thwarted love—he was high-strung and excitable—and tormented by guilt that his parents were making such a sacrifice to give him an expensive education, Frank spent a week haunting night clubs and drinking heavily and in a moment of extreme depression slashed his wrist. It was a severe wound. He was wildly excited and his parents took him to a highly reputed and high-priced private institution. The mere fact of incarceration seemed to do the trick: although acutely psychotic on admission, Frank very rapidly recovered and after a short stay he was sent home.

Frank always said he wanted to be a professional man—and he idolized doctors. All his life, he recalled, his parents had made remarks like: "It's nice to be a doctor." So it came naturally to him to think of himself as destined for the medical profession and to despise business, which people engage in without idealism, "just to make money." So, with his four undergraduate years behind him, he entered the medical school of another Ivy League university, again a world-famed institution, in the fall of 1954. But as the spring examinations drew near he became disturbed and could not face the ordeal. He was sent to the university clinic and hospital. He recovered quickly, as before, but it was a mortifying experience. As he said afterward, being there at all was bad enough, but just as bad was having nothing to do and being seen there in "psycho" by his classmates.

After two weeks he was transferred to the private hospital in his home city where he had been four years before. He was released after a week. It was early April 1955. He returned to the university against the assistant dean's advice, but he did not sit for the examinations. At the urging of his parents he loafed and rested all that summer.

When the fall term opened in 1955, Frank went back to repeat the first year of the medical course. He could not keep it up, however, and he left the university, this time for good, in the spring. He explained that seven or eight hours of reading and studying a day were "too much" for him. Again he had a summer of rest and recuperation.

Frank by now had begun to face the facts of medical education. He, or his father, owed $1400 to his undergraduate school and a similar sum to the medical school, as well as huge hospital bills. And so he turned to dentistry as a compromise. For one thing, study for it was shorter than a medical course. As a medical student he had been admitted to an accelerated program, giving him two years of credit for one year of work. Dentistry, too, was a well-respected profession which, as he now began to appreciate, would bring in money quickly. So in the fall of 1956 he applied for admission to the dental school of still a third university. This, as all Frank's choices, was a school with a national reputation. Meanwhile his father had arranged for a private psychiatrist to treat him. He was in the middle of a course of shock treatments when the dean of the dental school telephoned to say he had been accepted. Mr. Monaco was away but his wife borrowed money from her sister-in-law and sent Frank off at once by plane. She always felt guilty over having cut short the treatments, but she knew about the long waiting lists of the professional schools and at the time saw it as Frank's great chance.

In his first year of dentistry, Frank declared he had at last found his métier: it intrigued him to work alternately with books and then with his hands. But this bright beginning did not last. By mid-November, he had become manic and confused, and two weeks before the examinations his father was sent for. When he reached the campus, the distracted parent could find no trace of the boy. His room was in disorder and his roommate could only suggest the names of likely haunts. Finally he found him in a tavern, disoriented and giving the impression of being intoxicated.

Having a deep fear of state institutions, Mr. Monaco arranged again to have Frank admitted to the hospital where twice already he had been a patient. On admission Frank kissed nurses, clowned and acted "high"—to keep from thinking of the horror of being there, he explained later. There he stayed for three weeks in November of 1956. He was released at the beginning of December and again his father called in the private therapist. But at the end of three weeks, on Christmas Day, he had to be rehospitalized.

Frank had gone with a friend to a wedding, although he barely knew the principals. But during the celebration, he said, he grew depressed at the thought of marriage which for most young people means severing the parental tie. He himself wished very much to be married but the thought of leaving home was agonizing, and he wondered if he could bring a bride to live in the basement of his parents' apartment building. He drank heavily and was taken home truculent and confused. His father called in the private psychiatrist who again began a series of treatments. After some initial improvement, Frank began to slip and in the end he was taken to another private hospital in the Boston area and, after forty days, was transferred to one of the state hospitals that serve Boston. Mr. Monaco, distracted by a bill of $1000 from the psychiatrist, could no longer afford to indulge his prejudice against state institutions which he thought of as waystations to oblivion, but it was an unexpected relief to him to find the treatment in this hospital more aggressive and effective than any Frank had experienced.

THE HOSPITAL PERIOD

This stay in the state hospital, which was the study hospitalization, lasted from early February to late April 1957, but actually Frank had been hospitalized continuously for over four months by the time it ended, since he had spent six weeks in a private hospital just before this admission.

At the outset he was a difficult patient. He was "high" and violent, sexually aggressive to the nurses, masturbated openly, stripped off his clothing, loudly denied his illness, and was uncooperative in therapy.

All this, he kept insisting, was to take his mind off the awful fact of incarceration for mental illness: "All my education! And look at me now!" he moaned. He soon grew quieter and spent the balance of his hospital stay lying in bed, reading or brooding. He took no interest in occupational therapy or hospital industry and sought no outside work—nor did he seek work at any time during several terms in hospitals. He made many friends, however, among the patients and was gregarious and talkative. But, as in the university clinic, it was a constant mortification to be discovered there by his former classmates from the medical school, for it dramatized the gulf between his current situation and theirs.

The hospital gave Frank time to think. On the recommendation of the doctors, his father now disclosed to him the full extent of the family's indebtedness on his account. Frank cried. Now he painfully reviewed his situation and only arrived at a miserable state of indecision. Should he take a job as soon as he was released in order to earn money and reduce the bills? Or should he go back to dental school, set up a practice as quickly as possible and bring in money that way? He had not burned his bridges, at any rate—when a fellow student offered to buy $750 worth of instruments from him Frank refused, for he wanted to keep the way open to return to the university. But at best it would be some years before he would be earning.

To go into business, which he regarded as mere money-grubbing, would mean altering his life's outlook. Since childhood he had idealized doctors—but the courses were hard and he was sure he would "crack up again" if he undertook returning to school. He reasoned that he "hadn't what it takes" and blamed the repeated psychotic episodes on the strain of having attempted what he really in his heart of hearts did not want to do. And he admitted to himself that what he wanted was a sports car, *immediately*. He would like to be able to live like his friend, an attorney's son, who had a convertible and "all kinds of money. He could go to the race track every day and drop a twenty-dollar bill and think nothing of it." A red sports car, spending money, a college education and, after all that, a wife and family, and a home of his own. But this certainly entailed an immediate job and the abandonment of professional ambition.

Of course there were other professions, some of which required shorter preparation. He entertained the idea of industrial management.

And he studied a brochure describing a course in public health. As a professional man, no matter which profession, he could take holidays just when he wanted them—another advantage over business.

His father had been working in the evenings for the past year and his mother had taken a political job—all in an effort to keep abreast of the mounting bills and, as Mr. Monaco put it, largely in vain, for they seemed to need more money than ever. If Frank *did* decide to return to dentistry he knew his parents would give him every penny they had but he could not ask them to send him away to school; he would have to be content with studying in one of the local universities and living at home. But that brought him squarely before an additional dilemma: although torn, he believed he had to leave home to achieve personal autonomy.

One argument for returning to dentistry was that after four or five years of practice he could reward his "wonderful parents" by buying them a house with some land about it, as his father had had in Italy. "I've known many wealthy fellows," he said, "but I never knew anybody with parents as wonderful as mine. They have worked hard all their lives and what have they got?" His father should retire on the land and enjoy his declining years. But Frank never told his father this. He did say, from time to time, "Give me two or three years and I'll take care of you," to which his father always responded by saying he would have his pension and did not need help. And Frank felt he owed his father grandchildren. He certainly wanted to get married and thought it was time. And here he faced another impasse. He could have a wife by giving the word to Victoria, his father's god-daughter. He and Victoria had grown up together and she was in love with him. But she was too much like a sister for Frank to "have any fun with her." Fun with girls was important to him; he often referred boastfully to his strong sexual drive and used to appear in the hospital smeared with lipstick which he proudly exhibited as proof of popularity. But because of his particular relationship to Victoria he preferred even blind dates to evenings with her. Characteristically, he let the matter ride; she and his parents considered they were engaged but Frank never actually committed himself.

There was still another complication—his military service. Until now (he was 24 years old) he had been deferred as a medical student. If he left that category to take a job, he would become 4F because of his illness. This would stand in the way of employment and was at all cost to be avoided. As a matter of fact the Monacos were all acutely sensitive to possible stigma and had shared the knowledge of Frank's prolonged hospitalization only with Victoria and his former roommate. Prone as he was to deny reality and deal in subterfuges, Frank even contrived to make a public virtue of his plight: "My father," he told the interviewer, "pays to keep me here as a subject of research!" But he was preoccupied with the irreconcilable circumstances of his situation and appreciated the hospital as a refuge.

THE POSTHOSPITAL CAREER

Frank left the hospital at the end of April 1957. His father, discussing what he should do next, would begin with the happy phrase "Now that he's cured. . . ." The boy had had almost six months to reconsider his life. Some of the puzzling incompatibilities solved themselves; others he settled by default. It was too late to re-enter the university, so that question could be put off until after the summer. His Selective Service classification was still as a deferred student, and he was under no pressure in that direction—at least for the time being. He lamented the time his illness cost him, and vowed he would not rest on going home but would get to work at once.

On his second day at home he applied at the dental college of a local university, only to learn that registration was filled for the next two years. Of course he knew he would have had to live at home if he had enrolled there and living at home, he said, was his greatest problem: "I can't develop at home."

He consulted the openings listed in the student placement bureau of the university where he took his baccalaureate, but they disgusted him: department store jobs "fit only for high school boys"; clerical work at pay offensively low. His early elation at being home gave place to apathy and despair. "Look where I've ended!" he exclaimed. "How am I to know that I won't break again? It's your self-respect that goes." However, for the next three weeks he threw himself into the search for work. Eventually he faced the choice between two possibilities—one was selling insurance, the other was paper work in the loan department of a bank. Neither appealed to him, yet he knew he could not stand the summer with nothing to do. "There's nothing in business, just money-making." He began to talk of social work which, at least, was doing something with and for people. Even the bank job, if it meant recommending clients for loans, had its good side.

The trouble was he was in a hurry. He asked the interviewer, "After all those years of study, does your Ph.D. really pay off?" He recast his ambitions, giving first place to a car and an education, then stipulated an income of not less than $85 or $90 a week with prospects of advancement, and finally faced the question, "Do I really want a job? I'm not lazy; I'm ambitious. But I don't know where to direct my steps." In the end he decided to take a year to make up his mind whether he would return to his interrupted professional training or cast his lot with business which, purposeless and unworthy though he had always thought it, at least meant an immediate income.

He had come to no decision about jobs when his father persuaded him to take tests for employment in the insurance company in which he himself had been working for so many years. But it came to nothing. Frank was "not aggressive enough," Mr. Monaco complained. Frank, on his side, complained one did not need to know anything for that kind of work and $75 a week was too little. His father then found him a political job that paid $47 a week for three days of work and when Frank again complained it was not enough, he offered to pay him the difference making up the sum the boy thought he should have. Frank turned down a second patronage job and then the father hit upon the idea of traveling and selling for a wholesaler. Both were pleased when Frank found a place with a tobacco wholesale house. But when his prospective employer learned his draft status and the reason for it and realized that Frank could not get a driver's license, he refused to hire him. After that Frank was offered, but then refused, a position as organizer of suburban health groups at $67 a week. Again he considered the salary too low; moreover, he was intimidated by the fact that most of the others who worked there held M.A. degrees.

By this time father and son had come to the conclusion that Frank had best say nothing about his Selective Service classification. Strictly speaking, he had lost his exemption as a student but the sympathetic local draft board had told him there was no need to hurry. Frank took the matter hard: "I don't mind being 4F for myself. But what will I tell my children?"

Frank was presumably still Victoria's fiancé, but he was seeing a girl he had met while in medical school and, at the same time, another whom he knew as an undergraduate. This third girl hurt him deeply by suddenly refusing his invitations. He seemed destined to be dogged by girl trouble.

He was living at home which brought the inevitable conflicts. His parents believed that they "just let him alone" . . . "just let him decide for himself" . . . and so on. But actually his father never ceased his efforts to take charge of his son's life. "Why must you see him so often?" he demanded, referring to a former patient, for it made him unhappy to think that Frank should consort with other mental patients as though they could be his natural friends. "It's all right to sleep late, since you're convalescing," he would say. "But make up your mind. If you want to land a job you have to apply first thing in the morning." And yet the whole time the Monacos kept telling him to "Take it easy." For they, too, had not made up their minds, but Frank found their insinuations an insupportable invasion and there was constant bickering.

By arrangement before he left the hospital, Frank was to report weekly to his therapist. But he began to miss his appointments. As he saw it, if he went to the doctor it meant he was ill again. If he did not, it meant he was well. So, in reality, when he most needed help he was most disposed not to seek it. Nonetheless, he surmounted a minor crisis of depression in late summer and in the end he was to stay in the community for over three years, during most of which he was employed at work which he enjoyed and for which he certainly had no need to feel apologetic.

After three weeks of hunting, Frank found a job through the placement lists of his university, selling pharmaceuticals for a wholesale drug firm. This, his first real job, was a good one, conforming to all the standards he had set up. The pay began at $84 a week and a delightful feature of the position was that it brought the use of a company car, even for personal purposes. As his name remained on the rolls of the dental college he had briefly attended, he was still classified as a student and exempt from the draft. Many of his associates at work were pharmacists.

But curiously, although he could be reduced to tears by the bare mention of the debts incurred on his behalf, he contributed nothing to paying them, nor even to the family's expenses, except sporadically. He explained that in June when he first got the job and for the next two months he had to buy all sorts of things—clothes, records, a record-player, and so on. But he planned to put aside some money when September came, hoping in a year to have saved as much, perhaps, as $3000 toward his return to dental school. Four and a half months later, however, he had given his father "some money" to help pay off the debts but he had not saved anything.

He had been too busy all that summer in his new job to see his therapist, but he returned to him for advice and moral support at a time of discouragement when he had been reprimanded by the sales manager for neglecting the reports and paper work which were the only aspects of the work which he disliked. He weathered the crisis well. From his weekly performance he anticipated no difficulty in making the quota of sales assigned to him. In fact he was such a successful salesman that the general manager wrote him a congratulatory letter—and then he began to take advantage of his accomplishment, to loaf. He enjoyed contact with doctors, but what hurt him, he said, was "seeing the fifty out of three hundred doctors who were bad doctors, dragging down $40,000 a year," and he concluded he himself was too sensitive and too interested in people to stay in this job for life.

By November Frank had begun giving his father his paychecks and asking back whatever he needed, sums which, although they were considerable, were never questioned by Mr. Monaco. His illness in the current year had cost $1315, yet they allowed him to think that all the bills but one of $1400 due to the medical school had been paid. "He has worries enough," explained his father. "Why give him more?" And so Frank continued to be a child in money matters. The interviewer heard him inviting a friend who suffered from muscular dystrophy to bring his family and dine with him at a restaurant; but his father stepped in, reminding him they were in debt. Mr. Monaco spoke of the incident with fond pride as though it proved Frank's generous sympathy with the unfortunate.

Frank was now nearing the age of 25. He still thought of returning to dental school and of marrying. He spoke of his father as being the right age now to enjoy grandchildren and felt he owed this to him. He wanted a house of his own (never an apartment) and it was to be near his parents, as this was the custom in Italy. In July he was going to have to make some sort of decision: either he would re-enter the university and continue to be exempted from the draft; or he could be shifted into the class of 4F, a price he was very loath to pay. He could, of course, marry and go into dentistry. He had plenty of girl friends; yet, although he had a car to drive, money to spend and free evenings to devote to them, he felt some girls might be afraid to marry him. "Mental illness is ruining my life," he moaned.

He began to have very serious doubts about dentistry as the career for him. Had he liked it, he wondered, because all through those last two terms in school he had been "hopped up" ? And suppose he graduated and began to practice, only to find that the fine work and the concentration were "too much for him"?

For seven months, until February 1958, Frank sold drugs. In the easy belief that he could fill his sales quota without effort, he would go to work late and end the day early. "It's only the married fellows who have to hustle," he argued. He took doctors' secretaries out on dates although it was against company rules, sought out former classmates and got orders from them, played basketball with them, and spent his off-hours with them. All this did something to feed his ambition to return to his first choice of a career. But his friends, he claimed, all envied his car and the money and evenings free of study: "It's one-twentieth of the strain of graduate school," he boasted. "If the fellows knew how good it is there wouldn't be so many of them in school." But he never fooled himself and there were times when his mood was black. He acknowledged to himself that he was no good at studying, and he stopped going to his fraternity meetings because "lots of those fellows are not good as I but they're getting ahead and I'm down." After six months he grew seriously worried about his sales record, which was now a glaring contrast to what it had been. "The trouble is," he admitted, "that I'm really no salesman." He worried incessantly about losing his job, and he worried that it should worry him.

The axe fell in February: he came home highly upset. He had quit, he confessed, at the same moment as he had been fired. It was a clash of personalities; the field manager wanted him to do everything *his* way: "Carry your bag like this," . . . "Greet the customers this way"— remarkably like Frank's father! And Frank had neglected his paper work. He rebelled and left the company, but he cried when he broke the news to his mother. Typically, Mr. Monaco called upon the general manager but could not induce him to step in. And he did his best to comfort Frank: "You're young. I lost jobs when I was young, too. You can afford to when you're young." Although he had been a good earner, somehow the family was no further ahead. Frank used to get money from his father to supplement his own earnings, then went to his mother for more; and she, naturally, had to go to her husband to make up her deficit. Indeed, Mr. Monaco encouraged Frank in more than one form of irresponsible behavior. Although angered that the boy never helped with household tasks in a family where both parents went out to work, he at the same time suggested extenuating circumstances: "Frank has mail to answer . . ." etc., etc.

It was just when Frank lost his job that Mr. Monaco bought a house, because "Frank needs more privacy." Frank took advantage of his enforced idleness to help with the moving. "If we had only known how much better this is," exclaimed his father, "we should have moved years ago." In fact the whole family were persuaded that if they had had more commodious living quarters Frank would not have fallen ill. Yet they admitted it was not a wise move. Mr. Monaco, who had borrowed all the money for it, even the down-payment, from his wife's brother, declared that he would be dead and buried before it was paid for. The loan was insured, however, and there was to be no hurry about repaying it. Still, the new house cost them at least $50 more a month than the apartment; and there were still mountainous debts to be met.

Mrs. Monaco described Frank as over-elated about the new house. He painted fences and porches and furnished a basement playroom which had its own entrance, planning a party there to take place on their second night in the house. And now he thought he should have to live at home for four or five years more to help pay off the mortgage. His father declared the house was to be his if he would take care of it.

Selling, Frank began to realize, was more satisfying to him than graduate study. Yet a professional career had not quite lost its spell and he went back to the idea of some professional pursuit with a shorter preparation. All the while he found it hard to admit his plight: "How could it happen to a guy like me? I'm athletic. I'm intelligent. How could I fail like that?" He hunted employment persistently, turning down, as before, openings which did not meet his specifications. He explained to a personnel manager that he was 4F because of high blood pressure but the company doctor exposed the deceit. Thereafter he resolved not to mention his draft status to prospective employers.

After a month of seeking a job he got a place in a federal tax office (how he obtained the job is not known), evidently not expecting to be there long; and indeed, four weeks later he joined the Army Signal Corps. On April 20, 1958, he left for Fort Dix in high spirits. This was a sensible move, for in July his draft status would change. Frank entered the Army under a plan whereby a man served only six months, but undertook to be on active reserve for five years after that. He acted on Mr. Monaco's urging, for the father was of the opinion that while Frank might be able to stand six months of Army life, the usual two-year stint would be beyond him. He even liked the Army.

Quite characteristically, Frank was in the midst of a love affair at the time he joined the Army. A girl he knew from his days at medical school had come to Boston with her husband for the spring and summer and she and Frank revived the old flame. The Army separated them, however, and when Frank was discharged in September she and her husband had already left town.

In September Frank's Army service was finished. It had been just what he wanted. He had lost forty pounds and looked fit. He was supposed to be engaged, but always spoke noncommittally about it. He was depressed on re-entering civilian life, but things brightened when he found a place which brought him the gratification of capitalizing on his university studies—teaching English in a surburban high school. To all appearances he made a good teacher. During the summer of 1959 he went for a short trip to Los Angeles, and he seems not to have worked at all during the vacation. The interviewer met him on the street, driving a red convertible with a beautiful blonde, a fellow teacher, beside him in the front seat; both were in tennis clothes. In that short encounter he gave the impression of one who is satisfied with life, but he looked ill. Plainly he now had attained most of the things he wanted; it remained, as he remarked, to marry and settle down.

In the succeeding fall Frank moved to another suburban high school where he taught physiology and biology. In the summer of 1960 he took a short trip abroad and somewhere in Europe suffered a concussion in a traffic accident. On his return he was depressed and paranoid, as he had been at the same time the year before. He complained that "the kids make fun of me behind my back." With the help of private therapy in the next two months, however, he recovered and terminated treatment. Mr. and Mrs. Monaco were satisfied with the turn his career had taken and proud of having a teacher in the family.

As that winter progressed Frank's movements began to mystify them. He went off for long weekends at some unknown place and during the week came home very late from unexplained engagements. He struck them as tense and unhappy. By March 1961, he was again markedly paranoid and threatening. He lost all interest in teaching and found it impossible to concentrate and prepare lessons. He visited lawyers and the chief of police in an effort to have them circumvent "a plot" against him. His behavior in the classroom grew more and more bizarre and inappropriate. Finally in mid-May the principal suspended him for a Thursday and Friday. But he hung about the school, manic and threatening, and on Monday was definitely suspended.

He now suffered from megalomania and religious hallucinations. He spoke of himself as an agent of God, boasted that he could teach without preparation, and was so conversant with the law that he could control the board of education. Two days after leaving the school he drove off to a Roman Catholic shrine, telling his parents he was getting all the help he needed from the priest there and was putting himself in God's hands. He left the family car there at dawn, came home without it and throwing his things about in great disorder, packed as though going away. He told the family he was moving at last into an apartment of his own. In great distress, they called the police, who took him to the state hospital where he had been admitted twice before. Later they learned that a month before he had had a love affair with an airline hostess.

It took force to bring Frank to the hospital and once there he behaved wildly, manic to a degree he had never reached before. Yet a stay of ten days with medication brought him back. He kept insisting that he should return to his classes and to his apartment. It is not certain that he actually had leased living quarters or in any way positively committed himself to an independent ménage, but there is no doubt that he made much of the claim to have made the break at last and quitted the parental household.

He was released at the end of May. But the respite was to last only seventeen days. In mid-June 1961, he was admitted to a state hospital outside of Boston and was still there in August when contact with his case terminated.

DISCUSSION

The story of Frank Monaco adds to this series of careers, as affected by mental illness, the instance of a man who was deeply committed to a choice which crystallized in childhood but brought him to incompatible situations from which he was delivered by short, temporary retreats. Seven times in nine years (1952-1961) he withdrew into mental hospitals; for half a year the Army protected him from hard choices in the competitive world.

Victor Norton was a man who successfully sealed off his illness and hospitalization and was confident he could deal with his problems himself. Illness swamped Harold Lang before his career had achieved any form. Illness, although pervasive, in the case of Arthur Jackson was less devastating—it reduced him to a career on a lower level. And Frank Monaco, although from boyhood he wanted to go into medicine, was not the equal of his own ambition, and illness gave him a face-saving way out and directed his career into new channels.

Career Pattern

Up to the time he finished his undergraduate course, Frank's life followed a straight line, with a medical career as the goal. It was when he entered into professional education that he failed to cope with life. At the age of 24 this threw him for the first time into the labor market for a job.

At job-hunting, then and later on, he showed himself capable and persistent, almost the equal of Victor Norton. He knew exactly what he wanted from a job and refused those that did not offer what he wanted. Some jobs were "fit for high school kids;" others paid too little. He was not for a moment deceived by the token jobs his father found him through political connections nor tempted when his father offered to make up the wages to something more in keeping with the boy's education and intelligence. It took Frank two months to find his first real job—that of selling for the wholesale drug firm; and he held it for seven months.

It was apparently personal differences which caused him to lose the job as well as poor performance. The manager's tendency to try to control him must have been too painfully like his father's determination to do likewise at home. That his salesmanship, excellent at the outset, should deteriorate may have been because Frank never respected business and was finding it hard to reconstruct his life-goals. Nevertheless, on being dismissed, he straightway applied himself to job-hunting again and found the place in the tax office. Paper work had never appealed to him (and his dislike of it entered into his failure in the drug-selling job) but it seems probable that he sought a place which he could easily give up and indeed after four weeks he left it for the Signal Corps. This, again, was a well-calculated move, well-timed, and one he had to make. In selecting the six months' program of active service he appraised his staying powers cannily.

As a drug salesman Frank did well at first; then his record fell off. This was not because of illness, as was his later failure at teaching, but willful neglect. He did not believe in business or respect it, and he made no effort to stabilize his career in it. Then he went into teaching and for three years did well. His profession drew on his university work and there appears to have been advancement in moving from English which was not his forte but did get him into the school system, to biological science, which was. This was probably the best available profession for which he needed no further schooling—and Frank had come to see that he was not cut out for studying.

His career was now following one profession and getting ahead in it; in the last three years of his known history it had achieved stability. True, he was often ill, even when a teacher. Although etiological questions cannot be addressed here it is known that the bombardment continued, undiminished, at home and that his troubles with girls persisted. It may be hypothesized that his work at last was satisfying but his personal life was not and the trials in the latter occasioned manifestations in the former.

In the twenty-six months following the study hospitalization—which was the point at which he gave up professional education—Frank held three jobs, each one in a different field, calling for its own skills. This was experimental, exploratory. Then having learned by doing it that he did not want to go into business, although it brought adequate and immediate monetary rewards, he threw his lot in with the teaching profession and from the first was upwardly mobile in it.

Qualifications for the Labor Market

Unlike some of the other cases, Frank entered the labor market late. His protective and indulgent father seemed ready to give him complete support all through his college career and professional education. His summer situations were useful in giving him money to live on campus during the school year, but his first serious employment, with the drug wholesaler, was a real job. He got it during the recession of 1957 and entirely through his own efforts. He never accepted any of the half-dozen places his father found for him. When he gave up his lifelong ambition and settled on school teaching, he was adaptable enough to accept teaching classes in English in order to make a start, but lost no time in moving into subjects where he could salvage some of his university work.

He was apparently a subtle operator, winning his shrewd father's admiration of him as a salesman: for he knew how to balance his productiveness with the manager's disposition to raise quotas in consequence of good performance.

It was at this point in his career that Frank had his moment of truth; he was able to accept the fact (not wholly without pangs of regret) that to continue to prepare for dentistry was to invite disaster again. Realistically, he found a niche for himself in teaching, an admirable compromise in that it called for no additional preparation and yet made him a professional man.

Career Orientation

A child of immigrant parents from a neighborhood that was a foreign enclave in the city, Frank was a marginal man who must have started out socially handicapped yet through athletic prowess and some winning qualities made his way to popularity and also maintained a good scholastic record. He admits having smarted under the sense of being out of place. Then, too, it was a blow to him on entering medical school to find that among other able students he did not stand out. And when he, "the greatest," was reprimanded by the sales manager at his job, he could not endure being humbled and indulged in the outburst that provoked his discharge. Yet the high value he set on his own abilities must have been a powerful support.

During the study hospitalization, Frank began to reorganize his ideas of what he wanted in life. It was then that he left a pseudocrystallized choice to look into the alternatives. And from talk of "helping people" and "It's nice to be a doctor," he began to specify an income that would allow for some pleasures and indulgences, such as vacations at times and of lengths he would freely choose, a car, marriage, and a home of his own. He was, as his therapist observed, "very pleasure-loving." As he said over and over again, he wanted money and he wanted it quickly. Dentistry appealed to him as a compromise. It was a profession included among the healing arts, education for which was congenially divided between book work and handicraft, and, at the same time, an occupation with a shorter preparation and so more immediate rewards. He sought extrinsic satisfaction from work whose rewards are usually considered intrinsic.

Although an educated man who had passed through the best universities, Frank never talked of scholarly topics and gave an impression of intellectual unsophistication. One judges what he craved from a medical degree was the social standing earned with it, and the perquisites, particularly the enviable income. It is as if he saw himself not easing the sick and restoring health but commanding deference, earning undying gratitude, and driving a handsome car. In prolonged and frequent interviews he never mentioned the biological sciences as the content of his mind, but he did refer to being a doctor as an affair of status. When last seen, off to a tennis game in his red convertible with a beautiful girl as his partner, he seemed to have achieved almost all that he wanted from life.

Still to be won was a wife and a family. He spoke of grandchildren as something he owed to his "wonderful father." But when it came to moving away from home, he was still ambivalent. Toward the last of the interviewing, when he had either leased a place for himself or was on the verge of doing so, he was more manic and delusional than ever before. One suspects that the several girls to whom he was attached, in turn, must have recognized his immature inability to be weaned from home and to live an independent life in quarters of his own. The fault, apparently, was mutual: his father, noted the interviewer, did not know "where he leaves off and his son begins." Just when Frank had reached the point where he had the money and was conquering the ambivalence, his father, although deeply in debt still for the boy's education and illness, bought a house "so Frank can have more privacy." This thwarting, ensnaring gesture, was characteristic: all through his son's life he had determined just what the boy *ought* to be wanting and then anticipated it. But the trap was good for only a month: Frank escaped into the Army. There he had a reprieve from the tormenting problems of his career and, perhaps even more welcome and necessary to him, a respite from the insupportable pressure at home.

An objective to which Frank repeatedly referred was "to do something really big" to show his gratitude to his father and mother. When he thought of this he wanted to be a dentist, reasoning that in five or six years he could give his father a house and land, as he had had in Italy.

Career Contingencies: The Hospital

After he finished his second year of college, Frank was admitted for the first time to a mental institution. That summer he had been a hotel doorman; he had already worked as a summer camp counsellor. His work was before him and he had not yet begun the specific education for it when the first of the sudden stops that punctuated his life occurred.

It was a bitter blow to see his former classmates passing down the corridors as students and internes in his later hospital sojourns, while his own career was arrested. But he used the hospital as though it were a boardroom where he had meetings with himself to discuss policy. The hospital offered him a refuge from a too-burdened life, as did the Army and trips to California and Europe. And although his father was an unusually frequent visitor to the hospital, the boy at least could escape the unremitting supervision over his affairs which his father arrogated to himself. Loafing, reading, and noisy exchanges with his fellow-patients filled his days, and he took no part in occupational therapy or hospital industry but lived the effortless life of people on a winter cruise. On their side, whether by intention or not, the hospital authorities played an appropriate part: they set no stipulations on discharging him, made no requirement of a job to go to, or even of a plan for the immediate future. The moratorium was complete: no strings attached.

This is not to say that Frank ever visualized the situation as it is represented here. Perhaps he did. Or he might have turned the hospital sojourn into an asset, although he was always taken there at the instigation of others when his symptoms grew alarming. Whatever the sequence, however, it remains true that in the course of illness and hospitalization his career was drastically changed.

Career Contingencies: The Family

Frank said he gave most thought to the problem of living at home. Mr. Monaco set his two sons an example of industry, resourcefulness, and cheerful adaptability. He had weathered the depression while a greenhorn immigrant and then got himself a satisfactory job which he held zestfully for over twenty-five years. Consequently, he seemed to feel entitled to indulge in endless advice, slogans, and admonitions. Although the father's solicitous interference took the form of job-hunting for the boy, it is striking that Frank never accepted it; at least he did his own seeking. His mother was less intrusive but almost as paralyzing in her habit of waiting upon her son.

Although willing themselves to make extraordinary sacrifices to give Frank a profession, the Monacos did not expect him to make any. Even when he had a good income they never asked for a regular contribution toward household expenses. As far as we know they protected him from any experience of austerity, self-denial, or deferred gratification, except for the one incident when the father induced Frank to withdraw an impulsively given invitation to take a friend and his family to dinner. In short, the parents sedulously discouraged their son in the cultivation of virtues in the possession of which they themselves were notable exemplars.

Although easily moved to tears by the mere mention of the appalling expense to which his education and illness were subjecting his parents, Frank did not assume his share of the family budget or the debts. There were occasions when he gave his father money, referring to the debts that were owed, but at the same time he would beg from both parents and so nothing was gained. Affectionate and emotionally dependent, he appeared to be considerate of his father and mother—as, for example, when he said he would not permit them to exhaust every penny to send him back to dental school, mindful that his father had taken to working in the evenings and his mother had gone to work for the first time. Yet Frank worked from June to September for the drug firm without giving up any part of his earnings. "I needed a lot of things," he said.

Here one detects again that immaturity and unchecked irresponsibility that characterized Frank's attitude to his parents and probably to his girl friends. And there are suggestions that his irresponsibility entered into his business dealings—in his loafing as a drug salesman, for example. There is, however, no sign of these failings affecting his career in teaching, as far as it went.

Frank, with his professional ambitions, gave the Monacos great pride and pleasure. His attendance at top-flight schools was, they said, not their idea but his own: "Frank always aimed at the best." But it was Mrs. Monaco who borrowed her sister-in-law's savings and packed Frank off on short notice to enter dental school. Certainly they inculcated in the boy throughout his childhood the belief that to be a doctor—his father's unrealized dream in *his* youth—was a wonderful thing; they could hardly have done more by way of sacrifice and savings to secure it for him. On the other hand, when business seemed the only thing Frank could find, the contempt for it with which his family had imbued him apparently stood in the way of his exerting sufficient effort to succeed at it.

Pattern of Career as Affected by Illness and Hospitalization

Frank's therapist complained that the patient constantly denied his own condition and took little interest in the treatment for, with his exalted self-image, he saw himself as dealing with his problems—including illness—all alone. But if, as has been suggested, hospitalization was a moratorium from perplexing situations, then this matters little. Just to get away even for a few days seemed sufficient to restore the patient; a religious retreat might have served the same purpose. If Frank made minimal use of the hospital's resources, perhaps he in reality had no need of them beyond the consultation with his therapist and the tranquilizing on admission which were the extent of his treatment. These were things he could have had outside of the hospital, for what he needed was a holiday from life.

While it provided the refuge he needed, however, he could not feel unmixed gratitude toward the hospital. He was filled with mortification and self-pity. Once he was caught trying to escape. Moreover, he was painfully sensitive to anticipated stigma. It was his bad luck to be seen as a patient by his former classmates; but as far as is known, none of them rejected him. And then, when just about to be hired, he lost a job by having explained that mental illness was the ground for his draft classification. Thereafter, he represented his status as that of a deferred student. Yet the Signal Corps accepted him. When the study hospitalization began, the family kept his condition and whereabouts a secret. Frank was furthermore afraid that his medical history would alienate girls. He told the interviewer the ego-bolstering lie that he was in the hospital at his father's expense, as a subject of research. Stigma was not, however, a lasting problem, and for the most part, in any case, it was imaginary.

The study hospitalization was fateful in Frank's history. He went in a badly battered medical and dental student and his educational career ended then. When he emerged from the hospital, his work career began and he was able ultimately to realize his professional aspirations by becoming a schoolteacher, although this entailed lowering his sights. It seems clear that the change in occupational choice, as well as the end of career preparation, were the direct results of the illness and hospitalization.

When, after almost three years in the community during which he functioned well and appeared to be gaining what he wanted from work, Frank again became ill, the crisis this time seemed not be occupational. One suspects that it arose in long-standing and unresolved conflicts at home and in his relationship with girls. It seems likely, however, in view of the bizarre behavior which resulted in his suspension, that the school administrators would not rehire him subsequently or even give him a recommendation to take elsewhere. One can only speculate, but it is possible that this last siege of illness and hospitalization might have as its aftermath another major career change if Frank were to remain employable.

PART *3*   MARRIED MEN

6 WORKER TO WORKER: PETER STONE

Although he had spent over twenty years in a profession notorious for making wrecks of its devotees, Peter Stone, pianist in a dance band, was still able to cope (although he might complain he barely made enough money to keep his wife and three children). In the twenty-three years of his working life which had begun when he left high school at 17 and ended with this record when he was 40, he was hospitalized on three occasions, spending a total of nine and a half months in the hospital. Since he was, of course, a member of the musicians' union, he was always promptly provided with jobs when he was in the community, so that he was at work virtually all the time.

His story was told in the course of seven interviews with him, five with his wife, four when both were present, and one with the hospital therapist.

THE SETTING: PAST AND PRESENT

When he went home from the study hospitalization in the late summer of 1957, Peter Stone was in his thirty-sixth year. He had been regularly engaged for about three years before this interlude playing the piano with a "combo" in a cocktail bar in downtown Boston; it was a good band and its leader was widely popular. Peter expected to rejoin it after release from the hospital.

Of medium height and slender, Peter looked like a dancer in a character part in a Sadlers Wells ballet. His features were sharp and birdlike and his hair waved high on his forehead in a long crest. He was a careful dresser. The bright yellow silk shirt he wore when first seen by the interviewer suggested an artist but one who while venturesome in cut and color of clothes, yet was not *very* bohemian. In conversation he was discovered to have in him a streak of the homespun philosopher, much given to stale, dogmatic interjections like—"You can't beat city hall!"—which gave his hearer the impression of a phonograph record, wearily repeated.

Peter had been married sixteen years. The parents of his wife, Joan, lived immediately across the street from them. They owned the two-apartment building where the Stones, at their invitation, had occupied the first-floor apartment since 1946. However, they sold it soon after Peter had gone to the hospital. The old people were retiring on a pension and needed their capital. Joan's mother had made it a condition of sale that the Stones were to have their lease extended for two years without a change in the $45 rental—with the result that they paid $20 a month less than their neighbors. Up to this time Joan's mother had been giving them expensive necessities, such as their refrigerator, washing machine, and bedroom furniture, but Peter, who had always tolerated her generosity, actively resented it when he became mentally ill. As he saw it then, such aid raised doubts as to his masculinity and continued employability.

The senior Stones lived in Boston, but at some distance away. They were a musical family. In Italy, Peter's maternal great-grandfather had been known as a fine musician. His mother, now a woman in her sixties, belonged to a minstrel show made up of eight or nine grandmothers who called themselves "The Daffydoodlers," dressed up in costumes of the Gay Nineties, and accepted engagements to entertain at clubs, bar mitzvahs, and weddings. But high blood pressure invalided her and she became financially dependent on the children who were still at home—two adopted nephews. His mother's sister was a dancer and another aunt was a musician. All Peter's brothers played musical instruments. One, who had a job in a print shop, had worked up a combo which accepted engagements after working hours. Two others although not professional musicians played on the side. It was a close-knit tribe. Peter and Joan called on his mother every Sunday after Mass and usually met some of the others there.

Peter's father was captain of a freighter plying the coast in short hauls so that he was never away from home for long. "He took us around a lot," said Peter. "We were very close, all of us." When he died, before Peter had finished his junior year in high school, the boy went to work to help support the family and that was the end of his formal schooling.

Joan, like her husband, was Boston-born but her parents had come from Lithuania over forty years before. Of her two brothers, one was a priest in Connecticut; the other, a pharmacist established elsewhere in Massachusetts. She was a sensitive, fond, and indulgent wife. Her attitude toward him was often like that of a mother generous to the point of unwisdom. They never had money to spare and occasionally meeting the rent turned out to be a crisis, yet Joan was always paying installments on something and usually it was some musical instrument for Peter. He had a piano, a $750 vibraphone, and had had three accordions, some hundreds of dollars worth of records, a large stamp collection, and a $750 car, which was perpetually in need of repair. There had been his fees at a local conservatory of music and a $185 mail-order course in art. It was small wonder that Joan welcomed her mother's gifts for the household.

The Stones were sentimental about South Boston. Peter loved to walk down their street to the waterfront where he would proudly point out to the children the old army dock where one of his aunts had for years held the important post of recorder of ships entering the harbor.

When Peter came back from the hospital in 1957, his older son, Harold, was 17 and a senior in a nearby Catholic high school. Shirley, now 15, was in her second year there. She was the bright student of the family. The youngest, Walter, was an 11-year-old in the eighth grade of the Catholic elementary school which the other two children had attended. The family lived comfortably in an apartment furnished in no particular style. On their pleasant, well-kept street their building was matched by all the others—a unit in identical confronting rows of two-flat structures. For the most part they ignored their neighbors; Peter said they were "all politicians. If they're friendly it's because they want your vote. So we just don't bother with them."

A chronological summary of Peter's work career and hospitalizations is as follows:

1938: Peter left high school in his junior year after the death of his father and worked at a variety of jobs. He worked principally as a musician, with bands, and as an accompanist, music teacher, and arranger, but in between music jobs he worked as a butcher, shoe salesman, and so on.

1940: He married his childhood friend. Their first child, Harold, was born within the year.

1941: He took a course at a local conservatory of music.

1942–1946: Peter was rejected by the Army as "neurotic." He then worked for an unspecified period as a welder, but was discharged because of poor health.

Peter spent seven months in the South Pacific as a musician with the USO.

1951: He gave music lessons, held jobs arranging music, and spent two months in Korea with the USO.

1953–1954: He played the piano in a well-known dance band. In 1954, he quarreled with the band leader over salary owed him. He accused the leader of stealing music credits for his arrangements and cheating him of money due for singing lessons he gave a politician's daughter. He was taken from the city hall (where he went in hope of getting his money and made a violent scene) to the state hospital by the police.

Between early April and late July 1954, he spent three months and nineteen days in the hospital. This was his first hospitalization; he was 33 years old. His wife appealed to Aid to Dependent Children (hereinafter referred to as ADC) and received $275 a month during the hospital period.

1954–1957: Soon after release Peter found a job through the union in a band playing at a downtown hotel. He stayed with this job for two years and nine months, almost the entire length of his community stay. Early in 1956 he passed a qualifying examination and became licensed as a securities agent to sell stocks, but never actually undertook to do so. He gave up teaching and most of his arranging, finding his job with the band seven nights a week too strenuous to permit additional work.

At a time when his wife Joan was nearing the end of a difficult pregnancy, Peter grew paranoid and catatonic, and was taken back to the hospital at Joan's instigation. This hospital stay, the study hospitalization, lasted two months, from early July to early September. The family again received ADC support during this period.

On release, Peter was encouraged by the ADC people to get well and rested before returning to work. They also recommended that he consider retraining in another occupation. This eventually came to nothing. Eight weeks after release he took a band job found for him by the union. After five weeks he left this for another job; both jobs were at hotels.

1958: He stayed with this dance combo, and that summer he and the family went with the group to play at a shore resort.

He continued to play with the combo that fall, and in November, anticipating Christmas expenses, he took an additional job selling in a department store. But in December the combo was

discharged by the hotel, and Peter was laid off by the department
store a week before Christmas.

1959–1961: Peter did three one-night stands in January 1959. On February 1,
he got work in a trio at a roadhouse. He played with this group
until February 1961, spending summers at the shore resort and
the rest of the year at the roadhouse.

In February 1961, he became ill again, quarreled with the other
members of the trio, and was asked to leave. For three weeks,
manic and paranoid, he was unemployed. He then made attempts
to assemble a college band, but the players would not stay with
him because they disliked the kind of places that were hiring
them.

At the end of March, Peter was admitted to the hospital for
the third time, after having spent three years and almost seven
months in the community. He was released from the hospital
in mid-July, after a stay of over three and a half months.

In the twenty-three years between the ages of 17 and 40, Peter
worked almost continuously as a musician. From the time of his first
hospitalization in 1954 until the end of his third hospitalization in 1961,
a period of seven years and three and a half months, he spent a total of
nine and a half months in the hospital and six and a half years in the
community. He was unemployed during several short periods while in
the community; the total time he was unemployed was six months.

THE PREHOSPITAL CAREER

"When I was in school," Peter recalled, "I used to play in small
bands—school bands and neighborhood outfits. It started out with
dance dates when we were in high school and one led to another. I
was very young when I started . . . mainly I think playing instruments
was just enjoyable. I didn't look much further than that. First it was
with the piano. Then later I played trombone with the band. So when I
left high school at 17, when I was in my junior year, I went to work
immediately, playing for weddings and social events and clubs and anything I could get. I also worked at other things: in a meat market and
selling shoes. But anything else was always extra, just something in
between music jobs. One thing about music: you can always get a job.
Good times; bad times; bands are always working. People always want
their music, even in a depression . . ." He brought home "good money"
from the beginning, but for some reason his earnings went to the family. His brothers' earnings did not.

It was not always straight playing. Peter gave both singing and instrumental lessons. He made musical arrangements. His combos went in for the novelty acts and skits to which a band without star names must resort. "There are those that create," reflected Peter, "and those that copy. I guess I'm a copier. If a good technique came along, I'd use it. Somebody else would work out the idea and then maybe I'd pick it up . . . I've never created."

The Stones were a happy and affectionate family. Joan could remember that Peter's mother "kept almost open house. I was one of the crowd that visited their home." In 1940 Peter married Joan, his childhood friend. "A good marriage," he pronounced it eighteen years later. "We've had a good life together." Soon after he was married he had his only professional instruction in music when he attended, for about a year, a local conservatory of music. When the war came he wanted to serve but was rejected as "neurotic," so he worked in a war plant as a welder. But that did not last long, for he was in poor health, lost weight alarmingly, and eventually was discharged.

Although declared unfit for military service, he was attached to the USO in 1946. Later he and Joan recalled with amusement that he, a military reject, during seven months spent in the South Pacific with the USO survived a tidal wave in Hilo and the explosion at very close quarters of an ammunition dump; and in 1951, when he rejoined the USO, he added to his ordeals performances actually under fire in Korea and a broken leg. For many years after that he would wake up from time to time screaming and clawing, reliving harrowing scenes at the front, and Joan used to keep a light burning at night so that she could creep out of reach. In retrospect she connected all this with his mental illness. But he declared that it was "hard work and no fun but I felt good."

Civilian life was not easy either. "Sometimes he'd come home from one job early in the morning," Joan reminisced, "and say he had to leave town for ten days and before I'd know it, he'd have a bag packed and would be gone and I'd be left with the kids . . . I don't think he knew what they looked like till they were grown. I'd say that ninety-nine per cent of the raising was done by me."

In the next few years Peter was attached to a band with a good reputation, and in the summers he sometimes played at resorts where he could take the family. He played for five hours in a hotel nightclub, then stayed up until 5 a.m. after arriving home, making musical arrangements. He arranged the song hits for several stars, some of which were recorded. In the afternoons he gave music lessons, amused himself with the children (by his own account), or his duties as the officer passing on merit awards in the Boy Scouts (a life-long hobby), or with his stamp collection; ate dinner; and went off to play in the dance band until after midnight.

He had brought his paycheck to Joan from the first week after they were married, and she gave him back a 10-dollar allowance from it. In an occupation where, as she remarked, men seek relief from tension in drugs or drink, Peter developed no bad habits. But they both spoke of his life as stressful: "Lots of men go down to Chinatown after the show is over and take a couple of hours to unwind before going home," explained Peter. "You know, working in the music racket with all the saloon noise, the biggest thing you look forward is to come home to peace and quiet and to get away from the crowd."

Later, talking about his life, Peter commented that there was a time when he had set his sights high: "Everyone does. Then you spend the rest of your life waiting for a break . . . For example, you make a record . . . If it gets to the public, then all of a sudden you might have a hit. But you never know what's going to hit the public . . . Sometimes there's a pay-off to a disc jockey and he plugs a lousy tune that couldn't stand on its own; and all of a sudden it's a hit. Sometimes the break comes and sometimes it doesn't . . . Lots of people have got the basic talent but whether or not you get a break is another matter."

In 1954 he ran into difficulties with his employer, the band leader. The leader had induced Peter to give singing lessons to the daughter of a politician connected with the mayor's office. It was vaguely understood that the recompense, at least in part, was to be in political favors. Then Peter discovered his boss was stealing credit for musical arrangements he had made and was privately collecting for the singing lessons. Moreover, for years the leader had been paying the band's salaries very irregularly. Personal relations with him grew more and more acrimonious. He began to accuse Peter of anti-Semitism and breach of contract. For six weeks Peter worried and could not eat or sleep. At home his behavior was odd and unpredictable. He made Joan swear on the Bible that she was not a Communist, ripped a crucifix from the wall, hid mysterious notes all over the house, tried to replace all red articles with white, and wrote letters accusing "Reds and Jews" of plotting against him. He ran up huge bills for a new car and for instruments, leaving Joan to keep house on what money was left. Yet when she thankfully accepted money and gifts from her mother he grew resentful. All the same, Joan appears to have recognized that he was "not himself" and never let these things come between them. His mother and his brothers were all sympathetic but their help did not go beyond moral support.

Then, one day, getting no satisfaction from his boss, Peter finally went to the city hall to see the singer's father and demand payment for the lessons. But he was put off with a patently false story of the man's absence from town and in his rage and indignation grew so wild and noisy that he was taken away by the police to the state mental hospital.

This was Peter's first hospitalization, at the age of 33. It began on April 2, 1954, and ended three months and three weeks later on July 21. His illness was diagnosed as schizophrenic reaction, paranoid type. Put at once on drug therapy he very quickly responded. When Peter was released he learned that Joan, with no money coming in, had appealed to ADC and the agency had been giving her an allowance of $275 a month. He was incensed at the news that the family had been publicly supported—although he had no ideas as to how Joan might have managed otherwise. Of course the allowance stopped when he went home. And he made so much fuss over her accepting help from her mother that, for the sake of peace, Joan put a stop to that second resource.

For the next two years, the Stones could not get any health insurance. "The insurance man," Joan explained, "said we were bad risks, and, boy! he really hit it on the head! We both got sick. I lost my kid (by miscarriage) and Peter was in the hospital." To which Peter added, "Citizens are a good touch. You pay out for years and then at the first excuse they drop you. But then, like I always say, you can't fight city hall."

Through the musicians' union, Peter promptly found a job at $64 a week with a combo which was playing in a popular night club. He was now working seven nights a week, an exhausting schedule from which he sought relief, but in vain. "How many musicians can get out of night work? I couldn't do it . . . Not with a wife and three kids." This job lasted about two years and nine months, that is, for most of the three years between his leaving the hospital and shortly before his readmission.

Early in 1956 he took the examinations and became registered as a securities agent to sell stock—"You have to have pull to take the exam, but I passed it." But he never availed himself of his license and in the end he let it expire. He said it was because he could not face losing the money of his clients. His tone suggested he considered the stock market essentially immoral.

He had given up the teaching which had made his too-short nights even shorter. And except for working for an organist friend, he gave up arranging, although he regretted the $50 to $100 extra which he could earn thereby "in a couple of weeks." Nevertheless, he found life demanding and grew tense and "nervous." Joan knew it boded no good that he began suffering from nightmares again in the spring of 1957: they had been a portent of his first breakdown.

Underlying Peter's uneasy state of mind was anxiety over Joan who was nearing the end of a difficult pregnancy. Eight years before she had lost twins at birth and had been desperately ill, and this time again her symptoms were ominous. Peter seemed to be serious when he announced they should get rid of the obstetrician and that he, himself, should deliver the child by Caesarian section. He was unhappy, too, over 11-year-old Walter who, to his mind, did not have enough space to play in, and he took out his misery on the next-door neighbor who refused to let the boy cross her garden or even play on the sidewalk in front of her property. One day he dug up her yard and dumped barrels of garbage on it, then tore up their own garden and his mother-in-law's across the street, searching, he told everyone, for a bomb planted by his enemies. This frenzied activity was the culmination of bizarre behavior that had begun a few weeks before when Peter could not recall how he had got himself to work or what had happened during the day. He had moved all the pictures in the house to one wall, adopted rigid poses, avoided metal, washed his hands incessantly and, as before, went without food and sleep. He grew morbidly religious, collecting holy medals and declaring he was going to join the Franciscan Order. There came a day when he started talking hour after hour and did not stop. Distracted and not well herself, Joan called his mother who said, "It's up to you. You do what has to be done." Joan called the police and they took him to the hospital where he had spent three months, three years before. He had been brought there, that first time, from the city hall and his children and the neighbors were not witnesses to what must have been a distressing scene. This time the trouble was right in the neighborhood. It was hard on Joan, but she found comfort in a discovery; that in her block there were three or four others who suffered from mental illness, a fact that had not come to light until then.

THE HOSPITAL PERIOD

It was the first week of July 1957, when Peter was admitted for the second time. He was to remain there until the first week of September, an interlude of just over three months. He was now 36 years old.

At the hospital he responded well to drugs and very soon was permitted to visit at home. He spoke of himself as in need of "a good rest"; he just didn't feel he "could take life"; but by the time he was released he reported feeling truly restored in mind and body. Throughout his stay in the institution he insisted that his trouble was analogous to physical illness, to be cured by rest and "TLC" (tender, loving care). His therapist thought that he would improve when Joan's pregnancy terminated; indeed, when in mid-July her baby was still-born, he took it calmly.

A talented professional musician, he was supposed to have been assigned to music therapy, but the hospital authorities humorlessly gave that up when it turned out there was no music therapist on the staff. Instead, he did some instructing in trumpet, worked with the hospital band and the choral society, and helped with a public concert. He worked in hospital industry in the mattress factory, "just long enough to make a new one for his own bed," as Joan pointed out, laughing. He worked in the occupational therapy division until he "graduated," having made a wallet and an ashtray—"one of everything. When you finish the moccasins you graduate."

"One of my gripes," said Peter later, referring to occupational therapy, "is that instead of helping patients, they were forced to make one thing or another; and that made them dependent. They'd be much better off if they could get out on their own . . . If you do something because you don't want to do it but are forced to do it, it doesn't help . . . The best thing for people is independence. If you don't have independence then you don't have anything. For example, you must want health. Then you have to be free enough to work it out on your own."

Confidentially he told the interviewer that he was not suffering from a mental condition but instead from the pain of a calloused foot, an occupational hazard of the pianist. "I winced every time my foot touched the pedal. But the average person does not see the difference between pain and insanity . . . This is an insane asylum. So they think that if you're here, you're insane. Now if you're not, then the problem is making the mental adjustment to the place. Thorazine helps. It let's you relax." Some time later he enlarged on his theory: "It's a pill. The patients come to the hospital and take a pill and then they slow down. That does it."

Meanwhile Joan was having trouble at home. Convalescing from her ill-fated delivery she now was told she could not have the ADC allowance again, because she and Peter had invested their savings, $200, in a twenty-year investment plan. Since the money was in his name, Joan could not convert their holdings into cash. Moreover, had she done so at that point, they would have had to lose nearly one-half of their investment. Refusing to help, the ADC worker told her to go to her church—a suggestion later regretted, for when Joan did so, the priest in a fury sent someone from the district attorney's office to the relief bureau. The outcome was that the Stones were paid benefits again. But Joan said nothing of all this to Peter; she remembered how outraged he was when she had applied for help before.

The Labor Day weekend gave Peter an opportunity to spend several days visiting at home and immediately after that he was released. He faced out stigma from the first moment. Almost defiantly he went to church and took a seat beside the neighbor whose garden he had devastated.

He left the hospital on September 6, 1957. He had made no move to find work on his own before re-entering the community, confident the union would get him a place.

THE POSTHOSPITAL CAREER

In the first few weeks after his return, when he was supposed to be resting and gathering his forces, the ADC people suggested to Peter that he take a course in electronics and qualify for an occupation where he would be under less strain. "And the income from music is miserable for the amount of work you put into it," expostulated the agency's worker. It appealed to the Stones to find an easier life for Peter. So he took aptitude tests. Another proposal made was automobile mechanics. "They're always advertising for mechanics," Peter agreed. "Maybe sooner or later I'd get a little garage of my own . . . There are lots of guys with their own places. There are more cars on the road every year . . . Well, there have to be more garages and more mechanics to take care of them." Or he might take up drafting, said the worker, or be an electrician. But would the ADC supply an allowance while he was training? "Personally," said Peter, "I think they should. This is a case of handicap." For he would have no choice but to continue working, presumably with the band, and this would mean that only his afternoons were free for classes—unless the family could be supported from some other source than his earnings. He rejected the worker's idea that he might learn the auxiliary trade by correspondence; he had tried that, years before, in art lessons, and had no faith in the method.

Two months later, in November, the Stones were still hopeful something would come of it. But in January Peter admitted that it had ended in "nothing specific. I'm still in music." He simply could not afford to take the two years of full-day training which were required in most of the programs suggested by the agency. The social worker, he complained, was simply wasting his time now with advice to apply at factories and other simple-minded recommendations familiar to Peter (now 36 years old) since his high school days. Training in a trade, it turned out, was either a matter of full-time days of study and work or part-time courses for years at night school—all with no training allowances. "But they've got plenty of money for training," Peter pointed out. "And it would be worth their while; there are five potential votes in this family! If it's a matter of deserving help . . . I qualify. But it doesn't look like it would work out. I think I'd better stay with the band. It's something that I know. If schooling comes to me, then I'll grab it. I'm not holding out for it, but if it comes, then, fine! It's a matter of bettering yourself when you get the chance. But I'm in the musicians' union and there are always jobs available."

For the first time, Peter, who had always met stigma head-on, complained of it. Proclaiming that one must go to politicians for jobs in these days, he added that even prisoners can get jobs through their parole officers but mental patients have no one to turn to. The idea of making use of his license to sell securities never seriously occupied him: "It's legalized robbery!" Yet there is no evidence that he was actually handicapped. As Joan said, "Most everyone has been very nice about the whole thing. The majority feel bad for him—sure, there are usually one or two wise guys out there (at the job) but mainly they're real good."

When asked about his sentiments about staying in music, he replied, "Well, it's just work; like anything else." Joan was more specific: "He's just not happy at any other work. I said, 'It's up to you. If music makes you happy, then stay with it. There's not much pay, $64 a week, but it's steady.'" She wondered if he might not seek daytime work, however, and a more restful regime. He was quite positive about giving up teaching: "I used to have a place downtown for it. But that's long ago. The kids just tear the house apart if I teach them here at home." As to the band, they were all congenial friends. They had taken up a kitty for Joan and given her $45 when Peter had been taken to the hospital. But the job lasted from 8 p.m. to 1 a.m., seven nights a week, with an hour of commuting added to each night—clearly too strenuous for Peter. It would take him two hours to get to sleep when he reached home. "The noise is pretty tough . . . The shows are lousy and blaring like a foundry . . . With rock-n-roll they're getting away from music now-a-days."

For nearly two months (it was now early November) he had been in the uncomfortable position of holding off from his old place in the nightclub combo in order to recuperate. The ADC was ready to pay the family $68 a week until December, but Peter was anxious to get back to work, rested or not—"I'm the man of the house, I shouldn't be laying around. I feel small when I do." He wanted to put a stop to the ADC payments. Then the band leader had a breakdown and was sent to a mental hospital and his place was taken by a good friend of Peter's who urged him to rejoin them. But no one knew how long this man would be in charge. Moreover, Peter thought it was a bad sign that he was working all day, beginning with an early television program, and most of the night. He was rescued from a decision, however, when the union found him a place playing the piano in a popular night club. It was the place where he had worked at the time of his trouble in 1954, but the personnel had changed. So the family's ADC allowance came to an end in November 1957.

After a month, Peter switched to a hotel combo where he had Sundays free. He liked his fellow musicians and much appreciated the fact that one of them transported him to and from work and that the place was not too noisy. The callous on his foot which interfered with his pedalling and had plagued him for years had subsided now into a minor nuisance. Best of all, this job was to stretch on into the summer when they had a contract at one of the most popular resorts in the region. Here the combo was to play for $35 a week more than they earned in town. It was a trio, Peter and two brothers, one of whom played the guitar and tail drums, flute and saxophone; the other, the accordion and several other instruments. They had a good reputation among musicians and the night club public. The trio expected their winter and summer contracts to run on into the next year. Life was looking rosier for Peter.

But Joan struggled chronically with money problems. Peter wanted a new car. An old car, they reasoned, is always in need of expensive repairs. But a new car would cost too much. Joan made him agree in December to wait until April, by which time, she hoped, they would have put aside $500 for the downpayment. But she was haunted by the fears that he would fall ill again, they would be unable to meet the payments, and all they would have invested in the car, license and insurance, would be lost. The children, too, wanted things. Harold, who had been making a little money washing dishes on Saturdays at a hospital, was expected to keep himself in small supplies, shirts and shorts, for he was not paying board. But he made a scene about paying for his high school graduation suit. Yet if Joan paid for it it would have to be with money saved for the car. She had already had to dip into those savings in April to pay the rent. Harold wanted a tape-recorder for his graduation present and Joan's brother had offered them one for $80 which had originally cost $200. In the spring of 1958 she had just managed by ingenious austerity to clear up the medical bills of the previous summer. (They knew the state hospital would not make trouble if they ignored the hospital bill; they had learned that in 1954.) Of course, Shirley wanted new blouses and sweaters. And now the youngest, Walter, was clamoring for a new baseball glove. "Where's the money going to come from?" wailed Joan.

They bought the car in late spring, just in time to use it in moving down to the beach as the summer contract began. And they bought Harold a new tape-recorder, paying for it in installments. "It cost over $200. But it's well worth it to get a good piece of equipment rather than spending $80 for a piece of junk," Peter moralized. At his insistence,

Joan had bought a new coat and dress for Easter. It was her first spring coat in five years.

They had a "marvellous" summer that year (1958). They had a beach cottage and indulged in cook-outs and picnics every few days. Peter had arranged some music for the owner of a golf course at the resort who, in return, had given the whole family club privileges for the season. Harold had stayed on two weeks to work in town, then worked on the golf course for ten days for pocket money. They went back into town in September in good spirits. In eleven weeks they had put 2000 miles on the car and paid rent there and on the apartment in town, but as Joan cried triumphantly, "We got by!"

But their good luck did not last. Just a month before Christmas 1958, the hotel changed on very short notice to a Negro band. Peter took the blow hard for he had made great plans for Christmas and even taken a job on the side, selling in a department store, for extra money. Then the store laid off the extra workers a week before Christmas. He had just applied for unemployment compensation but having been for so short a time on the payroll, he received only $32—less by a good deal than he would have gained by applying immediately after the music job had ended and remaining unemployed. It turned out to be, as Joan put it, "the lousiest Christmas we ever had." But her mother gave her a new washing machine.

Now Peter was out of work. Joan worried about the payments on the car and the tape-recorder but she prudently reasoned, "pushing him won't help him to get a job, so there's no point in pressing him. He wants to get back to work." So, as she always had, she coped, some-how. By borrowing from her mother she was able to keep the car on the road by renewing the license and paying $51 toward the year's insurance on it. There was still the monthly installment of $60—"but that's not till the 18th and this is just the 8th, so I'm not going to worry till the time comes." Of course there was the $45 rent for the apart-ment. But Peter picked up a job for New Year's Eve and two more nights and Joan added $5 she had been given at Christmas; and that covered the rent for January. Her father had just been pensioned, and now she realized that the help that had so often providentially come from that quarter was about to end. Peter had the promise of a job, however, in a roadhouse on the highway, beginning in February 1959, with the trio in which he had played the previous winter and summer.

The Stones now began to be plagued with a peculiar form of persecution which they could not explain. Taxicabs kept arriving at their
house—eight in the first week, four in the second, with the report they
had been called and given that address and asked to hurry. "Somebody
must be cracked," said Peter in disgust. "For peace-loving people like
we are," Joan interjected, "who don't even talk to the neighbors, I
just can't see it." This was one of several small incidents. But at least
Peter never suffered from stigma on the job.

As Peter remarked later in that spring of 1959, the new job turned
out to be "all right; but it's a long ways off." He began to think of
himself as old at 38: "You get old fast in the music business. It's all
partly the noise, partly the hours . . . And once you get old in the
music business, you've had it. You start getting grey hair and you're
out unless you're established . . . unless you're someone like Benny
Goodman, who could go on forever." Once before, he commented,
"When you get older you don't have the energy you had when you
were younger. But as long as I have energy, I can always work in the
music field. Talent and energy give security there." But Joan was always closer to reality than he: "I think the only thing that would hurt
Peter now," she said, "would be if we lost the car." Being out of work
was a problem he seemed able to survive—he relied on the union and
it had always found him work—but the knowledge of the money they
had invested in the Chevrolet lay on the minds of both. "The car is a
lot," conceded Peter, "Of course, it's hard to pay for it . . . but we
enjoy it. We got out a lot . . . We had to pay $65 excise tax but we
made that O.K."

Money, Peter concluded, was the thing that meant most to him, as
it did to everyone else. Of course he set a high value on being able to
work and having a profession. Yet despite financial worries, the couple
seemed to have entered on a pleasant phase of family life. Peter was in
splendid health, sleeping and eating well and enjoying a "spin" in the
car with Joan each afternoon. The car was their pride and joy, but a
real burden, for they discovered there are "a thousand and one expenses," even with a new car. But, as Joan put it, "Peter's got cigarettes
in his mouth and food in his stomach. What more do you need?"

The children were doing well. Eighteen-year-old Harold had gone
into the Air Force for four years in the fall of 1958 and was talking of

making it his career. He had spent the summer in radar school in Mississippi, where he was building up his own bebop band. Shirley was a popular student in high school, captain of the color guard, and a member of the band. But this year they had had to tell her they could not give her the money for the summer tour with the school which they had financed for her the previous year. Walter was a good student and the center of a wide circle of friends.

Peter's job at the roadhouse ran from 7 p.m. to midnight, but it took an hour to get there. To the great joy and relief of the family, the summer contract was renewed and they were to go back to the beach again in June.

After interviewing was terminated in July 1959, nothing was recorded of Peter's story for a year and a half. In early 1961 he was still playing the piano in night spots with the trio he had joined in 1958. But in February he began to make absurd accusations against the brothers in the combo, complaining they were "hard-of-hearing." He shouted at them during performances and disturbed them and the audience with odd gestures, and finally had to be let go. This was the first time he had ever been discharged. At home Joan noted a return of disturbing symptoms: he was not eating or sleeping well and he spent hours in compulsive occupations, sorting and throwing things out and holding himself in rigid postures. He resented Joan's interest and threatened her and Shirley, who was in terror of him. He seemed to be listening to mysterious voices.

Three weeks after losing his job he grew more rational and set about getting together a college band. But the players objected to the "dives" where they were engaged and eventually they disbanded. Thereupon Peter grew worse—argumentative and paranoid. Finally he attacked strangers, bumping into them on the street, and once he sat for fifteen minutes, jabbing his elbow into the neck of a passenger sitting next to him on a bus. He began digging up the back garden, as he had done once before, burying all sorts of objects and casting suspicious glances toward the house as he did so. But it was when he assumed toward Joan the role of a small child, even to calling her "Mommy," that she became really frightened and called the police.

He now entered the hospital for the third time, almost three years and seven months since he had last left it. It was the end of March 1961. His illness was diagnosed again as schizophrenic reaction, paranoid type, but this time the term "chronic" was included, and at 40 years of age Peter was defined by the therapists as one who could look forward to recurrent breakdowns and sieges in the hospital. By June, he was allowed to go home for weekend visits and then for a week at a time. Information about the case came to an end on July 19, 1961, when he was released from the hospital on a trial visit and was reported to be "returning to work with his music."

DISCUSSION

To these studies of careers before and after mental illness and hospitalization, Peter Stone adds a second variant of "Worker to Worker." The first, Victor Norton, was a bachelor, a contrast to Peter with a wife, three children, and a wide network of kin and in-laws. But each had at home a warm source of encouragement and loved individuals to serve as models of industry and responsibility. In Victor's case there were his brother, Leo, and his mother; in Peter's case, his parents and his mother's musical clan at an earlier time and his wife in the present. It may be partly because they were supported by visible examples and positive, affectionate expectations that each was able to compartmentalize his illness, Victor more completely than Peter, and keep it from destroying his career.

But more far-reaching and significant are the likenesses between Peter, the musician, Arthur Jackson, the physicist, Carl Duncan, the would-be artist, and Frank Monaco, the would-be physician. Each was dedicated from childhood to a quite specific conception of himself in his chosen profession. But their fates as former mental patients showed few points of resemblance. Peter and Arthur were already established at work when illness intervened and Peter was able to return to it; Arthur was ruined as a physicist and slipped down the occupational ladder to truck-driving and furniture-moving. Carl never became an artist but drifted among low-grade jobs, a kind of occupational hobo. Frank's original ambition evaporated and he compromised on an alternative career.

Career Pattern

Music was Peter's life and in the twenty-three years of his working life covered in this history he never did any other work; nor was he, but for short periods, ever without work. He was an adequate performer whose competence was never questioned and who was never discharged from a job except at the end of this account when he was obviously very ill.

During most of his case history, Peter's jobs got progressively better. The roadhouse contract, combined with a summer contract at the beach with the same trio, year after year, was certainly the best position, from his own standpoint and the family's, that he had ever had. He was patently more ravished by illness than he had ever been when, at the end of the record, he was playing in what seem to have been unpalatable "dives." Until then his associations had all been creditable and one may only speculate as to whether or not, when he recovered from his last bout of illness, he returned to reputable connections.

As a high school boy, seeking work to support a widowed mother and several brothers, Peter said he went from place to place. Later, as a union man, he relied upon the organization and during those eight weeks of the only period of any length when he was unemployed, he had a place waiting for him when he felt well enough to take it. No doubt he was exercising good judgment in taking time off, and meanwhile financial support was continued by ADC; yet this put him in the uncomfortable position of not assuming the support of his family. "I feel small if I'm loafing around the house. I'm the man of the family." When he found himself unexpectedly losing two jobs almost at the same time, the band and the department store work he had taken on for the sake of extras at Christmas, he rebounded quickly and was able to make the money needed for the rent with a few days of extra work. Albert Rossini, too, could depend on the union for work, but the difference was that Albert was as content to live from unemployment compensation as from his own earnings.

Music was the unchallenged center of his working life. He was committed to it as though it were his fate. He made deliberate changes in order to be able to continue in it, reducing the stress ("Music and aggravation don't mix. You can't have both. They're like water and oil.") by cutting down on his undertakings on the side. Music bound his childhood, adolescence, and adulthood together and gave them continuity and stability and a certain sameness. It was the same with his hobby, scouting: a middle-aged paterfamilias, he had been a Boy Scout since "den" days under a scoutmaster who, three decades later, was the leader of his younger son's troop and still Peter's closest friend.

In his work and in his hobby, Peter's past and his present were alike. It was as if he had never grown up; or, equally, as if he had never been a child.

Qualifications for the Labor Market

From the time he was a high school boy entering the labor market in the depression, Peter appreciated the fact that "people want their music, in good times and in bad," and was full of assurance that he need never be without work. His choice crystallized very early and he never gave serious thought to an alternative. He acquired skill at the piano and a number of other instruments, made arrangements, and taught singing. A year after his first child's birth, he took his first professional lessons, and some years later qualified as a securities salesman, although he never took advantage of it.

Dedicated though he was, he still could take a critical look at his profession, as he did after his first hospitalization. And although he regretted the loss of extra income, he made concessions to his own fragility which enabled him to continue in the occupation he had learned to love as a child.

Career Orientation

On the only occasions when he gave even passing thought to other work, he was under pressure from the ADC to take courses in electronics, drafting, automobile mechanics, and a variety of other employments all of which would, in reality, require his full time to learn—impossible for a man with a wife and three children. The whole proposal was inappropriate and ill-conceived. Although there was no scheme to pay for the classes, he was induced to spend time taking inappropriate tests and given gratuitous advice to haunt factory employment offices in the hope of finding something. Apart from this interlude in which he played a passive part, his behavior in job-seeking and job-accepting was proficient. As for his contemptuous repudiation of hospital industry and his poor opinion of occupational therapy, a man of his age and experience could hardly think otherwise.

As would be expected of one in the arts, music in itself was Peter's reward. Creative and autonomous to a great degree—even in a band and of course in arranging and teaching—the life of a musician was just what Peter wanted. "He is not happy in anything else," said Joan.

And colleagueship with his fellow players meant a great deal to him; he repeatedly spoke of the pleasant relations between himself and the members of the various combos he was in (with the obvious exception, of course, of the band leader who cheated him). He himself never grew lyrical over the call of music, however, and when asked what was proving important to him in the year and a half since he had been released from the study hospitalization, he named money first, then the ability to work and having a profession and a steady job; and he added, "It's good to be able to walk around in the afternoon. Some people can't; they are tied to their machines." (His tendency to paranoia revealed itself in his complaint that he dreamed once of becoming known in the music world and "almost got there several times, but someone always kept me down.") The rewards to him were both extrinsic and intrinsic.

If Peter named money first in listing what mattered most to him, it was largely to be explained by his own financial ineptitude. The family kept barely abreast of its debts. Joan once said that Peter could rise above crises at work but the one unbearable blow would be to lose the car. Yet her husband was reckless with money and more than once almost missed the payments on it. He accepted Joan's pampering of him with expensive and dispensable gifts of musical equipment; he complained when Joan appealed to the ADC for support of the family although there was no choice; he resented Joan's mother's generosity; and they somehow justified buying a $200 present for Harold on his graduation at a time when paying the rent was an effort. Nevertheless, it must be said that with the help of Joan's good management he was able to provide a comfortable home and many small, and some great, pleasures for the family.

Career Contingencies: The Hospital

The tense and taxing life of a dance musician was not ideal for Peter from the standpoint of health. As in the case of Frank Monaco, the hospital took him out of the world when it became too much for him and sent him back more or less resuscitated. Perhaps it was only with these relatively short and widely spaced releases from stress that he could continue, although he reached the age of 33 before he was first hospitalized. The record ends with his being committed for the third time, following over three and a half years on the outside, and it is suggested that this will occur again and again. If that was the price of playing the piano, Peter was apparently ready to pay it, while making all concessions, short of leaving the profession entirely, which would make it more bearable.

One is struck with the absence on the part of his therapist of any expression of interest in what was to become of his patient when he was released. The hospital staff appear to have assumed no responsibility for seeking out for him a *modus vivendi* in which he could stay well. The bulletin board, as Peter once remarked, listed all sorts of openings but at the end came the warning that these were not for mental patients.

Career Contingencies: The Family

None of these stories reveal so much support from the family, moral and financial, as Peter Stone enjoyed. His parents-in-law provided him with an apartment at a very low rent and gave the family expensive pieces of household equipment; his wife treated him like a loved and quite spoiled child. But she did not put any pressure on him and was deeply sympathetic with his troubles and his dreams. "All I can do," she explained, "is give him what he wants. After that, all you can do is hope for the best. He's been very happy-go-lucky in the past few months. That's a good sign." If her permissiveness brought them to bankruptcy, it may have been the price of Peter's sanity; in any case she had a justified faith in his ability to continue earning a living, just as long as he was well. And when he was incapacitated, she was able to cope by invoking the ADC.

In his slightly bohemian vocation, Peter was inspired by the examples of musical relatives, running back at least to a great-grandfather in Italy whose fame had become a family legend. Peter himself appears to have picked up technique at home. He was a grown and married man before he had professional instruction. He slipped into music easily. Encouraged since childhood by talented kinfolk, he took from them a conception of himself as a musician who would do well at it.

Although not sophisticated in those matters, Joan held a therapist's attitude toward her husband, her idea being to save him worry and make his life easy and pleasant. She did not press him about money, said nothing of it when she had to "borrow" from the savings for the new car to pay the rent, kept the children quiet during his daytime sleep, took upon herself all disciplinary problems, and bought Peter almost anything he wanted.

Pattern of Career as Affected by Illness and Hospitalization

Peter simply denied he had an illness of a mental nature. Perhaps the conviction that he was not psychotic bore him up and helped him face out stigma so successfully. Stigma appeared in strange guises. There was the time between his second and his third hospitalization when Peter's wife was driven distracted by unexplained appearances of taxicabs she had not called. A neighbor called names and drove the younger child off the street. These things were annoying, even hurtful; no other among the eight cases was subjected to this sort of torment. But they had no lasting effect as far as one may judge and, more important, they had nothing whatsoever to do with Peter's employability. He got and held jobs and was not made to feel self-conscious about his history of mental illness by his colleagues in the music world. The union ignored it and placed him whenever he needed it. And on his part, he showed astonishing boldness in confronting the neighbors when he arrived home.

Yet he was realistic in saving himself from too early a re-exposure to the strain of band-playing and night life and at least verbally and in connection with other people he conceded an association between illness and tension on the job. Undoubtedly his first hospitalization, at least, was related in his mind to job-connected frustration and anxiety, and he was realistic in attending to the ADC worker's proposals of easier work; and realistic again in rejecting her unrealistic suggestions.

As in Frank Monaco's case, hospitalization gave Peter a rest and relief during which he reconsidered his job and made his life easier for himself thereafter. The hospital itself actually did very little for him that entered into his working life: as was said of Arthur Jackson, he was "not a partner in therapy." However, he did pick up where he had left off.

7 WORKER TO WORKER: DAVID FIELD

David Field, a cabby with bright red hair, is remarkable among these cases as the breadwinner of an accident- and illness-prone family known, so it was said by a case-worker, to every social agency in town. In the years this case was followed, there was no time when the household was not receiving medical or financial aid thanks to which, with David's own earnings, they could just subsist.

David's first hospitalization for mental illness, in a private sanitarium for six months, occurred when he was 15 years old. He was 33 when next hospitalized, and during the following five years he entered the same state mental hospital four more times and spent a total of six and a half months there. His sojourns in the community, of which the longest lasted two and a quarter years were, for the most part, times of almost continuous employment, chiefly as a cab-driver.

His life as worker, family man, and patient was reconstructed from information gleaned in the course of three interviews with David, six with his wife, eight when both were present, one with his mother, one with both his parents, seven interviews and a conference with workers in three social agencies, and two interviews and a conference with hospital personnel.

THE SETTING: PAST AND PRESENT

In the spring of 1955, when David Field was first interviewed, he was being released from the state mental hospital after a stay of thirty-two days. Chubby and cheerful, with an attractive childish grin, he had a hail-fellow-well-met air that suited his loud-patterned summer sports clothes. He came from a local Jewish family and lived with his wife, Nelly, in what was described as a third-rate neighborhood in the newer, better part of a public housing project. In an older slummy section of the neighborhood lived his own parents. (David and Nelly had improved their lot before this case history came to a close by moving into a still more desirable block of the project.) To be eligible for residence in the project one could not be earning more than $3600 a year. The family paid a rent of $32 a month for four bright, sunny rooms, heat, and utilities.

The Fields had four children: Bella, a 10-year-old, Jonathan, aged 8, Marvin, the genius of the family, aged 4, and Polly, who was born two months before David had gone to the hospital. Nelly was a neat, even tasteful housekeeper but was reported as always frumpy and badly groomed, sallow of skin, talkative by habit, and a persistent nagger. Yet, unattractive as she might have appeared to the eye, she nonetheless made an agreeable impression by the gentle and appreciative way she spoke of her husband and his valiant efforts to make ends meet. Although he was unable, she admitted, to give his wife and family much of this world's goods, he was "good-natured, kind, and good."

David's father, a small man, heavy-set and usually seen in dirty working clothes, son of a Russian-Jewish socialist, had come to the United States in 1905. He was jovial and generous, much loved by his daughter-in-law, and by his son as well; although David never got over resenting his father's failure to send him to engineering school at M.I.T. The elder Fields both had slaved all their lives, however, and twice were able to offer him a substantial loan so that he might achieve his heart's desire, ownership of his cab.

A phenomenal talker ("My sickness is talking; I can't stop."), David's mother was aware of the compulsion under which she labored and mixed Yiddish and English together in a helter-skelter flow of words. She was quick-witted and open-handed. David also had a married sister, Rachel, five years his senior, who with her husband and three children lived near enough to enter into his affairs from time to time. They all liked Rachel's husband. After the manner of Jewish families, they expected to help each other and be helped. Among his kinfolk, David was regarded as studious and brilliant, although his mother had her reservations.

Nelly's parents were of Polish descent but their name had been anglicized. Nelly had had a pinched childhood and hoped for better things for her own children. When she was 4, her parents separated. Her mother managed to eke out a living from her earnings as a charwoman together with welfare payments and arranged for Nelly and her 7-year-old brother to live with their grandparents. The mother, a cardiac cripple, was still living in 1955, and in the same part of town as the Fields.

Shortly before the study hospitalization Polly was born, terminating what Nelly had found a trouble-beset pregnancy. David was anxious about her, as the births of the older children had been attended by various complications. Then, too, Bella was threatened with appendicitis and David's father, weakened from a stroke the year before, was being treated for a burned hand. Thus David came home to a houseful of invalids—a state of affairs to which they all had grown unhappily accustomed.

A chronological summary of David's work career and hospitalizations is as follows:

1938: David suffered his first psychotic break at age 15 and was hospitalized for six months in a private sanitarium.

1941–1942: At the age of 18 he graduated from high school and held a succession of jobs, including the managership of a service station and a brief period as a sales clerk in a hat store.

1943–1945: He was rejected by the Army but accepted by the Coast Guard Naval Reserve and worked for ten weeks at an arsenal, taking a machinist's course.
He then became an insurance salesman for about two years, until shortly after his marriage to Nelly in 1945. After his marriage, he began job-hunting again but found none he liked. He took to bed for a short time, whereupon Nelly left him for five months and filed first papers for a divorce. In 1945 after their first child, Bella, was born, Nelly rejoined David.

1946–1950: In 1946 David accepted a job as a cab driver for the first time. In 1947, when their second child, Jonathan, was 7 months old, they went to California. In Los Angeles David for eight months earned $90 a week in a tool-and-die shop. They then returned to Boston, and for a time David neither worked nor sought work, just as he had done shortly after his marriage.

1951–1954: David returned to taxi-driving and continued at this work.

1955: Their fourth child, Polly, was born in February. David for the first time considered borrowing $1000 from his parents to make a down-payment on his own cab but could not raise the additional $500 needed.
In April, he was admitted to the state hospital for a month's stay, and the family went on ADC. He returned to the community for twenty-four days, then was rehospitalized for two

and a half months, and was released at the end of August. During the rest of this year, he drove a cab illegally for one month, then worked part-time for the taxi company for three months as a radio dispatcher.

1956: Encouraged by aptitude tests and the advice of agency workers, David left taxi-driving and spent about four months as a car salesman, working for two different automobile agencies. By September, he was back to taxi-driving, as always for his original boss. In October, he changed for the first time to another taxi company whose cars did not hurt his back.

1957: He drove a taxi all year. Again he raised the question of a loan from his parents to buy himself a cab. In late December he was hospitalized for twenty-eight days, after having remained in the community for two and a third years.

1958: In January he came home for ten days but was then rehospitalized for seven weeks. When released, he returned to driving a cab and, in September, raised for the third time the issue of a loan from his parents to buy a cab.

1959–1960: In the summer of 1959 he had an opportunity for a straight business loan to finance purchase of a cab, and by October decided to go ahead with the purchase without a loan. In March 1960, after working at a furious pace and long hours to pay for the cab, he was again hospitalized.

Although hospitalized only six days, he gave up the project of owning his cab, returned to driving for someone else, and was still at it when the record ended in May 1960.

From the time he finished high school in 1941 at the age of 18 until the record ends in 1960, David had been in the labor market for over nineteen years. During these years, he was employed almost continuously, mainly as a taxi driver, except for short periods of inactivity and convalescence. From the time of his hospitalization in 1955 until the termination of the case history in 1960, he was in the hospital a total of six and a half months during five different admissions, the longest stay being for two and a half months, the shortest for six days.

THE PREHOSPITAL CAREER

David's had been the hard childhood so commonplace among the near-penniless European immigrant families of a generation ago. His father, a factory hand in a New England firm of shoemakers, left his job when the boy was two years old to achieve his life's ambition: he bought a little grocery store in a working-class suburb. The parents and their two small children lived in three tiny rooms at the back of the shop. There they stayed for seven years of unmitigated drudgery. Up at 4:30, the parents prepared breakfasts of fresh rolls, and so on, which David and Rachel had to deliver to the doors of various neighbors. But young David detested the business and began refusing to help at all, so that his outraged parents had to hire delivery boys. They sold the store and bought another which they lost in the depression, when David was 13. David's mother said that her husband had always been obsessed with having his own business, but store-keeping, to people as inexperienced as they were, was pure slavery. She added that her husband had the reputation of being a calm man, but in business he was always on edge and excitable. Mr. Field, following upon various vicissitudes, took a job in a shoe factory at $60 a week and was still working there when the case study began.

In process of time David qualified to enter a superior city high school where he made excellent grades for a time. But soon he was doing no homework at all and, to everyone's exasperation, missed a scholarship which all agreed easily could have been his. One detects a touch of the "wise guy" in the boy. Not only was he contemptuous of the homework which the others in school took for granted but also he constantly urged upon his harried father all sorts of inspirations which were to bring in quick and easy money. His mother, always skeptical, saw through him: ". . . he sells himself on his ideas and then he believes in them." If he asked her for $2 for pocket money she would give him 25 cents, whereupon he would beg the rest from his father. He was consumed with ideas for making vast sums.

When he was 15, David was possessed with an idea for an invention, a device for keeping butter at melting point on the stove without burning it. He was sure there was a fortune in it. His mother was discouraging from the outset and, as David complained later, everyone laughed at him. One day one of his pals overheard him boasting that he was planning to spend that night in a downtown hotel and fly to Washington the next day to see someone at the U.S. Patent Office about his invention. The tale was relayed to Mrs. Field who went to his room and found he had been packing. With the help of the police she and his father discovered he had gone to a movie for the evening, but when they went to look for him he slipped through their fingers. At 5 the following morning the hotel manager phoned the message, "Come and get your son." Although little more than a child, David, it turned out, had almost persuaded a neighborhood money-lender to let him have $1500, "no more and no less," to launch his invention.

At home David now grew sullen and uncommunicative. He spent his spare time in the stockroom of the store, tinkering with tools and busied with a mysterious project. One winter morning his mother awoke at 2 and found his bed empty. His father reported it to the police who, at 4:30 a.m., found him down at the docks in his shirtsleeves, dragging a bag of tools behind him. They took him for "some sort of radical"—which his mother laid to the fact that he gave a salute suggestive of the Nazis'—and they returned him to his family. He lost his appetite, could not sleep, and accused everyone of trying to hold him back. Finally his mother took him to a doctor who declared the boy would have to be hospitalized but warned them against a public institution. Although already in debt, his parents borrowed money to put him in a private sanitarium. There he stayed for six months, until the fall of 1938. David told his therapist at the time that he knew he had ability, but "all my life I've been failing myself."

At the doctor's insistence, the high school readmitted him with the understanding that he be put under no pressure to work. The doctor may have shared David's view that what had made him ill was being nagged at by his mother at home and by a "mean" teacher at school. Eventually he was transferred to a high school with more relaxed standards, but soon began to play truant and to make paranoid accusations. He was kept under occasional therapy for the next five years and grew much better. But the family always said his illness cost them a good business.

On completing high school David had to face the cold reality that he could not become a mathematician or physicist—Einstein was his hero—for his parents could not afford to send him to M.I.T. as he had been hoping, and he would not agree to any second-best university. He had to console himself with two correspondence courses in tools and machinery.

David now went from one small job to another, never staying long and never satisfied. When he was 18 he was employed at $18 a week at a gas station. To the family's astonishment he told them he had been made manager and when his incredulous mother went to see for herself, she observed with her own eyes her teen-aged son giving orders to middle-aged employees. A day or so later a car ran over David's foot, keeping him at home for something less than a week, and when he went back he was told he had been fired. ("And a good thing, too!" exclaimed Mrs. Field.) From that job he went to a hat store as a sales clerk and one or two other positions. "David is very unstable," sighed his mother, "especially about jobs."

In 1943, when he was 20, David was rejected by his draft board on grounds of his breakdown. To be declared 4F was a sore blow to his pride but he tried to laugh it off and, indeed, he succeeded, for he applied at once to the Coast Guard Naval Reserve and was accepted. This brought its reward: he was sent to work at the arsenal and took a machinist's course for ten weeks.

For a time David had a good job as a salesman but was anxious to make more money and left to enter an insurance company, where he stayed for two years. But he was given a bad route: the premiums were hard to collect and he grew discouraged. He was still selling insurance when he and Nelly were married. This was in 1945, when he was 22 and she was 23. Mrs. Field, who never quite approved of Nelly, said she was attracted to him by his good looks and his Naval Reserve uniform and married him because she "wanted pretty children."

Soon he left the insurance business and then for some months did not work at all. They moved into an apartment in his parents' home against Nelly's wishes, in order to save money. Then David gave up even job-hunting and stayed in bed. He did so, he said, because he was tired of his mother's nagging and wanted to spite her. Nelly could not stand his idleness, however, and served him an ultimatum: she would move out and live by herself. She had hoped to shock him into action, but she ended with five months of life on her own and even filed first papers for divorce. The first child, Bella, was born that year. Inauspicious though matters looked, the couple became reconciled and years later Nelly recalled with gratitude David's helpfulness when she and the baby came home from the hospital. "Things have been wonderful ever since," she said. She herself proved in the long run a strong and sympathetic helpmate. But it was not so wonderful financially: David eventually accepted work as a cabby, although he expostulated, "For a fellow like me, it's a dead end!"

For some months he drove at night. It was a hard existence. He saw little of his family and was overworked. Nelly's life was driven and lonely and her health was poor. David used to take several hours a week from his job, to do the laundry and spare her other tasks, devoted help which she never forgot. He tried repeatedly to get into other work but was always thrown back on cab-driving. At least he could always make a living at it: "You always have a dollar, but it's a different story if you need two for an emergency!" He gave up night driving for an unstated period and tried "skinning on the fly" (cruising about to pick up passengers). He tried, too, to build up a circle of regular customers. But this, he found, always led to loss—so much waiting and so much unprofitable driving across town to the regular patron's address. Like Peter Stone and his band-playing, David came to look on taxi-driving as the work he knew best. He drove a cab for years and was never discharged. But he never said he enjoyed it: it was just his job. And while he appeared to think of it as difficult and demanding, he kept returning to it, as though it were his fate.

In 1947 the couple took a trip to California which they looked back upon later as the low point in their fortunes. It was Nelly's idea. They announced suddenly to their relatives that they were leaving with Bella and the baby of seven months in the belief that life in the sun would be their salvation. It was true they both were in miserable health: David had suffered for years from a draining cyst on his back which made sedentary work a torture, while Nelly had been so prostrated with colitis that the social service department of the hospital where she was treated arranged to send her a housekeeper for two or three days a week, for some weeks.

The young couple began selling their furniture to raise money for the trip. But they were buying it on the installment plan, and it was not theirs to sell. Providentially, David's mother saw their advertisement in the newspaper and rushing over, shooed out the handful of customers who had just begun to foregather, and sent a certified check to the furniture firm "to cover up the whole thing and prevent worse damage." Eventually she got possession of the furniture and put it in storage. Then she gave a farewell party for them, at which she herself contributed several hundred dollars toward their expenses and others gave smaller sums. David and Nelly stopped first in Detroit where, through Mrs. Field's forethought, they were welcomed for a few days by her brother who gave them $75 when they left.

Los Angeles was a bitter disappointment. David, it is true, found work without delay as a machinist's helper in a tool-and-die shop at $90 a week. But he was put on the night shift and it was not a big aircraft plant, as he had hoped. Beside that, they found the cost of living inordinately high. Even harder to bear was the incessant rain. Then Nelly's mother and brother joined them, all unasked—not the happiest addition to the household. At the end of eight months, as unexpectedly as they had left, David and Nelly turned up on the elder Fields' doorstep back in Boston. David had lost weight and the cyst on his back was no better. He let Nelly do the talking. They were penniless and it was quite clear that they expected the old people to support them. To this Mr. Field consented but on condition that David have the cyst excised, a procedure which Nelly had always opposed. This time she gave in. David went into the hospital and she moved with the children into a small furnished apartment for which Mr. Field paid $89 monthly rent. He gave her also $35 a week for expenses and when she said it was not enough he gave her more. But she quarrelled with her neighbors and soon took herself and the children to a larger, unfurnished place.

On leaving the hospital, David for a short time did nothing at all. He did not even look for work, reminding Nelly painfully of the time just after their marriage when he had taken to bed and stayed there. But this did not last for he eventually returned to his old boss, driving a taxi.

In the years which followed, the family fortunes of the Fields showed no improvement over what they were before the California experiment. Jonathan was born in 1947, Marvin in 1951, and Polly early in 1955. The last baby was badly timed. Nelly had had to have her spleen removed and she was not robust. In fact her life now had become a succession of afflictions: she suffered from a blood dyscrasia which had made the spleenectomy necessary; she had severe sieges of colitis; her varicose veins were so swollen that her legs were constantly swathed in bandages; she broke her instep, then a toe; she had a hemorrhoidectomy. Then, several months before Polly was born, she overturned a kettle of boiling water and scalded her legs so badly that she had to keep to a wheelchair. During all these ordeals Nelly carefully kept in touch with various departments of the general hospital where she was continuously either an in- or an outpatient and during the last ailment contrived to secure once more the services of a housekeeper, paid for by a welfare agency. In fact, by the time Polly was born she had already been given sixty days of housekeeping at a cost of between $300 to $400, far more than the agency expected to spend on one family. But Nelly, according to the social workers, knew how to play one department against another to extract the maximum of assistance. Bella, now 10 years old, was suffering from emotional difficulties and was accepted for weekly treatment at a psychiatric clinic for children. "Every agency in town knows the Fields," burst out an exasperated case-worker.

Meanwhile David, who had been working all these years as a cab-driver, was bringing home from $55 to $60 a week, not quite half the money he took in from his fares. He found the life strenuous and his mind was always playing with some scheme or other "to bring in real money." It was then that he hit on an idea that was to haunt him for years to come: to buy a cab of his own and keep *all* of the fares. The "shield" (the medallion certifying ownership and the license) would cost $5000 and his parents offered to lend him $1000 of the $1500 down-payment. He would devote 55 per cent of the weekly "take" to paying off the debt, and he counted on doing it in two years. But he was growing bitter over his failure to raise the remaining $500. And he brooded over the fact that he and Nelly had been married ten years, had lived in a dozen places in that time, and now had four children, and were barely keeping abreast of expenses. In fact, except for the ample public assistance the family received, they would have been in real want of bare essentials.

Finally, David's affairs took an alarming turn for the worse. At a party in early April 1955, he grew so wild and boastful that Nelly in fright prevailed on her brother to go home with them for the night. The next day he was even more uncontrolled and under pretence of getting him medical attention for a rash, they got him to a general physician who warned them that a psychotic outburst seemed close at hand.

Then the sword fell. David was driving to the hospital to have a treatment for his cyst while en route to pick up a regular customer, when suddenly he thought he saw Nelly calling to him out of a window telling him not to work that day but to come home. It was the day Einstein, his boyhood idol, died. He tried to phone Einstein. The next thing he knew, he said later, he found himself in the seclusion room of the state hospital, but there is no other indication that he was really taken there at the time. Actually, he had got himself home but could not remember landmarks or the names of streets he had known for years. His vision of Nelly had some foundation: she had in reality felt uneasy and had urged him to stay home that day: "I should have known something was going wrong. Whenever David is loving to my mother there's something the matter with him." At some time during the crisis he told Nelly he would never drive again. She and his mother suspected that he had had an accident in the course of that day: but no one ever knew.

David now grew intensely excited and voluble over a scheme for "a cigar store on wheels," and for the two weeks which culminated in his hospitalization he talked of it almost literally all day and all night. He even consulted a lawyer about putting the idea in effect. Finally the exhausted Nelly had him brought to the state hospital. The family began to live on welfare funds from ADC.

THE HOSPITAL PERIOD

David was now 32 years old, and this, the study hospitalization, was his first since the six-month sojourn in a sanitarium when he was 15. At the hospital David was diagnosed as schizophrenic, manic reaction, and kept there for thirty-two days, from April 18 to May 20, 1955. Then he was sent home but had to return to the hospital at the end of twenty-four days. The second stay ended in August and brought the total time in hospital during these two admissions to three and a half months.

In the ward he showed no interest in other patients or the routine, as he was too engrossed in his own thoughts to give attention to anything else. In time he went to occupational therapy but left it in disgust when on having completed making a wooden rabbit, he was invited to "graduate" to weaving. At that point he demanded "man's work" and was given heavy chores of scrubbing and scraping in the greenhouse and put in charge of chrysanthemum beds. This he found tolerable. Once he scrubbed so zealously that he pushed his arm through a pane of glass.

When, after a month, he was released from the hospital the first time, the family faced the fact that he would be denied a driver's license for six months and would have to find alternative employment. They decided he should keep the books for the photography shop of Nelly's brother; then they decided that was "too mental" a type of work for him in his present condition; and finally decided he could probably sort photographs. This did not appeal to David any more than weaving had. He loafed, which everyone thought proper enough in a convalescent, and worried. Nelly tried to hearten him: "Honey, we're getting along on what we've got. We're all alive and well, thank God, and what more could we ask?"

For a week he had been unusually excitable. He talked incessantly, keeping Nelly awake until nearly dawn. He dwelt on the miseries of having no money and no work and failing those he loved best: "A good Jewish father," he said, "should provide for his wife and family and buy them things . . . He must be the head of his house, the breadwinner; and this is fundamental and basic, a basic fact of man as head of his house." He wondered if Jonathan would recapitulate his own disappointing history—a promising boy whose father could not afford to give him advanced education to help him to rise higher in the world than the generation before. But what was the good of being shown on tests at the hospital that you have "business ability" if you have no capital to start in business?—and so on. By day Nelly ingeniously thought up picnics and outings to tire him and make him sleep. She told him she would be willing to try to get along if he wanted to go to college at night—the only way he could do it. Nothing consoled him, however. In three weeks he was back in the hospital.

The crisis that brought him back to the hospital that June came one evening when his mother and mother-in-law were together in the younger Fields' apartment. David was not working. He had, with his boss's connivance, driven on the first day in the community, but of course he had no license. His employer, indeed, offered to get him his license through political influence, but Nelly was firm in insisting he could not stand the strain of driving yet. He was tense and anxious and for the first time in life irritable with the children. On this day he chanced to go into the kitchen in time to hear his mother accuse Nelly and her mother of exploiting him. Shaken with anger, he ordered his mother out of the house. She went, and quite in character phoned an apology the next day. But that night, sleepless and utterly wretched, he woke Nelly. She and a policeman took him back to the hospital before daybreak. He was carried, noisy and violent, to seclusion. There he covered his head and called on "Jesus and other gods" and ignored what went on around him.

But when Nelly went to visit him he seemed normal enough, except that he talked about money continually. He was released from the hospital on August 29, 1955, after a stay of two and a half months.

THE POSTHOSPITAL CAREER

David was in the community for nearly two years and four months after his second release. He returned to a home where things were going badly in ways peculiar to the Fields: "psychopathic, irresponsible, happy-go-lucky, with many psychosomatic complaints," ran the hospital's description of the family. Two or three weeks after he came home Nelly had to go to the hospital again and Bella, who at the tender age of 10 was cast in the role of virtually full-time babysitter for Polly, was going twice a week to the psychiatric clinic. Her mother said she was "persistently malicious." Nelly was almost as much a problem, public and private, as David. She looked on four children as at least one too many and wanted, as she put it, "to be a lady," with time for employments more diverting and elegant than domestic chores. (As part of being a lady, with David's consent she induced the hospital to sterilize her a year after Polly was born.) No sooner was she out of the hospital than she rushed Bella and Marvin to the clinic with what she took for sure signs of polio; but she was mistaken. Nelly was, in the words of one of the many case-workers kept busy by the Field family, "infantile, demanding, and petulant." It was generally recognized that she was a great giver of morale to David, but nonetheless she seemed to want him to be dependent. "To feel adequate," asked the case-worker, "does this woman need a sick husband?"

The family had been receiving sufficient support from ADC to cover the needs of four children but Nelly shrewdly guessed that David would come to rely on it, and she had it stopped without his knowledge. David boasted to the interviewer about money "put by," but this was pure face-saving. It was not long before Nelly fell ill again. This time she was smitten with functional blindness, brought on, according to the hospital, by the fact that David was now reassuming charge of the family's affairs, asserting his authority, and finding fault with her management of the household. And he himself was in a precarious state. He would talk nearly all night about quick ways to make money and he needed constant tranquillizing.

Disqualified temporarily from driving, he nevertheless went back to his former employer and drove a cab for a month. Then for three months he tried radio-dispatching part-time at 75 cents an hour: "girl's work," said David scornfully. Moreover it was night work. Nelly saw with alarm that he was getting more nervous. By January 1956 he left the job and was hunting for work. This went on until March when he regained his license and become a cabby once more. But it was obviously a strain and Nelly was more than ever sure that he ought to give it up, once and for all.

David's affairs, ever since he left the hospital, seemed largely the concern of counsellors in vocational rehabilitation, family service workers, and clinical psychologists. He went through a dozen tests and was shown to be potentially an excellent machine operator and designer and to rate very well in business ability. He "broke the top" in the test of engineering aptitude. The vocational counsellor advised him to take a two-year course in electronics at a downtown technical institute. He recognized himself that it was not a practicable proposal for a man with four children and a wife chronically ill. But he found the idea delightful: it was a step toward what he had wanted since boyhood. At one time he seemed persuaded that the family would be publicly supported while he went to college to study mathematics and physics and fit himself for a profession suited to his abilities. But this was wishful thinking, encouraged by at least one of the agencies. It was decided, however, that he should wait six months for fuller recuperation. Nelly urged him to hold out until fall (1956) in the hope of "something good, to get us out of the rut." Meanwhile, they agreed, their creditors could wait and they determined not to worry over debts. The vision of a free education lingered, sustained by encouraging gestures from the vocational counsellor. But David and Nelly eventually faced the fact that their immediate business was to feed and house the children. Obviously support had to come entirely from David: a delicate person like Nelly could never add outside work to her household duties. They had moved to a new apartment in the housing project where, for $32 a month, they had adequate space and all utilities paid for but the telephone, and to that extent were better off than before. But they refused to associate with their neighbors, "people from the laboring class, not middle-class as we are." Their ideal of how to live was to have owned a three-flat building whose middle floor would be their own; but they knew that was impossible, as things were, and enjoyed what they had.

Now once again they were receiving ADC, to the extent, this time, of $90 every two weeks and David was in a position to nurse unrealistic hopes. He reverted often to his ambition to own his own cab and brooded over his bitter disappointment in being unable to raise the last small part of the $1500 payment. "Today," he observed sadly, "it would cost at least $2000 more to buy."

In the spring of that year (1956), David was behind the wheel of his employer's cab, but he decided he should act upon the revelation of the aptitude tests and applied for a job as an automobile salesman. He was picked as one of four applicants at a Ford agency. For two months he spent little time on the floor but was on the road, building "connections." This was important, not only to create customers but also to hold them, for a buyer became the salesman's customer exclusively, once he had bought a car from him. If David could sell two cars a week he would earn an average of $50. In his first weeks with the agency, David sold a few cars, but by mid-June, after ten weeks of effort, he had not sold any more and was beginning to look for another selling job. Discouraged, he fell into the habit of hanging about the house for hours at a time. He knew it was dangerous for him to return to cab-driving, but there seemed no alternative.

As a beginner, David had been drawing from $30 to $60 a week at the Ford agency, although he had made no sales yet. After a few sales he sold a car for which he was not paid the commission: the manager had sold that customer a car five years before and claimed him for his own. David wondered if this was not his way of easing him out, and eventually left in disgust. For three weeks he tried a Chevrolet agency. But selling was hard as the summer went on. The customers were waiting for the 1957 models which would reach the market in October. He had the bad luck, too, to suffer a slipped disc which kept him home for a week.

As autumn set in, David gave up selling and resigned himself to cab-driving. Yet he was not quite reconciled to it and when the October models came he consulted Nelly about returning to the automobile agency. "Do so," said Nelly, "if that's what you want." But he went no further with the idea. He went to work as a cabby but with a different employer for he had found the seat of his car was hurting his back and although his first boss gave him several models of car to drive, nothing seemed to suit him. He switched companies when he found one with a make of car in which he could drive in comfort.

When David entered on his eleventh year as a cabby he made $65 a week. But the family needed more than that. Virtually during all of the year of 1957 he spent working as a cabby for his second employer. Among cab-drivers he was unusually stable: cabbies change firms because they want a better route or because owners sell or retire a car and fail to replace it; they do not expect to stay indefinitely with one firm.

He was leading a full, perhaps a too full life. He belonged to the auxiliary police and that took one evening a week. He was on the executive committee of a burial society and belonged to a Jewish lodge, which claimed two evenings more. He had not had a vacation in years: he could not afford it for it would be time when he was spending money and making none—a bad side of cab-driving. He speculated sometimes on the feasibility of leaving the younger children with his mother while the elder child went to a camp provided by one of the agencies and taking two or three days' holiday with Nelly.

Few jobs appealed to David but the idea of a small business had always lured him. Not a grocery store such as his father had had but perhaps a service station. He once confided to the interviewer that he "had his eye on a place"—this was when Nelly was out of earshot. It would take between $3000 and $4000 and was a real temptation; if he could only raise the money. On the other hand, why would he go to all the trouble and investment to make, say $75 a week, if he could do as well or better driving a cab—and much better if it was his own cab? But returning to solid ground, he had to admit that things were little changed from what they had been before he was hospitalized, two years before. Still, the family was fed, housed, and clothed, which he conceded was the main thing—that, and that the children should "grow up to be good people, do well in school, and keep their health."

But matters were not going well with David. As December came on, he was sleeping both during the afternoon and at night—a bad sign, as Nelly well knew. He had to come home for a midday nap; he stopped work at 4:30 and rested again after supper. In between times, Nelly said, he was "none too coherent." The indispensable breaks in the day, of course, cut down his earnings and he worried all the more. Already he had much on his mind for he was definitely borrowing from his parents the $1000 toward the $1500 down-payment on the medallion for his own cab. He saw this as his only chance to rise out of the financial depression which had engulfed the family for so long. But to buy a cab now he would have to make more than he had hitherto, more, certainly, than he was making in the curtailed hours his health seemed to demand. To keep the family now was costing more than he earned. The fear of failure and of falling ill again haunted him day and night. It was mid-December 1957 and he had to decide by the first of the year whether to gamble on taking in $175 a week, if he had his own cab, for the next five years. At present he was making about $75 a week; the larger proportion, of course, went to his employer.

Nelly was hopeful, even enthusiastic, at first. "It's something he's always wanted," she explained. But she knew, too, that he was obsessed, that he would drive the cab day and night until the delicate balance of his health would be reversed. She had found a way to raise the last $500 but by now was afraid of the whole project, for in talking with another cab-driver she had learned what a burden it would be.

Then David, just as she foresaw, broke down again. He was taken by the police to the hospital during Christmas week and she called off the deal. She appeared to sense what the therapist had divined: that David in some obscure way felt the need of dependence on his mother and embraced the opportunity to be in her debt. David himself had moaned that "it was no wonder" he was a failure, when he kept on ignoring her good advice. But he consciously sought autonomy, yet knew himself emotionally incapable of it.

Four weeks later, on January 17, 1958, he was sent home. But in ten days he was back in the hospital again, ranting expansively about buying the cab. His mother was his most frequent visitor.

This time he remained in the hospital until March 21, a stay of one month and twenty-two days. Then he re-entered the community for two years and was a cabby all that time.

He had not been three months out of the hospital (it was the summer of 1958) when he was seized again with the longing for his own cab. He was working long hours and had never done so well in his life. But there was no family life any more and Nelly knew—David, too, in all probability—that it would end in catastrophe. "I cannot stand the success," he lamented.

Soon after David returned to his home Nelly had another operation, her mother was hospitalized with an embolism, and when the two women came home the family was again provided with a house-keeper—by still another agency, the ninth to help the family since David's hospitalization early in 1955. Nelly's mother took care of the children. Bella by now was a happier girl. They had moved to an apartment they all enjoyed, overlooking a park. Here there were more Jewish youngsters and Bella had congenial age-mates. School was more challenging. But Polly was the problem child by now. Indulged by her two big brothers and her parents, she had become a household tyrant. And now it was Polly who had to be escorted weekly to the psychiatric clinic. Meanwhile David's mother, always overpoweringly and insistently helpful, gave the family a car—and promised she would manage to get herself living quarters in their building.

The hankering after a cab of his own gave David no rest. All through the fall and winter of 1958 and the whole of the next year he slaved for it. In the summer of 1959, for the first time, there was some prospect of a straight business loan toward the purchase of it. By October he decided to buy it without borrowing, pushing himself to the limit of endurance; and in the end he paid the price he and Nelly knew he would have to pay: in mid-March 1960, she brought him to the hospital. He was now 37 years old. He had been robbed at gun point and the loss, putting forward as it did the day when the cab would be his, overwhelmed him. Heartbroken and at the point of exhaustion, he went wildly manic. But he was kept in the hospital only six days, then released.

When this study of his history was terminated in May 1960, he was apparently well and back again behind the wheel of a cab. But it was not his own cab.

DISCUSSION

David's story could be constructed as a composite of elements taken from several of the other histories in this volume. Throughout his career ran the *motif* of longing for his own cab: his illness was evidently connected with his efforts to achieve it. And here he resembled Arthur Jackson and his dream of a physics laboratory and Frank Monaco and his ambition to be a doctor. But there were differences. Of the three, Arthur alone received neither help nor encouragement from his family with respect to resuming his original career. Frank compromised on a second choice of career; Arthur and David never gave up until their efforts culminated in breakdowns. But this is what can be seen. To pass on to inference: while the other two were steadfastly committed, and early in life, to their objectives, David always thought of cab-driving as beneath him. He broke his heart over something he did not greatly admire, a temporizing goal.

David, too, was like Peter Stone. As if it were a tropism, the one was drawn to cab-driving, the other to piano-playing; and each knew he was courting disaster, but like moths near a flame, kept returning to the lure. Among the particular qualities which make David and Peter stand out among all the other cases were that they were into their thirty-third year and had been for fourteen and sixteen years, respectively, in the labor market before the study hospitalization. David stands alone as one who, despite almost continuous employment, could provide his sickly family with food, shelter, and medical care only with an astonishing amount of support from eight or nine welfare agencies. He depended so much on public assistance that it might be more accurate to describe him as "marginal worker to marginal worker"—if worker were to imply adequacy as a breadwinner.

Career Pattern

No doubt from sad experience, David's mother learned to look on her boy and his schemes with a skeptical eye and spoke of him as very unstable as a worker. In him, at least in his earlier years, high-flown ambition and bombastic assurance (which, with his youthful flair for invention might always have produced something profitable—but never did) made an uneasy combination with hard-driving devotion to the work at hand. Thus at 18 he either talked or worked his way into the managership of a service station but held the position for only a week or so. Yet his mother's dictum was not entirely just, for this was the cabby who later on worked a fourteen-hour day, seven days a week in a frenzied drive to buy his cab.

Entering the labor market at 18 when he had finished high school, David made it quite clear that he aimed at something higher than his father's grocery store. He was still a boy when he launched on the escapade to patent his cooking utensil and when he scored his comet-like success at the service station. He was 20 when, after the Army had rejected him, he got himself accepted by the Coast Guard Naval Reserve through which he got a course in mechanics—a small consolation for not being able to enter engineering school—thanks to which, as he once pointed out, he could service his own cab himself—if and when he could acquire a cab. At 22 he was doing well at selling insurance, and

it was only after he had been at it for two years and had married that
he left it in the hope of something better. All during the California
interlude he had well-paid work. David might have been called unstable,
meaning he did not stay long in one job, for he had a dozen employers
in the nineteen years of his working life traced in this history. But in
1946, at the age of 23, he drove a cab for the first time and except for
about nineteen months (six and a half months in the hospital, about
one month in convalescence, eight months in California, and four
months when he tried to sell cars) it was still his occupation when contact with the case was terminated in 1960. To this very considerable
extent his career at work became continuous and could be called
stable—yet always hazardous, for his recurrent illnesses were apparently work-connected.

Once a cabby, he always had driving to fall back on and he sank
back into it thankfully at critical points in his working life. In eleven
years of driving he had only two bosses and there is no sign of complaints about his work. Indeed, he had a second employer only because
of the good and sufficient reason that the cars owned by the first employer hurt his back.

While it is true that for a time after the study hospitalization, when
he was ordered to rest, he did permit himself to play with the ambitious
projects laid before him by the welfare workers, yet when it came to
the serious business of going back to work he needed no help in re-
entering the labor market as a cabby. At the job-hunting that followed
his several hospitalizations he was proficient and wholly self-dependent.
On the other hand there were the two occasions when he grew too
discouraged to seek work at all. At these times, Nelly's gambit of
threatening to leave him and once actually doing so was a layman's
shock treatment that worked.

In the nineteen years in the labor market David got no higher than
an employee in a low-level occupation. Despite heart-breaking effort
he never attained the status of entrepreneur which cab-ownership
would have conferred. Two handicaps blocked his way and they were
ones he could expect would always make his path thorny: poverty and
illness. Indeed, between 1955 and 1960 the tragic round had been thrice
repeated: he borrowed to buy a cab, drove himself mercilessly to repay
the loan, and ended in the hospital. The project on which he launched
was highly inappropriate in view not only of his precarious health but

also of the fact that the public assistance without which the family could never have coped could have been withdrawn at any time and in any case was not supposed to be for long.

False hope and heartbreak were the only outcome of the proposal that he be put through college and the family supported by welfare funds. He took seriously the suggestion to try selling and worked at it for four months. But the impracticality of these test-based schemes was clear to him (as it was to Peter Stone) before it was recognized by those who proposed them and in his life story they stand out as a digression—and a cruel one, although well-intended—that contributed nothing but discouragement to the solution of his dilemma.

Qualifications for the Labor Market

On the several aptitude tests which David took after the study hospitalization he showed himself as excelling in "business ability," but as he said himself, of what use is business ability without capital? It was on the inspiration of the tests that he engaged in selling cars, with disastrous results. When, however, he simply went job-hunting, he was able to meet the exigencies of the market and always turned up something: a job in a hat store, in a service station, in a tool-and-die shop; he sold insurance, and then he became a cab-driver, committed, it is true, by default, but only the psychotic episodes broke in on his pursuit of cabbying.

David recognized the job offered him in his brother-in-law's business as calling for concentration which was beyond his ability at the time. And he ultimately left one cab company to work for another whose cars did not hurt his back. In short, he knew, on the whole, how to make the best of his skill and ability; but within limits. He had "big ideas," but, as more than one student has pointed out, many a boy from the working class never scans the full spread of the labor market, and with his none-too-adequate education David was probably unaware of a variety of what may have been suitable possibilities.

Yet it cannot be said of him that one job led to another or that he exploited what he learned in one position in the one that succeeded it. And it must be admitted that he threw all his strength and spirit into a vocation that he could not tolerate. If he ever actually succeeded in buying a cab it could only be at the cost of the unremitting devotion to work which had on three occasions brought him to the hospital.

Career Orientation

Cruising the streets in a cab whose major profits went into the pockets of another, David was constantly preoccupied with the idea of bettering his condition for he felt guilty that he was not able to "buy things for my family, as a Jewish father should." Of cab-driving he said, "For a fellow like me, it's a dead end." But as to selling, he exclaimed, "I can sell anything!" There he overestimated his powers.

What could he have made of his life? In his immediate circle David found no models of a career. His father's occupation repelled him and in idolizing Einstein he had picked an example impossible for a high school graduate to follow. Thus he was foregoing the supporting inspiration of a guiding star. He was emotionally a dependent individual and the lack may have given him a certain feeling of rootlessness. There is no evidence that he longed for the *status* of cab-owner, as distinct from the owning of a cab which he certainly did desire most heartily. That status would have brought him barely closer to Einstein than he was as a cabby. Surely he still would have yearned hopelessly to fit into the world of mathematicians and physicists.

As mentioned above, he did not so much *choose* cab-driving as resort to it in the absence of something else. He was too intelligent to wish his choice to crystallize on a blind-alley occupation. But, of course, the longer he remained a cabby, the less were other pursuits open to him. It was, in short, crystallization of choice by default.

When he talked of what he wanted from life, David mentioned first the children; his hopes for them were that they "grow up right, be good in school, and be in good health." Although the wish was modest, it was not easy to accomplish. They were doing well in school, but David had no more prospect during the time of study of giving them higher education than his father had had when he was growing up; and their health left much to be desired. He also wanted to move to quarters where the children would have a better class of neighbors and, in particular, Jewish playmates. The latter he and Nelly achieved. The couple once spoke of their ideal of housing: a three-flat building which they would own and whose middle floor would be their home, but they pointed out at once that this was a dream, and meanwhile they were content where they were.

Like Peter Stone, David expressed no enthusiasm for his work; it was "just a job" and one which each recognized as destructive for one of his fragility. It was purely a means, the only means at hand, or so it often seemed, to other desiderata. He wanted to own his cab not because he set any value on ownership itself, but so as to secure the cab's full earnings. His immediate goal was simply subsistence for the family, a minimal aim which for months at a time he could achieve only with the help of welfare agencies. It was only at first that he resented public assistance; Nelly prudently had it stopped at times when she saw he was relying on it. He once spoke of wishing for a small business, a service station, but, as when discussing living quarters, he promptly dismissed the idea as beyond possibility and not to be taken seriously.

David exhausted himself with long hours and no vacation—conditions which a cabby may set for himself—but if he did not like it, his was a plight very common in the world of work.

Career Contingencies: The Hospital

As in the case of Frank Monaco, and to a lesser extent in that of Peter Stone, the hospital provided David with a moratorium during which he reconsidered his unsatisfactory existence and revived his old regrets that he had not pursued his education further. Then, as the time approached for him to return to the community, the hospital initiated the vocational testing which, for months thereafter, made him the relatively passive victim of a debate among the agency workers on the subject of his future. All this to-do came to nothing but meanwhile time was lost and his anxiety and disillusionment compounded. This must have been all the more distressing in view of David's remark that he felt obligated, on returning to the community, to better, if he could, his family's situation. The occupational therapy he was offered struck him as pure insult; he was given "man's" work only at his own insistence.

To turn from questions of occupation: hospitalization helped his *personal* situation significantly by removing him temporarily from his over-helpful yet demanding mother and his houseful of neurotic and somatic invalids. But the respites were short: the longest lasted only ten weeks.

The first hospitalization came in a period when David was casting about to find the answer to the vital question: "What shall I be?"—a question which, at the age of 32, he had already left too long unanswered. Thereafter he re-entered the hospital when the pressure to buy his own cab became intolerable. But always, when he emerged, his life continued just as he had left it.

In passing, it is of interest to know that David, alone among these cases, expressed curiosity about his own illness and how he behaved when in the throes of a psychotic break. He pestered Nelly with questions about how he was delivered to the hospital and what he talked about in his seizures of manic volubility. He complained that the doctors do not tell the patients about the unconscious and the deep nature of their affliction. There is no information as to whether he was a satisfactory partner in his own therapy—indeed he seems to have received minimal treatment—but there is evidence that he was deeply interested in his own condition.

Career Contingencies: The Family

It must be said to Nelly's credit that she gave David strong and loving support. She rarely put pressure on him but showed a willingness to make a sacrifice if it would get him what he wanted by way of an occupation. The social worker, however, raised the question whether Nelly, whom she described as petulant and infantile, did not suffer from a psychological need to have a sick husband. Perhaps she did.

At least there are surer grounds on which to assess his mother. Beyond a doubt, the elder Mrs. Field judged her son hard and put heavy demands on him. David himself, it must be remembered, attributed his illness at 15 to the intolerable pressure he endured from his mother and one of his high school teachers. On the other hand, the senior Fields were generous and helpful. Due to Mrs. Field's quickness, the young couple owed the saving of their furniture; to her open-handedness they owed cash for the California trip. And Mr. Field supported the none-too-grateful Nelly and the children on their return. Her own mother was a liability to them.

Nelly's inexhaustible resourcefulness in extracting the maximum of public assistance on several occasions supplied the family with food and medical care. She was always able to see that the gap was closed between what David earned and what they needed. So, like Arthur Jackson, David demonstrates the man whose story is very much the story of those about him. David's parents presented him with no model he cared to copy and apparently there was only one significant other—

Einstein. The family was more disposed to dampen his youthful exuberance than to give it active direction, poverty-stricken and overworked as they were. And Nelly was lenient and indulgent. She could be so because she was always able to talk the welfare agencies into taking over the family. But if she had shown she expected David to assume the full burden, would he have acted differently? As will be seen, Arthur Jackson's wife assumed the household responsibilities during his illness and hospitalization and he himself was never after that the complete breadwinner. Peter Stone's wife, however, used the opposite tactics, with opposite results.

Pattern of Career as Affected by Illness and Hospitalization

"There is a scar on a person, the stigma of having been insane," David once said to the interviewer. His mother had declared that mental illness was "not nice"; his mother-in-law did not conceal deep shame at his affliction, and David claimed that it sometimes complicated his job-hunting, although as far as is known he did not allow it to deter him. As a cabby he could not suppress the fact of his illness since he lost his license thereby—in itself evidence of stigma. It will be remembered, however, that his helpful employer was ready to use political influence to recover his license, and at one point let him drive a cab illegally for a month. He then gave him work as a radio dispatcher for three months, and although David despised this work, he himself recognized the precariousness of his mental and emotional balance and consented to work a short day and a short week, at the cost of reduced earnings.

Nonetheless, although he accepted the judgment of others and associated cab-driving with his recurrent illness, and at one point made a desperate effort to establish himself as a car salesman, he entered the hospital a cabby and when he left he became a cabby again for the same firm. His most intensive efforts went into planning and saving for a cab of his own, although he knew that the attainment of his goal could only lead to an even heavier burden of work than he had carried before.

8 WORKER TO MARGINAL WORKER:
ARTHUR JACKSON

Arthur Jackson was 33 years old when he became part of the study in 1958. He had been in a state mental hospital for nine weeks, the study hospitalization, and was about to be released at the time of the first interview. As a physicist who specialized in spectroscopy, he had enjoyed a professional education and had progressed through several positions as an experimental laboratory man, gaining in status and salary with each move. He had patented several inventions. But he had already suffered several psychotic breaks and during the previous ten years had spent a total of almost a year institutionalized as a mental patient.

The study hospitalization lasted from February to April, and when he re-entered the community, he accepted work as a driver and packer in his brother-in-law's moving firm—a job he had taken once before when too ill to work at his profession. Two months later, in June, Arthur was admitted to a different hospital and this time, including brief stays in two more institutions, he was out of the community for about seventeen months, although during much of this period he was allowed to go home frequently on visits. There followed one year free of illness when for a time he held a well-paid position as a physicist once again, and took night courses toward completing work for a graduate degree in one of the nation's leading universities. But in the spring of 1961 he was readmitted to the hospital. Soon after he was transferred to a Veterans Administration hospital and was still there when contact with the case ended in September of that year. Arthur himself was seen six times. His wife, Hannah, was interviewed on eight occasions and various therapists, familiar with him and his story, on five.

THE SETTING: PAST AND PRESENT

Arthur was born in a South Shore suburb of Boston, the sixth child in a Roman Catholic family. His grandparents were local people. At the time of the study hospitalization, his elder brother, Daniel, fifteen years older than Arthur, a physicist with seven children, was employed in the south by the federal government. Theresa, the next child, was nine years older than Arthur. She lived with her husband and their one child in New York. Closest to Arthur and five years his senior was the second son, Tom, an accountant living in the same suburb as Arthur. Then came two married sisters, then Arthur, and, finally, Natalie, a year younger, the mother of four, who lived in Spain.

Arthur's parents were New Englanders of Irish and English extraction, well known and respected in the town. Arthur's mother died at age 70, two years before this study began, after a long illness. His father had been a helper in the dining-car department of a railroad and on retiring went into insurance. He was 72 at the time Arthur entered the study and lived in the same town as Arthur. Occasionally given to interfering, the father could appear inconveniently as a power to be reckoned with in the family. Thus Arthur's wife, Hannah, complained that once when Arthur was hospitalized his father decided that her car "should be taken off the road" and refused a check written by her mother to cover insurance premiums. Throughout the long history of Arthur's illness, his own family, according to Hannah, was prone to consider him as her business, refusing responsibility for him while criticizing his wife's efforts to carry on.

The family of Hannah, of Irish descent, entered into Arthur's story more than did his own. At the time the Jacksons began to participate in the study Hannah was 35, two years older than Arthur. Rita, Hannah's sister, lived across the road with her husband, Ned, and small children. Ten years older than Hannah, she was a local school teacher. Her summer cottage on the shore provided Hannah and Arthur and their small children a haven on the holidays. A second sister, Violet, five years Hannah's senior, was also a teacher in the town schools and Edna, three years older than Hannah, was the secretary of the local superintendent of schools; her husband worked for the telephone company. Finally, there was one brother, Henry, a "foot doctor" who lived near by and was seven years younger than Hannah. They all lived within easy reach of each other and their parents and were a united and affectionate clan.

Hannah's grandfather had founded a moving business which eventually he passed on to his son. (He had gone to a school of accountancy but abominated a sedentary indoor life and found in the moving business an escape from desk work.) In process of time his son in turn transferred the business to his son-in-law, Ned. Just at that time Arthur's condition made it impossible for him to get placed as a physicist and Ned offered him a place as a driver of one of the two moving trucks. In his brother-in-law Arthur had a sympathetic and considerate boss: Ned himself had once been a heavy drinker and he claimed to understand "what it is to try to come back." Hannah's father, having given up the moving firm, then turned to work in the family's gas station which was just a few steps from the houses in which his two daughters, Hannah and Rita, were living.

Arthur and Hannah had three children at the time of the study hospitalization. Maxine, aged 9, was in the fourth grade at school; Ada, a 7-year-old, was in the second grade, but 3-year-old Larry was still two years away from kindergarten. "I'd like to send them through college," said Arthur. "Of course that's a few years off. But we'll leave it up to them. If they want to go into nursing or secretarial school or get married, whatever it is—that's up to them. But one thing, we'll scrape the bottom to send them through school if that's what they want." This was, then, a family of lower-middle and working-class origins in which the educated and ambitious husband and father with his psychotic difficulties stood out from the whole clan connection.

Arthur and Hannah lived in a plain clapboard house of seven or eight rooms kept in impeccable order, located on an unpaved lane behind her father's gas station. Two smaller houses shared the site, with no pretense at gardening. In one lived Hannah's sister Rita, her husband Ned, and their children, The furniture in Arthur's house was plain, utilitarian, comfortable, and of the overstuffed period. The interviewer described the house on a summer evening as lively with sounds of children's laughing and scuffling coming from upstairs.

Living side by side as they did, Hannah and Rita saw each other daily. When Hannah took up teaching to support the family during Arthur's illness, Rita looked after Larry, the baby, and when Hannah went to teach night school her mother came over and took charge.

Not only did Ned give Arthur employment when he needed it, but also he and Rita, as well as Hannah's parents, helped out from time to time with money. Thus Arthur is pictured as a man of original mind, with professional skills, literally fenced in by members of his wife's close-knit clan, each of whom was ready to leap in the breach if necessary, as though it were the most natural thing in the world: a strong contrast to his own family.

Arthur Jackson's career may be summarized as follows:

1943-1946: In 1943 Arthur was 18. He had completed one year of college and entered the Navy for almost three years. In 1946 he resumed his college education.

1947: Having completed his war service, which included radar and other technical courses on eight univeristy campuses as well as ten months' duty in the Pacific, he got his B.S. in physics at a good Eastern university and took graduate work toward a Ph.D. He was at the time a research assistant in the spectroscopy laboratory. He was 22 years old. He and Hannah were married this year.

1948: He now took what seems to be his first job, as a consultant to his elder brother who was a physicist. He went in the spring to his first "real" job as a junior physicist with a large corporation at $3600 a year. His first child was born and he suffered his first psychotic episode. He had to leave the company to be hospitalized. This was followed by three other short intervals of hospitalization totaling three months of the year. All four admissions were to a private hospital.

1949: He was for the first five or six months in a Veterans Administration hospital, diagnosed as suffering from schizophrenic reaction.

1949-1956: For six and a half years while in the community he was an "idea man" inventing spectroscopic devices in the commercial laboratory of a man who became a family friend, and he was earning $7500 a year. He grew overemotional and confused and finally gave notice in February 1956. He at once found a job in an Air Force research center, at $8650 a year, but was discharged in December, in a highly excitable and paranoid state. At this time he first became possessed with the idea of setting up his own consulting laboratory.

1957: In January and February he was "unable to work" but was consumed with his dream project of a laboratory of his own. In mid-February he was arrested for holding up motorists on the highway at knife-point at midnight. He was said to be afflicted by paranoid delusions, was hospitalized by court order, and spent two and a half months in a state institution. Released

in May, he found it impossible to get employment as a physicist and in October accepted work in his brother-in-law's
moving business. When business slackened in the winter he
drew unemployment compensation.

1958: In January he reverted to the idea of his own laboratory, became manic again, and was returned at the end of February to
the state hospital. He stayed there nine weeks until the end of
April. This was the study hospitalization. Released then on
trial visit, Arthur went back to his brother-in-law's moving
business. But at the end of two months he became deeply depressed and was rehospitalized, this time at another state hospital for seventeen months. During this hospitalization, he again
worked as a packer and driver in the moving business, being
allowed home for days at a time. He talked of accepting very
soon one or the other of two positions in physics.

1959: In January Arthur again bent his energies toward setting up
his laboratory during the periods he was allowed home on
visit. In March he escaped from the hospital to New York.
Immediately hospitalized by his sister there, he was returned
three months later to the hospital from which he had escaped.
In November he was granted an indefinite visit home, and returned to the moving business.

1960: He continued in the moving business, working forty to fifty
hours a week. In November he found employment in vacuum
physics and was formally discharged from the hospital. His
salary was $8700.

1961: He worked as a physicist and also, in March, set up his own
laboratory. In February he and Hannah agreed to separate for
six months. In late March he became violent and was returned
to the hospital by the police. Sent home in April, he was excitable and threatening and was taken back after three days.
In May he was transferred to a Veterans Administration hospital
and was still there in September.

Of the eighteen years between the ages of 18 and 36, Arthur spent
three years in the Navy, got his B.S., did some graduate work, then
worked about nine and a half years as a physicist and about one and a
half years as a mover's helper. The last-named employment often overlapped hospitalization which, in the eighteen years, totaled two years
and eleven months.

THE PREHOSPITAL CAREER

When Arthur had completed one year on a church scholarship at a
Catholic college, he was taken into the Navy's V-12 program, under
which he studied at eight institutions, including a radar school and

midshipmen's school. At the end of two years he was commissioned and
stationed as deck officer on a Liberty ship carrying fuel oil in the South
Pacific. When his military service ended (he saw no fighting), he came
home and took a B.S. in physics in 1947 at an institution of much higher
standing than the one to which he had gone first. He went on to take
graduate courses and at 22 was a laboratory assistant at a university of
world renown. That summer he and Hannah, his childhood friend,
were married.

For a short time he was a consultant to his elder brother, a physicist.
A year later he got a job as a junior physicist at $3600 with a large
corporation. Six months later, when his first child was born, he apparently became suddenly psychotic, a response, according to the therapist, to the realization of family responsibilities. His job ended with his
hospitalization.

In that year, 1948, Arthur was hospitalized three times more in quick
succession, amounting to three months. All four admissions were to a
private hospital. He was depressed and confused, the diagnosis being
schizophrenic reaction, catatonic type. At the beginning of 1949 he
was transferred to a Veterans Administration hospital, where he stayed
for a little less than six months. He was released for a trial visit of the
customary year's length, during which time and the ensuing year he
kept in touch with his psychiatrist as a private arrangement.

This was followed by five "good" years when he had no psychiatric
help. He was now in the employ of a friend who had a physics laboratory where he worked on spectroscopic instruments. He described
himself as an "idea man . . . solving problems with simple devices,"
some of which were patented. His salary was $7500, probably low for
this highly technical original work, but Arthur continued in it for
over seven and a half years, until 1956. He gave as his reason for remaining his lack of confidence in himself to succeed elsewhere. He
enjoyed a somewhat paternalistic relationship with his employer and
the wives of the two men were friends. It was characteristic of Arthur
to set himself very high standards and to drive himself to long hours
of work. A gifted, even brilliant physicist, he was thought of as a man
of inventive gifts who would go far, and a perfectionist to whom
autonomy at work meant a great deal, although combined with dependence upon an indulgent employer.

Hannah said he began to be quarrelsome and erratic in early 1956.

He became too confused and emotional to work properly, yet he repudiated the well-meant recommendations of his boss and associates to seek medical advice. Finally, he gave three months' notice and left on February 1, 1956.

In Arthur's mind his work at the laboratory was now of minor interest in any case, secondary to an all-consuming ambition which was to keep appearing in his career like a thread of fate and become a great bone of contention between husband and wife: to set up a consulting laboratory of his own. The idea took possession of him several times in the period of the study and assumed a characteristic form. It would begin with what Hannah called "telephonitis": he would telephone frantically to all sorts of people at all hours. He forgot to eat, slept only two or three hours out of the day, and came home at dawn. Then he would leave home armed with credit cards and take a room in a downtown hotel where he went in for high living with, it is suggested in the hospital record, women as well as men friends. As Hannah saw it: "Arthur has a marvelous mind but he does not have a business head. When he'd start thinking about the consulting laboratory he would be practical at first, but soon it would start growing into enormous proportions. It would become ridiculous. And we'd start getting very deeply into debt. . . . He hired a staff and began to set up an office operation and ordered some expensive advertising before the thing was ever on its feet . . . It would work if well managed—if only his temperament were different. He takes on all the work himself. He can't delegate anything. I just don't think it will work." When this mood was upon him, when as Hannah described him he was "high," she learned to identify it as the onset of illness, and a sign that he would have to be hospitalized.

His plans brought them some hundreds of dollars of debt but a month after he left his job at the physics laboratory Arthur found another one as a physicist at a nearby Air Force research center at a salary of $8650 and was happily able to pay off his creditors fairly promptly. But the job lasted only nine months. By December 1956, he had become so excitable and paranoid and so resistant to any suggestion that he needed medical aid, that he was discharged, a measure precipitated by his going to the FBI with some tale about the research center, details of which are unknown.

By now the second and the third child arrived but he seemed able to face these events somewhat better than the first time, although he was deeply depressed by his father's prolonged mourning when his mother died that winter.

In his "good" years, Arthur had taken a keen interest in the public affairs of his suburban town and had been elected by an impressive vote to the school board and as a town meeting member. He put his heart into their projects and is reported to have spent $300 of his own money on literature to promote a proposed measure authorizing the purchase of land for schools. But the vote went against him and he took it personally. This mortifying rebuff (to him) came when he was madly preoccupied with his consulting laboratory. Finally, one night in February 1957, he was picked up by the police while stopping drivers on the highway and demanding their car keys. He was convinced they were Communists with some grudge against him, whom, to save himself, he had to immobilize. He asserted that they were enemy agents, that the FBI and the Air Force were keeping watch on his movements, that he had been drugged, his cigarettes tampered with, and much else in the same vein.

The newspapers made a sensational item of the fall of a prominent citizen (it made an excellent news story) and the story went on for days, ending with the news that he had been committed by the court to a state mental hospital. Arthur was stung by what he took as a second instance of public ingratitude and wrongheadedness. Hannah, however, spoke of the townspeople as "wonderful"—ready to extend their help and friendship to him and to her.

As a patient, Arthur was, at least with regard to his behavior, encouraging. Although often depressed and withdrawn he mingled easily with his fellow patients, took part with interest in occupational therapy, and busied himself with patient government and with the photography section of the rehabilitation department. There is an indication, too, that he began attending an off-grounds social center for the patients, where he had several rendezvous with a manic-depressive girl—the therapist thought it was "an indirect call for help" and that this was not an isolated episode. If true, his wife gave no sign that she knew of it, but as the hospital record states, he would become a "playboy" only when "high" and on those occasions he was absent for most of the time from home.

A few days after he entered the hospital, Hannah reported, the school superintendent (Rita was his secretary, it will be remembered, and Arthur was a member of the board) "called me voluntarily and asked if I'd like to come back to teach. Of course I knew the superintendent before then but the point is that he volunteered the offer." She was engaged at once to teach household arts and home economics full time in the high school and she also took on two evening classes a week, all of which was made possible by the generosity of her mother and Rita who looked after the children, and by the fact that Arthur himself was permitted home visits at regular intervals. Admittedly, Hannah had assumed a very heavy program but she declared "I just love it!" Of course during Arthur's hospitalization her salary was their only source of income, a state of affairs which Arthur himself acknowledged with mixed feelings.

In May 1957, after two and a half months of institutional life, Arthur was released on a trial visit and went job-hunting. Hannah said he "went to every physics lab in town and nobody would hire him; he was too depressed." He returned to the establishment where he had been "idea man," but he was as high-strung and emotional as ever and at the end of three days he left of his own volition. He went on hunting jobs sporadically from May until October, with summer holidays spent with his family at Rita's cottage at the shore. Finally in October, Ned, who had recently taken over the family business, took him on as a truck driver and packer in the moving concern at $2.25 an hour. This undemanding job seemed to be just what Arthur needed at the time; as he said himself, he learned to move among people again: "I think there was good wisdom in it. . . . I had to face these people—especially after the headlines and all the publicity of my arrest. It took me about four months to get over it, to learn to be at ease with people in the community again." The hospital record refers to a job found for him by his former employer in a college physics laboratory, but there is no evidence that he accepted it; in any case this would have been for a brief time only before he joined Ned.

For three months all went well. Arthur's therapist left the city, which upset him, but he appeared quite capable of doing what his job demanded. In November when the moving business slackened he and Ned agreed that Arthur should collect unemployment compensation.

But although unemployed, Arthur was very far from idle; his vision of a consulting laboratory beckoned again. Late in January 1958, the mania of telephoning which Hannah already had learned to dread overcame him. Moreover, he hired lawyers to begin suit against the newspapers which had played up the story when he had been arrested the year before. He was seeing almost nothing of his friends, although he had always been gregarious and popular. His project consumed his days and large fractions of his nights and all his energy. He ordinarily enjoyed his children, would drive them into the country on Sundays or play games with them at home and, according to Hannah, they adored him. But now, as she said, he seemed not to want to be reminded he had a family at all; he simply did not see the children, even across the dinner table. He upset them, too, with his loud-voiced arguments and his incessant angry accusations of their mother.

Manic as he certainly was at this time, Arthur had a promising idea for his consulting laboratory, combining his interest in science with his interest in schools: to make and distribute electrical kits for use in high school physics classes. Beside that, he was seeking patents on a spectroscopic device which could distinguish what materials were burning in a fire, a chief use being that it could detect, perhaps, magnesium pellets planted by an arsonist—"just what a paranoid physicist would think up," remarked Arthur's doctor.

Toward the end of February his restlessness and hyperactivity had reached such proportions that he and Hannah each took steps to get him some psychiatric help, consulting several hospital psychiatrists and a social worker at the suburban family service center where Hannah had been receiving counseling for over a year. Finally, Hannah took him to a state hospital where an appointment was made for a diagnostic interview the next day. But it was too late. In a state of intense excitement, Arthur for some unexplained reason rushed off to Bridgeport, then returned and declaring he needed peace and quiet to work, took a room in a Boston hotel, and rented a car. He was said to be in a very confused state, and was rehospitalized from the hotel, apparently at Hannah's request. He was returned to the same state hospital which he had left nine months before.

There he stayed nine weeks, from February 23 to April 30, 1958. This was the study hospitalization and was the sixth time Arthur had been institutionalized, by now at three different hospitals—one private, one Veterans Administration, and one state.

THE HOSPITAL PERIOD

Arthur presented something of a puzzle in diagnosis: he was too friendly and had too good a record at school and college to run true to type, yet he was "obviously delusional." The therapist noted cyclical depression and classified him as suffering a schizoid reaction, paranoid type. Hannah, who was always more afraid of his "high" intervals than of depression, was frankly relieved to have him back in the hospital and devoted her energies thankfully to her school-teaching. On re-entering the hospital, Arthur conceded, "This has been very rough on my wife but I guess she loves me enough to put up with it." Nevertheless, he suspected her and others of "pushing" him into the hospital and sorely resented it.

As before, he soon occupied himself. In the patient government he was a ward representative, and he was made assistant manager of the coffee shop. "That's what I'm dressed for now" he said to the interviewer on their second encounter to explain his unpressed work pants and rolled-up sleeves. "It doesn't amount to much. There's nothing really managerial about it." The work took five half-days a week, in addition to which he was going home for weekends and working again with Ned in the moving business.

Following some weeks of good spirits, Arthur began to grow depressed, slow, and seclusive. Nevertheless his therapist, in consideration of the patient's wish to go home ("It will be wonderful!"), Hannah's concurrence, and his own conviction that a longer stay would bring "only diminishing returns," had him released for a year of trial visit.

The therapist suspected that Arthur might never be a physicist again. "He has deteriorated," he said, ". . . I'd be very surprised if he returns full time to physics . . . The demands of the real competitive world in physics are just too much for him. Given his two [*sic*] years of difficulty, I just don't think he'd be able to get back into the swing of things. What worries me now is that he only thinks of physics when he is in his grandiose mood, not when he's on the level." He pointed out that the patient this time said nothing about seeking a place in a laboratory but spoke, as though looking forward to it, of resuming work as a mover. Arthur himself did not refer to his inventions and his projected plan of manufacturing and marketing the electrical kits.

Instead, he explained to the interviewer that he was going right back to work on the truck this time; that he had, on his previous release from the hospital, surmounted the difficulty of facing the world again. "It's not my pick for the rest of my life," he said, "but it's just something to get back into shape with. . . . It's not easy to stay physically in shape when you're in the hospital. Also it's a matter of getting your mind accustomed to the regular day-by-day work schedule." Hannah commented, having Arthur's drug-induced slowness and Ned's patience and sympathy in mind, "I don't think he could work for someone else now. And I don't think he wants to get back into his field until he feels he can go without [the drugs]. He sleeps too much now."

Meanwhile, Arthur arranged to continue seeing his therapist, paying him privately—"My past experience seems to show that I'm susceptible to breakdowns, so I think it's a very good investment to stay with a private doctor, once I get out." The therapist's explanation was that Arthur wanted to get better without the hospital and by paying for it himself. In one of his infrequent references to his condition, Arthur explained: ". . . The problem became apparent early this year. I started promoting my own lab again and I got into a state where I should have known better. I should have realized I needed more rest than I was getting. But I just couldn't get myself to believe that I was running into trouble again. My wife and I just didn't hit it off. There was no hatred but there was a feeling of lost love. We were separated for about four months in our own household last year. I think as I look back on it now, it was my responsibility. And I didn't succeed at it. With the three children, I should have taken my wife's advice. I was getting more and more keyed up with the lab but I couldn't seem to break away from it. . . . Now we have complete understanding. Everything is O.K. . . . I feel good about leaving the hospital this time and I hate to return to it after weekends at home."

The packing and truck-driving were to give place in due time to one of two alternative openings which Arthur expected to follow up "within the month": the vice-president of a research firm was interested in his patents and a second company invited him to go into the retailing of an electric breadboard. The last-named proposition, he conceded, was selling, not science, but selling had been part of his work when he was on his seven-year laboratory job; although after all it was selling scientific instruments: "I wouldn't want to sell outside of my line."

Hannah cherished the hope that he might return to his earlier employer's paternalistic establishment but in sales, not research.

Their financial position, Arthur described as "not too good. [But] we've got pretty good assets. I've got only a $7000 mortgage on the house but we're about $500 in debt, mostly from my last attempt to get the consulting service operating. The job [involving his patents] would pay $8000 to $9000 a year and that should straighten us out in a hurry." Hannah had been dunned by his creditors and with her father's help had been making payments on the debts, a fact which Arthur discovered only by accident, much to his chagrin. One was for a $29-a-day hotel room. Hannah until now had not spoken of the money but when he learned of the bill collectors, she said, "Tell me, Arthur, what did you get for that $29?" But he denied all recollection of it and left her wondering if it was due to genuine amnesia or to shame and mortification. That spring as he left the hospital the couple counted on her salary and his income as a mover to tide them over until he could accept one of the well-paid openings offered him. When he told the interviewer, speaking of Hannah's teaching, "I don't particularly care to have her working like this. But I'll leave it up to her," he must have known that under the circumstances she could hardly choose not to work.

He left the hospital on April 30, 1958.

THE POSTHOSPITAL CAREER

For the first two weeks all went well. Delighted to be back at home with his children, free of the fear of meeting people which had tormented him when he had left the hospital on the previous occasion, Arthur was looking forward to attending the men's communion breakfast on Sunday, a well-attended affair which he had shrunk from twelve months before. For their part, Hannah and the children revelled in revived family life—"He's warm and very much here. He's one of us and not just a guest or a stranger in the house." She, too, saw the moving job as a face-saving alternative to the more demanding life of an experimental physicist but confessed that she "felt leery." She was sure the dream of his own laboratory would possess him again: "That's where our personalities really clash. I hit the roof whenever he mentions it." Although she admitted that if there were a partner with a good business head, it might be a practicable project. Of one thing she was certain—with returning strength, he would leave the moving business.

Then Arthur began to dread handling the truck on his own. "He's quite depressed," said the therapist. "It's comparable to last year at this time . . . a difference is that this time he's working. But he's working with great difficulty. He is considerably handicapped. So I don't know just how beneficial the working is for him. When he is left to his own devices he gets very agitated and feels incompetent. His usual function on the job is to pack the trucks to see that things are properly distributed. But he feels unable to do this. So he asked his boss not to schedule too much. Also he's not eating or sleeping well. He's got a real fight on his hands." Hannah interpreted his deepening depression as due to the belated realization that he might never get back into research again. And although she had insisted on how "good and friendly everyone had been," for the first time she began to wonder if her husband's lengthening record of illness and hospitalization might not begin to militate against him in the minds of prospective employers.

To the exasperation of Hannah and Ned, Arthur suddenly began to suffer qualms of conscience over having collected unemployment compensation in the preceding winter. He insisted he was guilty of theft from the government and talked of giving himself up. The old bills from his laboratory loomed large in his mind and despite Hannah's repeated assurances that they were paid and ought to be forgotten, he worried incessantly that "he had put us through all that." Unfortunately, the therapist whom Arthur had been seeing privately had left the city and he had no confidence in the stranger who replaced him at the hospital. Finally, on a day of black despair he cried out to Hannah, "Take me any place! To any hospital!" And when, the following day, he declared he was going to surrender to the police without further delay, Hannah and her brother brought him to still another state hospital where, through the mediation of an influential friend of Hannah's mother, he was admitted without delay. He was accepted by a horrified doctor who exclaimed "Heavens! Why did you wait till this late in the game? You've been taking a terrible chance with your children!" The diagnosis was schizophrenic reaction, chronic undifferentiated type, the symptoms being cycles of manic succeeded by depressed behavior. It was now June of 1958, just two months after Arthur had been released in such a hopeful state of mind.

Responding well to hospital treatment, Arthur was soon detailed to kitchen work and a stretcher unit and was reported as "the best worker on the ward." By August he was allowed visits home that lasted four or five days at a time. The improvement in his physical and mental health was striking. But in September, all was changed suddenly by a piece of administrative bungling in classifying him as a court commitment as a result of which his ground and weekend privileges were immediately withdrawn. Not only could he not go home, but also he could not go out to work with Ned. Arthur nevertheless was "basically fine. He's nearer himself," declared Hannah, "than he's been in a very long time." But she complained that he was getting no medical attention, no days off, no ground privileges, and had no activities. Leaving the children with Rita at the beach, she went to visit him every other day.

By October the confusion over classifying the patient was more or less resolved and at last he was allowed to go home again on visits. "He is just like the old Arthur," said Hannah. ". . . a big change. He's really wonderful!" And the therapist began to hope he could be "brought back to normal and kept there." Yet he warned, "I'm not going to send him out as a physicist. He's not a physicist now. He won't be a physicist again." He spoke of the patient's intellectual capacity as reduced by repeated psychotic episodes: he could be a waiter or a porter or a truck-driver but he was no longer able to think continuously or assume responsibility. Arthur was now taking weekends and other days off from the hospital and worked with Ned, as before. He reported it was working out very well and that for the time being he had no further plans. "I'm just taking it as it comes, you might say." Ned, on his side, was more than willing for the arrangement to continue for he had found in Arthur a superior employee, a good worker; moreover, he was happy to help him earn money.

By January 1959, however, they were all less sanguine. Arthur was growing ominously quiet and anxious again; the cycle was apparently repeating itself. He had borne up well at the packing and moving but when Christmas was past he fell into depression, complaining that the task did not use his talents and it was degrading. "But my father was a moving man all his life and now Ned is one—and they can hold up their heads," cried Hannah. Finally he stopped work altogether and, although his doctor had instructed him to stay away from physics for a year, he proposed to find a job teaching high school physics and chemistry. His efforts met with no success but suddenly, to Hannah's despair, he stopped talking about teaching and began the familiar mania of telephoning, and all the other wild gestures that meant he was bent, once more, on establishing his laboratory. In mid-January he left home, armed with credit cards, found a hotel room, and launched upon the entertainment of "friends" which, as Hannah was now sure, included women friends. Through his old employer, he sent word to Hannah that he had engaged a lawyer to start separation proceedings. Hannah, horrified at the prospect of more bills, requested the hospital to end his home visits and before the end of the month he was reinstated as full-time patient.

Arthur was much exercised over Hannah's action and vowed he would sue all those who had sent him back. He grew deeply resentful of her job and told her they should have another child, to keep her at home—a remark which betrayed his frustration and the mortifying awareness of the lengthening intervals when her salary was all they had to live on. He became so difficult to manage that in the end he was assigned to seclusion in an old building where he destroyed every-thing breakable within reach—a type of behavior he had not exhibited until now. Hannah decided against visiting him but kept in touch through Ned, two of his sisters, and his brother and sister-in-law, all of whom went to see him. Some members of his family looked on him as "unwilling to help himself, though he could if he would"; his father called him "stubborn and nasty."

Hannah herself had a heavy schedule of teaching which included an evening class and a second evening when she attended extension courses, aiming at an M.A. in education in order to gain a very sub-stantial increase in salary. Helpful as always, her family recognized Arthur as a sick man and trusted her judgment when she decided to seek a divorce. For Hannah was convinced that responsibility triggered Arthur's "high" phase and reasoned that he might recover if free and clear of his family. In mid-February she had new misgivings about the future, for she made the unwelcome discovery that she was pregnant—but it ended shortly in a miscarriage.

In March, Arthur escaped from the hospital. He hitch-hiked to a suburban town where he was able to cash a check big enough to pay for a bus ticket to New York, where his sister Theresa lived on Long

Island. The day after he arrived there, Theresa had him admitted to a general hospital, from which he was transferred in a strait jacket several weeks later to a state mental hospital in New York. Delusional and withdrawn, he was in what Hannah, who went to see him in the spring recess, described as "very bad shape." Hannah was told the outlook was discouraging, that Arthur might be in and out of hospitals for the rest of his life. "I don't want to leave him in the lurch," she said, and instructed her lawyer to hold up the divorce proceedings for at least as long as he was hospitalized.

Following the very first in a course of shock treatments, however, Arthur became "quiet and cooperative, friendly and cheerful," free of delusions and paranoia. Three months after he had arrived in New York, he was transferred back to the Massachusetts hospital from which he had escaped in March. It was August before he was allowed to return home on visits. He was reported as quiet but very happy: "If he plans anything," said Hannah, "it is always with the children." She was reconciled to his return from the New York hospital; in the hope that the course of shock treatment prescribed there would help him—as it did—she had at first opposed the transfer. And now they were reconciled and she was anxious to have him released and permanently returned to his family.

Her own affairs were thriving. She had had to refuse a flattering offer from a textbook publishing company, but had had a raise in salary, was put in charge of the school lunchrooms, and made advisor to the senior girls. She was planning with a friend to spend the following summer studying in Dublin, counting, presumably, upon her family to look after the children.

Arthur, too, seemed to be making good progress toward recovery. He was much occupied in the hospital's X-ray developing room. To his therapist, he gave his own explanation of his most recent breakdown: overwork from the moving job and a business on the side (his laboratory) so that he found himself with a working day of from sixteen to twenty hours, with the added burden of domestic difficulties which he did not specify. At Hannah's request he was permitted an indefinite visit home in November 1959, and he went back to work with Ned, taking on as much as from forty to fifty hours a week of packing and moving. This brought to an end a siege of hospitalization totaling seventeen months, spent in three different hospitals.

He apparently worked with Ned during most of the period from November 1959 to November 1960. In the belief it would stand him in good stead later on, Arthur began studying machine tool operation in a downtown technical institute two nights a week; at the time it gave him immediate interest and pleasure as a hobby. He wrote optimistically of all this to the superintendent of the hospital: "This schedule of work, studying, and future placement into my original work as a physicist is in accordance with a scheduled rehabilitation plan which [my doctor] and I had worked out after my release from the hospital. It has been most successful and I truly believe the lack of such a program previously, as well as my own impatience and pride, was the major contributing factor to my return to the hospital."

And now at last he was a physicist again. He accepted a job in vacuum physics at $8700 in late October 1960, and on the strength of it was formally discharged from the hospital at the beginning of November.

The hospital record now skips to the beginning of March 1961, documenting the fact that Arthur until that date was well and still in the community, which he had re-entered just under seventeen months before.

In mid-February of 1961, Hannah and Arthur separated by mutual consent for an experimental six months, and he took a room nearer in town. He had been visiting the family on a Sunday early in March and grew wildly impatient when Hannah delayed dinner with repeated telephoning. In a rage he ripped the instrument from the wall. The police took him back to the state hospital from which he had been discharged, where he was diagnosed as in the manic phase of a manic-depressive cycle.

His life had been full indeed. He related to the hospital personnel that he was working in a vacuum physics laboratory but also had opened a consulting laboratory nearby where he was perfecting his spectroscopic instrument for fire detection. To launch it on the market he had made an apparently vain trip to New York. He saw little of Hannah and was having an affair with another woman, for in fourteen years of marriage, he said, he and his wife had been "slipping" for the past eight years. He was worried about his favorite brother, Tom, who was in Boston to be operated on for aneurysm of the brain. (Tom died soon after Arthur was rehospitalized.) Godfather of one of Tom's daughters, Arthur had visited him in the hospital just the week before his outbreak. To add to all this, Arthur had been drinking heavily when admitted.

Although he was reported as still delusional, he was declared sufficiently in contact and control to justify release and he emerged on April 18. He was home for three days. In that time he never went to bed, put medicine in his wife's coffee, talked incessantly of sex, terrorized the children, telephoned at all hours and to inappropriate people. His return at once to the hospital was urged by the local clinic to which he had been instructed to report. On April 20 the police once again brought him back, manic, to the same hospital. After two months there he was transferred to a Veterans Administration hospital. Four and a half months later he was still there—at which time this record was terminated.

DISCUSSION

The case of Arthur Jackson adds to this array of stories of working life as broken into by mental illness and hospitalization an example among married patients of a man who is slipping. A promising, it may be brilliant, person with practical inventive gifts, he went down occupationally with each psychotic episode, then up again, but in a descending spiral, moving further from being an employable, productive professional worker toward becoming an unreliable, erratic person who failed first at the high level of his challenging profession and eventually could not cope with even simple manual tasks.

The word *marginal* applies to Arthur in more than one sense. In the first place, only rarely did he get his jobs in the open market and most of the positions he held were not, strictly speaking, competitively gained: as a consultant to his brother; as a frankly underpaid experimental physicist in the laboratory of a family friend, clinging year after year to the job because he lacked the confidence to find another; as an assistant in a college laboratory, a place found for him by his former employer; as a packer and mover in his brother-in-law's firm, work which for a man of his profession was in reality a substitute for a job. Finally, the attraction of a laboratory of his own which he so determinedly sought to establish was, according to his psychiatrist, largely that he would thereby be self-employed, evading the labor market entirely.

In the second place, his jobs were marginal in that they provided him with the equivalent of the sheltered workshop for the handicapped. His long-time employer kept Arthur on, confused and paranoid, until he, himself, gave notice. His brother-in-law tailored the work to suit Arthur's capacities of the moment and fitted him into the firm whenever he wanted work and was well enough to undertake it, indulging him in a way no ordinary employee could expect.

Finally, Hannah and Arthur's customary mode of life could not be financed by his earnings as a mover, nor, of course, in the long stretches when he was ill or unemployed, and it was only Hannah's salary that kept their house and maintained the family. Providentially, throughout his story, his jobs in physics, short-lived though they had become, were enough to rescue them from the serious money trouble repeatedly brought on by his laboratory ventures. So dubious a breadwinner, however, can be described as only an occasional mainstay of the family. In this respect, and only so, David Field, with his family's reliance on welfare agencies, was also a marginal breadwinner, but David was not an erratic worker.

One thinks of a marginal breadwinner as the ineffectual support of a family reduced to bare subsistence and, often, too, of one whose continuance as a unit is threatened. But this is not true of Arthur's family: through the ups and downs of the father's precarious career, it at least remained intact.

Career Pattern

Arthur had, in effect, two careers at work: sometimes he was a physicist; at others, he was a packer and mover. Subsequent to his first series of hospitalizations, he was able to hold one job as a physicist for as long as seven years and another for nine months, and after a second series of hospitalizations, again obtained a job as a physicist for five months. In his other capacity, he was indulged and encouraged; he came to the moving firm always as a convalescent and left it "as soon as he had got himself back in shape," that is, after recovering from the regimen of drugs and inactivity in the hospital. Then with renewed self-confidence, he would repudiate his packing and moving job and plunge headlong into preparations for his cherished dream of an independent professional enterprise.

He sustained neither role for long, except for the seven years with the commercial laboratory. Illness cut short his career, or careers, for months at a time. There is continuity in the sense of a sequence, often repeated, of the two careers—stability in neither. Somewhere in mid-career before he reached what seemed to be the point of no return in either of his two working worlds, he was an adequate performer. He was a respected physicist and held four good positions as such. And there were times, too, when he seemed to enjoy the moving business— "It's good to be with people again"—and spoke of it without reservation or apology. Also there is Ned's statement that he was a satisfactory employee. But the good periods came to characteristic climaxes: the physicist grew manic, too sick to work; the truck-driver impatient and ashamed, too well to go on.

While it is true that some of Arthur's jobs contained elements of sheltered employment, he was often a prompt and successful job-hunter. On leaving his friend's laboratory in 1956, he found a place without delay in an Air Force research center. When, fourteen months later, although he went to "every physics laboratory in town" he could not get work because of his deep and obvious depression, he accepted employment with Ned in the moving firm. Twice more, on leaving the hospital, he went to Ned's firm. The fact that it was not worthy of a physicist did not deter him from accepting it, when it meant that job or nothing. There is no information as to how he acquired the job in vacuum physics which kept him busy for five months and was the last employment before the case was terminated.

With regard to mobility, it might be said that he oscillated up and down and back again as he alternated between the laboratory and driving a truck. Of more significance is the general trend of his total career and this seemed a basically irreversible descent. Sympathetic Ned might continue out of family feeling to hire him despite impaired capacity. But the family friend who had had him for so long in his laboratory admitted after one disappointing experience that he could not rehire him.

It must be conceded that the work in vacuum physics which was his last job brought him a larger salary than he had had. In fact each time he found work as a physicist his income rose, although this might be accounted for by the change in the salary scales in the years of his work history. That the last job came to an end when Arthur suffered the most violent and disastrous of his several breakdowns raises the question how often thereafter he would be able to get placed as a scientist. For how long would he be able to work at all?

Qualifications for the Labor Market

Arthur's education as a physicist was of the first order. He passed through a number of educational institutions and, beginning with a third-rate denominational college, ended as a doctoral candidate in what is one of the world's best schools. An advantage he was not slow to exploit was that he worked on the frontiers of spectroscopy: he became an inventor in a growing field.

His occupational choice crystallized early and he advanced rapidly. A laboratory assistant at 22 while a graduate student, he became a junior physicist in an international corporation a year later and a year after that was taken on at more than twice his salary in a small laboratory where he invented instruments. Again, after seven years he accepted a research position at a raise of 15 per cent.

His fatal weakness, however, lack of confidence, showed itself early. His first psychotic break was diagnosed as brought on by fear of responsibility when his eldest child was born. He accepted the job with the laboratory at relatively poor pay for such a position but stayed in it year after year because he shrank from competing in the open market. Undeniably, he was inviting responsibility when he undertook to found a laboratory, but as has been suggested he may have looked on independent self-employment as a device for insuring himself against the risk of having to look for work and of being refused or failing. This interpretation of his project makes it look rational, purposeful, and appropriate, when considering his timidity. At no time, however, did he have the capital or, according to Hannah, the practical business sense which it demanded. Treating him as a sick man, none of the family offered help with money or brains. Yet the idea might not in itself have been entirely unrealistic: he had a good professional reputation and influential, well-disposed friends. But always when he busied himself with it he was "high." Credit cards seemed to do for capital and his own furious, unresting energy for executive ability.

A question arises here, which cannot be answered from the data at hand: Were Arthur's "high" periods brought on by overwork, as he and Hannah and the therapist thought? Was relief at escape from

the moving business followed by the awful realization of the burden
he was shouldering in his consulting laboratory, upon which he became
ill? Or did the manic phase of his ailment assert itself, whereupon he
threw himself into frenzied, unremitting effort? Or, a third possibility,
were the illness and the mad pace of work unrelated phenomena which
coincided by chance, but did so more than once? Illness may be con-
strued as a despoiler of his projects, or as with Frank Monaco as a
flight from something that was exceeding his resources of personality
and capital. Did illness rescue him when unnerved by a sense of inadequacy as a physicist? Whatever the answers, it seems clear that his
educational qualifications were equal to the demands of his various
positions, but his temperament was not. Frank Monaco, another whom
high ambition and an early-crystallized choice launched on a course
he could not maintain, at least was able to remain in the professional
world; he did not take the steep plunge that Arthur did but, instead,
established himself in another field at roughly comparable status. In
other words, Frank, too, was salvaged as a worker by a change in
occupation but not at the cost of downward mobility. In another way,
Arthur may be compared with Carl Duncan, a man with a blasted
promise in place of a career.

Career Orientation

Despite recurrent illness and long periods of unemployability at his
profession, Arthur always thought of himself as a physicist, early
committed and persistently bent on continuing as such. Yet when he
had a chance to go in for selling scientific equipment, he adapted
himself to the change in orientation. Later on, he ingeniously thought
up a job for himself, combining the manufacture and retailing of
laboratory kits. Nonetheless, he made it plain he would go in for
selling "only in my field." And when he was reduced to moving and
packing he spoke of it as a temporary expedient while he grew used
to living in the community again and recovered from hospital life
and medication.

The physics laboratory was Arthur's love and his chosen mode of life.
He spoke of money rarely, and then chiefly in connection with his
wife's contribution to the family's income. His source of satisfaction
was clearly the work itself; the work of a successful inventor (he had
several patents to his credit) can be challenging, rewarding, even joyful.

His wife and his therapist took it as an ill omen when he once left the hospital, having said nothing about professional work but accepting it as forgone that he would go back to Ned's job; for on other occasions of release he appeared to take it for granted that he would require work in a laboratory. For years he stayed on in an underpaid job where the work and the associates were gratifying.

Nonetheless, Arthur had family objectives; he spoke of hoping to send the three children through college when the time came—"or whatever they want, nursing, secretarial school . . ."—and added, "we'll scrape the bottom of the barrel for that, if need be." We have no direct statements concerning his dream laboratory, but can conjecture that it offered, in his mind, the satisfying life of the physicist with inflated financial returns—for the plans are always spoken of as "grandiose" by Hannah and the therapist.

Career Contingencies: The Hospital

Arthur barely had launched on his professional career when he was plunged into confusion and depression by his child's birth, and a quick succession of short periods in the hospital followed. Thereupon he entered into a private arrangement with his hospital therapist which stood him in good stead. He kept in touch with the doctor for two years and then went without attention for five "good" years. Following his release from the hospital before the study hospitalization, however, he grew so dependent on his therapist that the psychotic episode leading to rehospitalization was attributed in part to the latter's absence from the city. The private financial arrangements were interpreted as the patient's way of getting better without the hospital and at his own expense, that is, entirely on his own. Yet the doctor complained that Arthur, for all this, never seemed to regard himself as "a partner in therapy. He never asks, 'what's wrong with me?'" It was as if his illness were an annoying distraction, like an infestation of mosquitoes that someone else was supposed to attend to. Only twice did he speak of it.

Hospitalization kept him from his profession for almost three years of the eighteen spanned by this study. He could work for Ned while at home for weekends and two- or three-day visits but his laboratory positions did not permit intermittent work. His therapists seem to have given no thought to what he could do when in the community beyond advising that he keep out of physics for a year—"the demands of the real, competitive world are too much for him now." Only Arthur himself thought of a compromise—his laboratory—that would keep him in physics but shield him from competitive job-hunting (although, of course, his enterprise would have to operate competitively). The occupations he found in the hospital—the kitchen and stretcher details, in the X-ray developing section, patient government, and as the assistant manager of the coffee shop—simply kept him busy and filled his days; they had no relevance to his talents.

It is very probable that his repeated illnesses, although never keeping Arthur altogether from physics, slowed down his advancement. Illness broke into his efforts to perfect, patent, and market one of his inventions. And yet, after he had been hospitalized seven times and more than four years after his last laboratory position, he was able to get a good job in vacuum physics and hold it for five months. Somewhat compensating for his fragility of the psyche was a strong measure of persistence and durability in his profession.

Career Contingencies: The Family

Arthur, like Albert Rossini, was kept a chronic patient by his relatives. He had three families: his parents, brothers and sisters; his wife and their three children; and Hannah's family. Of the first, his father and an elder sister played occasional parts in his story, grudgingly taking on some inescapable obligation connected with his illness and as quickly as possible relegating it to his wife. His children, a source of great pleasure when he was well, entered but little into the case. When he was ill he forgot them so easily and so utterly that the change in him was dreadful to bear.

Hannah and her kinfolk entered into Arthur's life at nearly all points, and Arthur's family and the hospital, by insisting that she make decisions, put her in control. Although often perplexed she never shrank from the burden and as time went on gave signs of rather enjoying it. Indeed, it is hard to keep Arthur's story from being Hannah's story as well. Loving, generous, and tireless in his behalf, Hannah found herself emerging from housekeeping to a gratifying career as a successful teacher as a consequence of his illness and with the backing of her family and the community. When the study ends she had worked up to the higher levels of salary, was a candidate for an M.A. in education, and was planning to go to summer school in Dublin.

Hannah's plans and projects were repeatedly threatened by Arthur's manic episodes. (His depressed phase, although equally pathological, seemed not to impress her as illness and at least he was more manageable at those times.) A crisis came when, recognizing the early signs of a manic phase, she was able to get him promptly readmitted to the hospital; for Arthur, too, was in the midst of projects of his own which were viable only at the expense of hers and which she, of course, had succeeded in thwarting. On the occasions when she was *not* the instrument of his return to the hospital, it was the police who would return him. To Hannah his dream laboratory meant only neglect of his family, the big bills, and the duns. She never recognized that to the sick man the dream may have been the most vital thing in life and the only way he saw open to preserve his integrity as a professional man and escape what he held to be degrading work. She talked of Arthur with intelligence and sympathy yet always as a problem to herself and the family and never as a human being in tragic distress. When he actually succeeded in setting up his laboratory, in the last year for which there is information, he and Hannah had separated. (Estrangement was the price of autonomy.) Then when he became disturbed again, Hannah had him hospitalized once more and dropped the divorce proceedings. If Hannah circumvented his efforts to re-enter physics, she and her family backed him unhesitatingly when he was driving the moving truck for Ned: Arthur docilely moving furniture under her brother-in-law's eye posed no threat to her personal ambition.

More than once Arthur objected that the moving business was beneath him, and Hannah retorted that her grandfather and her father and now her brother-in-law had always been able to hold their heads up—a gambit suggesting that, although proud of his record as a physicist, she was not unwilling to humble her husband and bring him to her own level. For Arthur stood out as the most intellectual and highly educated member of the two clans. Hannah may have had mixed feelings when, year after year, he returned to the moving van, but she voiced no regret that he had left his profession; nor is there evidence that his own family felt he was disappointing them. Although open-handed in helping when money was needed for the household, no one in Hannah's family ever helped Arthur to finance reinstating himself as a physicist. He stands in contrast to the other married patients in being one in whose career as a worker his in-laws played a more fateful role than did his own parents.

Pattern of Career as Affected by Illness and Hospitalization

In the eighteen years of his career for which there are records, Arthur made persistent, almost heart-breaking efforts to hold his ground professionally. He had crossed the threshold into the hospital eight times and lived within its walls for over three years. Yet he had worked as a physicist actually for over nine years. His illness was pervasive, entering into all facets of his existence. It threatened his family life and it broke in repeatedly on his various jobs. It brought his laboratory project each time to a sudden calamitous stop and there were weeks when the simple responsibilities in his work for Ned were beyond him.

Alone among all his relatives, Arthur seems never to have lost sight of himself as a physicist, although, often, the physicist was in overalls and driving a truck. But the therapist and his relatives concurred: as the doctor put it, "He was a physicist. He's not a physicist now. He'll never be a physicist again . . . He could be a porter or a waiter . . ."

Hannah spoke several times of how "wonderful and helpful" everyone had been in taking Arthur back into the community and in helping her to establish herself as a teacher. Explicitly she denied that he had been stigmatized. So it is puzzling to find her after his release from the study hospitalization opposing his effort to re-enter physics "until he was completely discharged" and arguing that his record would put him at a disadvantage in securing "the kind of job he wants." For there is no evidence at all that hospitalization stood in the way of his obtaining a job as a physicist when in the community. His patent fragility, that is, his illness, his family, and his demonstrable inability to perform were his undoing.

9   WORKER TO MARGINAL WORKER: ALBERT ROSSINI

Well or ill, Albert Rossini was paralyzed by self-consciousness and a crippling sense of his own worthlessness, a man so ill at ease in human society that he could deal with it directly only when bellicosely drunk. When out in the community he was tranquillized for a year at a time.

He cleaned railroad cars for a living and this was his principal occupation from the time he was 18 until he was 28. Out of that time, one year was accounted for by three sojourns in the mental hospital and he worked for almost eight years.

The following information about his life was gleaned from fifteen interviews with Albert himself, sixteen with his wife, two interviews with the couple jointly, one with his mother and thirteen with professional personnel.

THE SETTING: PAST AND PRESENT

Albert Rossini—known to everyone as Al—was leaving the hospital after a stay of almost four months when the first interview occurred. A dark, slender youth then 25 years old, he was good-looking despite the scars of acne. He talked of his longing to be home to play with his baby daughter and to give to his wife the little attentions which, looking back on his life, he realized he had never shown her—a "second honeymoon" as he put it. Driven by debt and penury, he had carried on in two jobs concurrently for two years but had been finding relief in drink; he came to the hospital harried and exhausted.

The young Rossinis, Al and Kathleen, his pretty, blonde wife, who was his junior by four years, lived in a pleasant apartment in a public housing project in South Boston. But during his stay in the hospital Kathleen had moved with the six-months-old Margaret into the house of Peter, Al's brother. Two years older than Al, Peter had married Kathleen's elder sister. It seemed natural enough that Kathleen, alone, pregnant, and worried should take refuge in her sister's house. But it created difficulties, for Al never ceased to brood over the fact that Kathleen, before their marriage, had had a few dates with Peter. The brothers were jealous on other grounds: they worked in the same factory, but the elder boy earned less and at the moment was actually unemployed, a consequence of a quarrel with the boss. To avoid trouble, Kathleen led Al to believe she had stayed there only for the first few days and was now at home.

Al's 55-year-old mother, a waitress, and his 17-year-old half-brother lived in one household, the Al Rossinis and the Peter Rossinis in two more, and there were a number of maternal aunts and cousins, as well as Kathleen's parents, her two sisters and two of her three brothers— all residents of South Boston, traditional home, first, of the Irish, and later of the Italians. The Rossinis belonged to the latter; Kathleen was of Irish descent; but all were thoroughly Americanized.

Kathleen led a difficult life, contriving by dint of extraordinary patience and sympathy to live at peace with a man given to prolonged moods of wordless dejection. That their always precarious financial plight was not worse was due to her capable management. Albert as an adult was beginning to resist the orders which all his life his mother had directed to him; Kathleen controlled him by tact and indirection. "Be home by midnight," his mother would call as he left to go bowling. —"Come home when you want to," said Kathleen. And when she was with him bowling and noticed he was drinking too much, she would say, "I'm tired. Please take me home." The two families always said it was *she* who courted him but at least she was under no illusions about what it was costing her. She knew before their marriage that he had already spent over four months in mental hospitals and now that he was ending another four months' stay, she admitted, "I don't see much happiness. I don't have a very pretty future with him. But they call it love."

Now, as Al was about to re-enter the community, they had a heavy burden of debt, a second child on the way, and were living on unemployment compensation paid by the railroad where he had worked for almost six years as a car cleaner. Kathleen frankly depended for her meals and Margaret's on the generosity of relatives and applied all her cash to debts and current expenses. The Rossinis had no savings, nor did they ever have any in the time of this study.

Al had his railroad job to return to but the therapist and his wife agreed there should be no more moonlighting; she blamed his thirteen-and-a-half hour working day as largely responsible for his breakdown. The interviewer found him more eager to "get back to work and be normal" than he was to rejoin his family. Indeed Kathleen had been pleasantly surprised at his expressions of interest in seeing Margaret again, for he rarely handled her at all and had acted as if she were a stranger who had invaded his home and monopolized his wife. From the boys of his gang that hung about the corner, one to which he had belonged since adolescent days, he could, according to Kathleen, expect a cool welcome. They had not come to see him in the hospital, and they said they were afraid he would "act funny" if he rejoined them. This was a bad prospect for a man so shy that he would stand tongue-tied and covered with confusion even when specifically invited to some social affair.

Al was emerging from the hospital "feeling good." He had needed a rest, and rest, sedation, and isolation from the many worries that had plagued him were just what the hospital supplied. But he was to continue tranquillizing medication.

A chronological summary of Albert's work history and hospitalizations is as follows:

1950: Albert graduated from high school at the age of 18, and obtained a job in a shoe factory which he held for one year.

1951: Through his aunt, he got a job in the railroad yards cleaning freight cars and loading ice.

1953: In February he entered a sanitarium for twenty-three days, was at home for five weeks, and returned to the sanitarium for five days. His mother then kept him at home for more than five months. He then took a job in a shoe factory but quit the same day. He did no further job-seeking.

1953-1954: He was in a state mental hospital for four months from late September 1953 to early January 1954. For a short time thereafter he worked as a janitor in a factory, and then returned to his railroad job, working from 4 p.m. to midnight.

1955: He married Kathleen, who continued in her job as a telephone operator. He then took on a second job, working for five and a half hours in the forenoon, in a plant making staples.

1956: He continued to work in both his jobs. Kathleen quit working in April because she was pregnant. Their first child was born in September.

1957: In early March he was overactive, paranoid, and depressed and his wife took him back to the state hospital. He was in the hospital almost four months, until early July. This was the study hospitalization. After release, he remained at home a few days and then returned to the railroad as a carpenter's helper. After two weeks he was demoted to his cleaner's job at less pay, and was then shifted twice more at varying rates of pay. In September he was laid off with forty other workers. He applied at several places without success, stayed home a week, then went job-hunting again. In mid-October, he held a job for a few days with another line replacing railroad ties. Hating it as "hard, dirty work," he soon quit. In December he first held a job driving a truck for two days but quit when assigned to a larger truck, then worked for the postoffice for about eight days delivering Christmas parcels. On December 28, a second child was born.

1958: He did not work for over two months and stayed at home. Then he worked for two days for the priest cleaning out the church basement. In March he got a job as a porter in a municipal hospital, working from 2:30 to 11 p.m. In May he obtained a second job, assembling storm windows from 8 a.m. to noon. In June after three months at the porter's job, he either quit or was fired. He then worked a few weeks painting houses for his wife's uncle.

At the end of July, through his aunt's intercession, the railroad recalled him on a day-to-day basis, on the 4 p.m. to midnight shift. In September and into October he was unemployed again, and in October he obtained a job as laborer in a machine-parts factory. Meanwhile his wife took a job as a waitress.

1959: In January he was laid off in a general retrenchment at the factory. In February he was recalled, but lost the job before the end of April. In April he was rehospitalized. His wife was again pregnant and quit her job, subsisting on welfare funds. Albert returned to the community in mid-August, after spending three and a half months in two institutions.

He stayed at home for awhile, and then in September obtained a job, through a friend, as a pipefitter's helper in a shipyard at a higher rate of pay than he had ever earned before. He was still working there when the record ended in December.

Of the total time in the labor market covered by this account, namely, nine years, Albert spent a total of one year in the hospital and seven years, nine months working.

THE PREHOSPITAL CAREER

South Boston-born Al's childhood was spent among second- and third-generation Americans of Irish and Italian descent. His roistering, hard-drinking father, always "out with the boys" and contemptuous of domesticity, died suddenly of a ruptured appendix when Al, the younger of two boys, was 13 months old. The parents had been married just five years. The mother married again when Al was 8 and again at the end of five years became a widow when the second husband, who had made a very strict and unloving step-father, died of a heart attack. "He died in my arms," said Al.

The boys, according to their mother, who was fortunately able to stay at home and keep house for them, were helpful and considerate. Both finished high school; Al with a satisfactory record. When Peter went into the Army their mother implored Al to wait until he got out before doing his stint. The boy consented but suffered pangs of conscience when his brother and his pals all went into uniform. At that time he enjoyed life: he "played" the numbers, the "nigger pools," the dogs, and the ponies and neither he nor his brother hesitated to ask for money if they wanted it for their various diversions. But no money from their mother was to be spent on drink: she had had enough of that in the turbulent years with her first husband.

Al began to look for work in 1950, as soon as he finished high school. Apparently he had no preferences but, as is common among the unskilled, he simply wanted some sort of job. By mistakenly going into the wrong building, he said later, he missed an apprenticeship he might have had; he did not specify what it was. He found work in a shoe factory and stayed there one year. Then a spinster aunt on his mother's side, who had been employed some thirty-five years by a railroad, secured him a job cleaning freight cars and loading ice into the refrigerator cars. The railroad was to become his mainstay and his chief employer for the next seven years.

When he was 19, he met Kathleen, who was 16, the daughter of an Irish letter-carrier and a cruel and domineering alcoholic mother who overruled the affectionate and ineffectual father. Kathleen was one of Al's first, and one of his few, dates. She said that in those days he was "full of fun and the devil," yet very religious: he never missed Mass. Still, her family objected to her having an Italian boy friend.

Kathleen had worked in an insurance office when she finished high school and was now a telephone operator.

They had been dating each other for about two years when the signs of Al's emotional and mental instability made themselves evident: one evening he took a girl out—it is not certain if this was Kathleen or another—and was tormented by voices which he believed he heard, calling "Mother! Mother! Mother!" The conviction came over him that the Roman Catholic Church was a source of evil, and he felt stifled by an overpowering fear of death and dissolution. Indeed the precipitating event, according to his mother, was the death of her much-loved brother, Al's Uncle Frank. Al's maternal grandfather had died two years before and soon after that his grandmother whom, as a child, Al had "followed around like a puppy." All his loved ones seemed to be dropping out of sight. He refused to go to his uncle's funeral, cried incessantly and drank heavily, although, as Kathleen reported it, he could not handle even one drink. A great resentment of his brother and mother possessed him.

A year and a half passed during which Al's seclusiveness and his abandoned weeping continued. Then, at Kathleen's insistence, his mother took him to a general practitioner who concluded he suffered from schizophrenia and recommended a private sanitarium. He went there on February 2, 1953, stayed twenty-three days, went home, returned on April 10, and left finally five days later. The bill for the twenty-eight days of care, over $1000, was taken over by the unmarried aunt who had secured Al the railroad job. Even more distressing than the bill was the fact that Al was, they all agreed, not at all helped by the shock treatments he had been given there.

When Al emerged from the hospital, he found that Peter had finished his military service and was home again, and he was filled with shame and guilt that he had not served. But the whole family rallied around him—he was a favorite of them all from childhood—comforted and coddled him, pitied him because of his illness, and excused him from assuming any obligations. His mother, in particular, kept him from work and treated him like an invalid. One day Al took a job in a shoe factory, but he did not like it and walked away at the end of half an hour.

Al was a "corner boy," member of a gang of youths chiefly of Italian background, who met nightly on the street corner and drank beer. He went back to them, drinking heavily and, as he put it later on, "feeling ugly inside myself." He did no work for weeks nor did he seek any. He began to get out of control, shouting all night, then sleeping all day or roaming the streets. "If only I had a father, he'd help me," he would wail. Remembering the months when he had been ill without attention, Kathleen urged his mother to get help and eventually she was advised to put him in a state institution. To her this meant the end; yet she could not afford a private hospital. Finally, five months after he had come out of the sanitarium she called the police and he was taken to the state hospital.

He entered it on September 21, 1953 and stayed three and a half months, until January 8, 1954. He was diagnosed as suffering from schizophrenic reaction, paranoid type. His mother visited him regularly as did his brother, his aunts, cousins and, at least at this time, friends from the corner gang; and now Kathleen was coming to see him, too. When he finally came home, they all agreed that this time he was vastly improved.

The hospital sent his mother a bill for $1200, but cancelled it on learning that Al had no work and she had almost no money. The boys' mother had fully expected them to take care of her when they were grown. But they left her to marry, and soon after Al's hospitalization she had had to go to work. By then, she was receiving $105 a month from ADC on behalf of her youngest son, the child of her second marriage, now half-way through high school. She had been working as a waitress for the past three years, seven hours a day, six days a week, and was earning $22 a week. She loved her work, she explained, and was only able to undertake it because her boy was "so good"; she could leave him alone at home without fear he would fall into bad company.

For the next three years and two months, Al was in the community. At first, and for a short unspecified time, he was a painter in an industrial plant. Then he returned to work for the railroad.

Kathleen meanwhile was growing insistent that they marry, but Al held back. He thought the Irish and Italians should not mix, and her family agreed with him. Her younger sister, it is true, had married Peter but there is no reason to think it was an unhappy union. Al's mother disapproved of Kathleen and indeed she blamed his illness on her—attitudes which she soon found ample reason to abandon. The

priest counselled a delay of six months to see how Al was tolerating
the return to the outside world and when this ended, he urged on
them a second half-year's wait. Then in February 1955, when he was
within a month of 23 and she was 20, they married.

Both recalled that first year as their happiest. Al's difficult moods
had vanished; even his mother conceded that Kathleen was turning
out to be a good wife to him. But her husband was not the fun-loving,
sociable boy of the past. He had turned anxious, serious, shy, and
inarticulate. Yet they spent their money on meals in town, movies,
and the races. She continued with her job at the telephone company
and Al, who loved to have "plenty of money" in his pockets, aug-
mented his earnings with an additional job from late afternoon until
midnight in a factory making staples. This job, which he may have
got through Peter—eventually both were employed there—brought
with it an advantage the railroad position lacked—Blue Cross insurance.
But even with his two jobs and her one, the pair found themselves
accumulating debts.

Looking back on those relatively carefree days, the young Rossinis
spoke of them as their best times because they did not worry about
money. True, Kathleen knew all along that they were gambling on
his health and the outlook was inauspicious. Al's two jobs put great
demands on his time but the railroad work, at least, was easy. He could
finish it in three hours, take two hours for a meal and loaf, drink beer,
and play cards in a bar nearby for most of the afternoon, go back to
punch the time-clock, and leave for home. The bosses let the men
alone, a circumstance which turned out to mean a great deal to Al.
Humble though it was, Al said he loved physical work, yet he repeatedly told Kathleen of his ambition to "make a million by the time
he was thirty."

Soon the couple overreached themselves. They expected a baby in
September of 1956 and Kathleen resigned from her job in the preceding
April. Al wanted a car and heedless of her plea that they wait until the
baby was born and paid for, he bought a three-year-old Ford. They
moved from their $12-a-month flat to larger quarters in a housing proj-
ect at $61, bought a washing machine and furniture; in short, they
went heavily in debt.

Al had been unreasonably worried about Kathleen when she was
pregnant, but the baby's birth did not bring him happiness. He wanted

a boy. A clumsy man in any case, he refused to handle the baby and looked on her as a competitor for his wife's attention and affection, and one whose care was one long vexation. He worried about Margaret and how they would raise her, about money and all the installments they had to meet; and he worried at the prospect of any social encounter. With the boys down at the corner he was painfully silent and uncomfortable, yet from time to time he made himself join them.

Some time in 1956, Al moved to the night shift at the factory, working now from midnight until eight in the morning and going straight from it to the railroad yards. This was taxing in the extreme; he and the family later on agreed that the two years of two jobs had much to do with his eventual breakdown.

Into the immediate circumstances of the study hospitalization entered, not a crisis of overwork, but, again, the death theme. A prize-fighter, a friend of Al's but not particularly an intimate one, died after a year's illness and his demise recalled all the loss and sadness of the family's bereavements of the past years and the fear of his own end which in those days was never far from Al's mind. For five days followings the wake he did not sleep or eat. When his talk became confused and irrelevant, Kathleen would reprimand him sharply: "That's sick talk. Stop it!"—and he would obey. At work, Peter noticed he was oddly silent and told their mother, who had learned from the earlier experience not to let his symptoms go unheeded. She told Kathleen who got the priest and at the end of the fifth day they persuaded him to seek help in the hospital. "You take me!" he implored Kathleen.

He signed himself in as a voluntary patient in the state hospital where he had been three years before, entering on March 8, 1957, and remaining there until July 3, just five days short of four months. This was the study hospitalization.

THE HOSPITAL PERIOD

On Kathleen's sharp orders he had been inhibiting "the sick talk." But, as she said later, "the minute he hit the hospital lobby, he started it again because he knew he could get away with it; it was almost expected." But he soon grew cheerful and controlled and begged to be allowed to go home to his 6-month-old baby and his wife to whom, he said, he owed a "second honeymoon." In fact he made four attempts to escape and twice succeeded in reaching his mother's house. (Kathleen and Margaret, the baby, were living with Peter and her sister, as noted earlier, but he was so wildly jealous of his brother that she told him she was either at home or at his mother's.) But once at the house he went wild and was promptly returned to the institution. On another occasion he turned up at his own house and Kathleen got the priest to persuade him to go back. And once Kathleen, who was leaving the baby with her sister and visiting him every day, had the bad luck to visit him when he was bent on escaping. He dragged her downstairs with him to the hospital entrance and in doing so broke her finger. On another day he punched her. His mother was openly afraid of him and she and Kathleen, who was distressed to find she had lost her magic touch with him, argued with him that if he ran home he would only grow violent and prolong his hospital stay. Yet the records describe the patient as "an angel on the ward."

In the hospital, in fact, Al saw things in a new light: he became conscience-stricken over his neglect of Kathleen. Yet his failure to share in the burdens of domestic life was a condition for which he held her to blame; but then, as Kathleen said, "he always puts the blame on other people." And he was filled with self-pity: as he saw his plight, "others grew big and strong but poor little Al never knew what was coming off." He took part in affairs started by the patients and began to enter into his own treatment as he had never done before—"It helps you to know yourself better if you talk about it with the doctor." He was in sore need of assurance, more particularly in the light of a new turn of events: Kathleen was pregnant again. He was terrified that she, like so many others he had loved, would die.

Recreational and occupational therapy did not interest him at all, but he grew eager to undertake real work. At first he worked two hours a morning with the hospital's paint crew; later he gave the forenoons to the coffee shop. And all along he spoke of his yearning to get back to work on the outside. As a union man he was, of course, in no danger of losing his job. But he claimed he had stopped worrying. (This was not so of Kathleen: she was tormented by their debts and the struggle to provide for herself and Margaret.) The therapist, anticipating that Al would not consent to stay long enough to "understand himself," had his voluntary admission changed to a regular commitment when he was in a violent phase and now his status as a patient was very different. For one thing, his driver's license was withdrawn.

More is known of the details of the Rossini's finances than is so of the other cases, thanks to Kathleen's clear grasp of the situation and her candor. After the manner of the unskilled laborer, Al had always brought her his whole wages so that from the beginning she had been in complete, and competent, control. His breakdown of course put a temporary end to his earnings and to the regular payments they had been making every month on their bills. Two months after he had entered the hospital they had begun to fall behind. Kathleen then applied for aid from the welfare agency but to her surprise and delight before it was acted upon the railroad for which Al had worked now for almost six years began to send her compensation checks of $70 every two weeks. And in June the project reduced their rent from $60 to $25 a month.

With the first $70 she received each month, Kathleen met the payments on the car—there were only two more now—and paid their rent and insurance. With the second $70 she paid all the small bills which left no money at all for the groceries, but she and the baby lived off the relatives. She had not been able to pay for the setting of her broken finger and now it was healing in a crooked way and showing signs of infection. She already owed a bill for an infected ear and never had returned for the customary examination after Margaret's birth. She knew very well she should be seeing the doctor in the matter of her current pregnancy; but what good would that do? It would mean more medical bills—she heard he was raising his fees—with bills, beside, for the vitamin pills she knew he would prescribe. Finally, as if all this were not enough, they had lost their Blue Cross coverage when Al's illness had compelled him to leave the factory job—and Kathleen would need that for the hospital bill for the new baby. If worry over money had contributed to Al's plight, it must be admitted the situation now was worse than ever. Kathleen agreed with the therapist, however, that when he returned to work there should be no more moonlighting. The therapist developed the interesting theory that a second job was his shy patient's way of avoiding encounters; the wife was confident they could live within his wages from the railroad job, alone.

The hospital released Al at the beginning of July. The doctor's prognosis was that he would do well enough "until someone else dies." The patient was sent home with a supply of tranquillizing pills and instructed to return weekly for psychotherapy and more pills. He was

25 years old. This was the beginning of a stay in the community that amounted to one year and nine months. The railroad paid the hospital bill.

THE POSTHOSPITAL CAREER

Four days passed before Al recovered from drug-induced grogginess and was able to return to the railroad yards. He still talked of the million dollars he was going to make before he was 30—that is, in the next five years—and argued that he had to have a second job again. Moreover, the railroad work left him plenty of free time and he wanted to be busier—perhaps the therapist was right in construing work as an excuse for avoiding people.

Back on the job, Al was happy to learn that he was to have a better job than the one he left, his seniority having given him claim on the temporary replacing of a carpenter's helper on sick leave. Now he made $80 a week—more than he had ever earned. This bit of good fortune lasted only two weeks, however: the sick carpenter returned and Al was "bumped off" and reduced to a lesser job at $70 a week.

The new job did not please him. He was busier now than he liked and the bosses were more in evidence. "I'd much rather be home," he lamented—a remark which gratified Kathleen who had longed for a domesticated husband, but at the same time made her uneasy. What if he stopped working when he was not even supposed to be ill? The change depressed Al and his old anxieties over money returned. "Besides," he moaned, "I can't talk to people any more." He avoided the corner boys and for the first time since he was married frankly enjoyed the comforts of home. His work was "just a job."

Kathleen, too, was harassed by their financial straits. The rent was due and all the first-of-the-month bills. The railroad sent no compensation check for the week before Al's return to work. So, as he had done all his life, he borrowed from his mother and his aunt, who always acceded to his importunings because he conscientiously made his obligations to them the first claim on his wages. His aunt had paid $1000 of his hospital bill for the spring of 1953 and Al had been paying the remaining $200 at the rate of $5 a week. To reinstate the Blue Cross coverage would take $30—it turned out it would pay for Kathleen's hospitalization—and that had to be paid almost at once. One ray of hope: Al had been in a traffic accident early in the year and their lawyer reported there was some prospect of his being paid as much as $300. But as things stood, their indebtedness was so substantial that, at Kathleen's urging, they paid back by way of bank loan. "Don't tell anyone," she begged him and he agreed; but the next day he went to the restaurant where his mother worked and told her the whole story.

As the summer wore on, Al grew more bored and unhappy. He had been put on a job that could be done in an hour. The "old-timers" filled their free time playing cards but Al did not belong with them. He who had always rushed off to work and enjoyed activity now seemed to have lost interest in everything. He could not talk and became more and more self-conscious and retiring, passing his spare time in dozing. Since his illness, he complained, "I've even lost my personality. Will I ever be myself again?" As he saw it, he suffered stigma on his own part, in his withdrawal from people, and at the hands of others. As to the corner gang: the married ones had "graduated" and there remained the bachelors, many of whom were hard drinkers, whom Al had neither inclination nor money to join. He revived doubts as to the wisdom of his marriage and he bemoaned the passing of his youth.

Kathleen suggested he enroll in the railroad's trade school, to fit himself for better-paid and more interesting work. But Al did not want to help himself: he just "sat around" at the yards and at home, miserable. So when he told the hospital therapist, week after week, that "everything is fine," Kathleen suspected him of doing so in the hope of regaining his driver's license sooner.

In the middle of August their luck improved. Al was moved into a job of jacking up cars which commanded better wages. He and a workmate finished work by 11 a.m., loafed in the bar drinking light ale until 3 p.m., then punched the time-clock, and left for home at 4. His mood brightened. He was quite happy spending the evenings watching television, but he and Kathleen also began going out with three other young couples to movies and night clubs.

When Labor Day came, Al was back at the old job of car-sweeping, at wages of $57, not the $70 he had been making at the end of July, but since he was working again, their rent was raised to $67. Still, they had at last paid all their outstanding bills. On the other hand, he had his driver's license back again and so the car, which had been stored in his aunt's barn, had to be re-registered. Moreover, the hospital expected an advance of $70 for Kathleen's impending delivery. Then, suddenly, they received $185 in settlement of the accident case. They repaid money owing the mother and aunt, registered the car, and had it put in order; and life was tolerable again. By mid-September, Al was back bowling with the boys, had played softball, and bought tickets to the Navy game. He was really enjoying Margaret, although he showed little enthusiasm at the prospect of a second child.

But in this hapless family good luck never loitered long. At the end of the month Al, with forty others, was laid off in what was all too plainly not merely a seasonal maneuver but a drastic and almost certainly irreversible curtailment of services.

Al applied for work at a factory producing automobile parts. It was a wretched experience for him. Totally lacking in self-confidence and tongue-tied, he did not expect to succeed simply by applying but he knew the president of the union and hoped desperately that he would recommend him: "He needs someone to speak for him, to get the job," Kathleen explained. For a week he drifted about the house in dejection; then took heart again. He avoided agencies but he said that he presented himself at twenty places asking for work; none needed him. He then went so far as to go to the employment office of the Commonwealth Edison Company, was overcome with terror, left without filling the application blank, and took refuge at home. To cap the climax, the television—the late show was the bright spot in his day—broke down. "I thought he'd die over that," said Kathleen. Desperately driven, he applied to the railroad for compensation and to his surprise a few days later received a check for $140, which turned out to be money to cover the two weeks missed at the beginning of his hospital stay. Al was now definitely unemployed.

On hand, the Rossinis had the railroad compensation, $100 saved from his recent job, and then the railroad began paying them $56 every two weeks. But this was not enough to live on. They had to meet payments on their loan at the bank, and Margaret should have had shots protecting her from various childhood ailments. Al paced the floor for days at a time, groaning "What should I do? What should I do?" He cried out that he had never really liked pushing a broom in railroad cars; but it was something. The possibility of learning a trade was sometimes mentioned but Al only retaliated, "How? What trade?"

While bowling one evening—at least he did find some fun in that, in those hard days—he heard of an opening in a factory making radiator thermometers, where he knew a union head. It was to be "nice work, not dirty," at "good" money although not as good as the $1.85 an hour he had made at the yards. But his hopes were crushed; the factory started laying off instead of hiring. Once he considered applying for the moonlighting job he had held before being hospitalized; but it paid only $1.25 an hour, the rate of the railroad compensation; so he had no interest in working there. Then, after a month of joblessness, the railroad found him a job with another line. He hated it from the start. The work was repairing or replacing ties. He had to rise before 6 to reach work by 7 and the bosses shouted peremptory orders and kept the men on the go. "I had no time to myself," Al complained. Moreover, always fussy, he was disgusted at having to step over piles of loose dirt and "there was nothing around but empty space!" Filled as he was with nervous terrors of all sorts, Al spent the night after the first day's work in sleepless loathing of his work—and quit on the third, together with half-a-dozen other men with families. He felt miserably guilty over leaving work when the family needed money so badly but kept telling himself and everyone else that it was the "best thing." It was toward the end of October.

It took him a week to settle down and face the ordeal of job-hunting again. He much preferred a railroad job to any he could think of but the yards were continually laying off workers. He wondered if he could become a fireman or a brakeman; but how was he to go about having himself transferred to another department? "I don't know anyone to speak for me," he wailed. Ideally, the job he wanted would be a "good job with good money," perhaps a trade, that he could settle in for the rest of his life—"But I don't know anyone who'd get me a job like that," he sighed.

By November the unemployment compensation checks were reduced to $28 a week, not enough to cover the rent. Kathleen would have asked to have the rent lowered but had fully expected he would have found work by the time the request was dealt with. They agreed there was no point in selling their 4-year-old Ford, for it would bring in very little and he would need it when he found work again. Their two mothers gave them dinner on three evenings a week and the young couple took the leftovers home with them for the intervening days and so spent almost nothing on food; but they saw to it that Margaret had two eggs a day. Al divided his days between sleeping at home and visiting the restaurant where his mother worked and where she managed to get him a full meal.

One day Al filled out a prize word puzzle in the newspaper and was certain he would win. By now he was talking of miracles—he even went to church daily to pray for one—for he saw no other way for them to be saved from want. He was enjoying bowling again and went out for beers with the boys on money borrowed from his mother. But when Kathleen needed money for cough medicine he told her roughly they could not afford it.

His mood changed again and he returned to job-hunting. Although he dreaded it he presented himself at a rubber factory for an interview and did fairly well, he thought. But he did not get the job. He applied at shipyards, mills, and docks, but in vain. He did no better with the advertisements.

In December their rent was reduced to $28 and again the compensation payments came: $40 a week, according to the rules, could be paid him for six months. But they could not meet the small regular bills, as for instance the telephone bill; their insurance was due; the car would soon need re-registering; and Kathleen still had no money for the advance payment to the hospital and the baby was due in early January. There was still the $200 outstanding on the old hospital bill for Al and $20 to the doctor. Their credit rating had survived their vicissitudes until now but they were fearful. And all this time since he had left the state hospital in July, Al had been taking pills at $7 a bottle. As a matter of fact he reduced the price, in effect, by taking fewer, on his own initiative. He was once told how to apply for a lower price for medication but when he got there the office was closed and he never went back. The therapist thought the hospital might help him to find work but Al let the matter lie.

Discouraged, pregnant, and lonely, Kathleen found Al's apparent indifference to their lot very hard to bear. Even harder was his family's habit of coddling him and telling him not to worry, that they would provide for his needs—although the truth was that between them they had not much over and above their own needs. "But if they are always so quick to help," Kathleen would ask, "how will Al ever become responsible?" Certainly Al was not loathe to exploit his role as an invalid and to welcome special consideration. And so while he observed that he enjoyed a "happier feeling" when loafing and liked being "free to come and go as I please," Kathleen sank into despair. By now the young couple had little to say to each other. Yet just two months before the interviewer had marvelled at her management of him: "She picks up inflections of her husband's voice and senses when a subject is going to upset him in the most delicate way." Yet Al was not *perfectly* happy. He noticed that the pills kept him from being alert and enjoying work and play as he used to and sometimes he admitted, "Loafing is awful. But I don't know what to do." Kathleen's complaint was that he worried only over himself and not about his lack of employment and the family's sufferings.

Shortly before Christmas he turned down a chance to drive a truck for the St. Vincent de Paul Society because the truck was "too big." By this time he had talked himself into an impasse: he would not take wages of $40 or $50 as he could draw $40 in compensation by doing nothing. He lacked the courage to face the tests imposed by the big companies on prospective employees; nor could he conquer his terror of being interviewed. It began to look as if his present state would become chronic. But Christmas was coming and suddenly his father-in-law reminded him about emergency work in the postoffice, delivering Christmas parcels. Al hesitated because this step might lead the railroad to stop compensation—although the postoffice would hire him for only three weeks at the most, and he would have to turn up to apply each day. Finally, Al decided to do it but when he found sixty-nine others there before him on the first day he dropped the idea. He spent the time dozing in the living room and refused to give a hand with the housework.

Two weeks before Christmas the priest told him that the truck-driving job at St. Vincent de Paul's was still open. The vehicle was a small pick-up truck. Al accepted. But he left after two days when the Society replaced it with a larger truck. Then his father-in-law got him a temporary mail job, delivering heavy packages from 6 in the morning until noon. It was good pay but it ended on December 24.

On December 28 Albert Junior was born. The Blue Cross paid $100 of the hospital bill; of the balance Al's aunt lent them $16 and they needed only $16 more. Perhaps Kathleen's pregnancy had been on Al's mind but in any case he became a changed man. He began to help his wife in the house, took affectionate care of Margaret, and even paid attention to the new baby. He said he would like eventually to have four children, but no more until these two were in school. He came to the decision to keep his car stored in his aunt's barn, thus saving the costs of registration until March when he expected a tax refund which should cover it; and was cheerful and happy once the decision was made. He had been too exhausted to go bowling while working for the post office, but now he returned to it. And all along he hoped and prayed the railroad would recall him, for if he had work he would not be so bored, or, as he put it, work would keep his mind "off the bore."

By the following February, Al was bowling and drinking regularly. A day came when, drunk and rowdy, he was thrown out of a bar and from the street yelled he would kill the proprietor. When his mother discovered he was spending on drink money she had intended for the family, she stopped giving it to Al and paid it directly to Kathleen.

His brighter mood was short-lived. Then he began to mope about the house, once again refused to lend a hand with the housework and, the television set being broken again, he just dozed and stared into space. Kathleen deferred going to the hospital for her postpartum examination: there was no money for it. Once more she grew anxious over their credit rating when the bureau denied receipt of a check for $5 she had mailed and declared she must mail a second check. She bought no groceries; they ate very little and what they did eat came from their relatives. She wondered now if they would have to apply for welfare; if so, the $19 they would be given weekly would not pay the rent and they would be obliged to move.

At the recommendation of the railroad, Al finally went to the state employment office. But there was no work to be had and applicants were many. Nightly he went down the street to the church to pray for a miracle and Kathleen was haunted by the fear he would break down again. From his talk it began to sound as if he would welcome it: "I felt happy in the hospital. There were not so many worries there as at home." And although he said he wanted work, he was sure it would tire him: "but I'm not too upset," he added. Loafing had its advantages, for it meant he had the chance to pick the job he *really* liked, and while he admitted he had never had such a job and did not know what it would be, he did know that he would not want work unless he enjoyed it. Worried sick over the two babies and the family's health and its future, Kathleen found these self-centered remarks almost unbearable.

In the first week of March the priest hired Al to clean out the church basement and paid him $25 for the two days of work it entailed. And the week after that, through a friend, he got a job as porter in the municipal hospital. She had spoken of it before but Al had not acted upon her tip. The job was still open and Al said he did not care for that sort of work, but he applied and got it. He was called a "medical worker." He worked from 2:30 until 11 p.m.—he was actually busy only half the time—cleaning operating rooms and transferring patients to or from surgery. He was surprised to find he could endure handling cadavers. The wages were only $47 a week but he had hopes of moving on to something better. His associates at work were nurses, internes, and one fellow porter. They were, he said, "all nice and friendly" but sometimes he wondered if he liked working among women and all along he declared he liked the railroad best, where he "knew everybody." But once at work, Al reported the job was "fine." He was not too busy and as a city employee he was entitled to certain fringe benefits.

And now he got the idea he would like to stay at that post for six months so that he might qualify as a regular civil servant and get an outdoor job in, for example, the Department of Public Works, or as a school custodian. As a newcomer he had a thirty-day appointment but he worked conscientiously to make sure of holding the job. Now at last money was coming into the house again. For two birthdays in the family that month, the relatives gave presents of cash and Al's mother kept up her habit of giving them groceries and things for the children. That Easter of 1958 Al and Kathleen felt so restored that they bought Easter lilies for the mothers and aunt, sent their spring clothes all to the cleaner's, and ordered a family portrait in color. That exhausted the cash they had on hand but they were abreast of their debts. They needed more baby furniture and equipment, however, and the car was still stored for they had not yet received the tax refund. But the project, not yet notified of Al's employment, let the rent continue at the low figure. The new job came just in time, for the railroad sent the last of six months of compensation payments just two weeks after Al went to work in the hospital.

Again Al hankered after a second job to bring in more money. He hit upon the idea of selling hot dogs at baseball games, but never followed this up. Then in April he received the tax refund, re-registered the car, and to his great relief was able to drive to work. Life was growing interesting again.

But as during all his life, luck never stayed long with Al. Trouble appeared in the guise of a shrewish head nurse who gave him sharp orders, worked him hard, and treated him like a servant. When she took to working two shifts, Al had her in command throughout his span of work. He took to drinking again and to Kathleen's consternation was driving often while too befogged to notice traffic lights or approaching vehicles. He still talked of wanting a second job, but slept so late in the forenoons that he had no time to look for it.

Another threat to Al's peace of mind was the impending departure of his therapist. He was still taking pills and still in psychotherapy and, a diffident talker under the best of circumstances, he dreaded beginning all over again with a new doctor.

Toward the end of May Al found a second job—putting together the frames of storm windows in a small factory. New at the work, he was taken on trial and assigned from 8 until noon. Kathleen did not approve but she hoped that, given more work, he would come home tired, sleep better, and grow quieter, even soberer.

Nothing ever came of his idea of entering the civil service, because he did not last the necessary six months in his first job. It happened in this way: the cranky head nurse ordered him to do a task which was not among his duties. On edge, Al refused. She forthwith had him transferred to another department where his duties were in the morgue and within two days he was either discharged or he quit; Kathleen was never sure which.

At this juncture Kathleen's uncle, a thriving contractor, passed on to Al some jobs of house-painting which he was too busy to accept. It was hard work but he said he enjoyed it. "Once Al gets something to do," explained Kathleen, "he is a good, conscientious worker." But it lasted only until the end of June.

Then, out of the blue, Al was called back at the end of July by the railroad. He was to be a "spare" on a day-to-day basis. Both he and Kathleen were delighted he was back at work he knew and which paid well—for in the months he had been laid off, the yards had looked rosy indeed. He was back at cleaning cars, replacing a man on vacation. But even if it were only for two or three days a week it was "better," they agreed, than the hospital job with the waspish nurse. But what hurt was that Al could have been back in the yards long ago. His aunt had happened to mention his name when men were being hired and the office, which had for some reason been under the impression he was unavailable, recalled him the very next day. "To think," wailed Kathleen, "that he could have been back there working all this time if he had only had the courage to go and ask!" Al's version was a complaint that his aunt had not spoken sooner—"Why wasn't she smarter?" And she could have got him back on a permanent instead of a daily basis "if only she knew the right guy!"

Al's hospital therapist left and when the new one took over he decided not to go back for treatment and not to take any more pills. He had been tranquillized for the whole year in the community. It was as if he proclaimed his restoration to normal life. He even went so far as to assert that thereafter he would control the family revenues, as a way of being sure he had money in his pockets—a statement that grieved Kathleen unnecessarily, for he never did so. On her side, she resolved to put an end to indulging him and to demand that he assume the full burden of responsibility that most married men take for granted. Her difficulty was that she did not know how to distinguish convalescent behavior from "normal bad acting," by which she meant drinking, loafing, and the selfish appropriation of money for his own pleasure. The first she could tolerate; not the second. Until now she had treated him as if everything he did were to be explained by illness.

After a month as a "spare" at the yards, Al was assigned to the 4-to-midnight shift, the one he liked best. There was a break for supper from 6 to 8, the work was done by 10, and on reaching home he could watch the late show on television. But Kathleen hated the long lonely afternoons and evenings.

Now some seven years with the railroad, Al suddenly began to take an interest in union affairs. Seniority, he discovered, is not effective outside of one's own department, but if a man speaks up he may be changed to another roster. Had he worked without interruption—as he might have done, had he only known—he would by now be enjoying seniority that would put him at the top of his roster. As it was, he had always accepted what was handed to him without question. It was all too true, as he said himself, that "poor little Al never knew what was coming off." Yet, although working only day-to-day, Al observed that things were "as good now as they'd ever been." And it would be perfect if only he could be sure of steady employment.

But Al's renewed connection with the railroad was short. In September of 1958, he was not working. In October he was a laborer in a factory making machine parts, a position he held for two and a half months when he was caught in a seasonal lay-off in January; but he was reinstated in February. He held the job a few weeks more but by April 1959, he was again unemployed.

On the recommendation of his doctor, Al when applying for a position never told of his illness and hospitalization: "it only gets you into trouble." If a form contained a question about mental illness he always wrote "no." "I'm not like the guys who *look* like patients," he said. "But I can tell it about other people—by their eyes." And when it came to work for the railroad he was, of course, completely secure: "It's a union job and they can't fire you." But in Al's case, fate took a hand. At the end of April, Kathleen brought him, paranoid, confused, worried, and overactive, to one of the state hospitals. As before, he made accusations against his wife and his brother and in the forefront of his mind was death which had robbed him of relatives and friends and would one day claim him, too. In these uncertain months of winter and spring, Kathleen had taken a job as a waitress. "If Al hadn't liked it or had asked me to stop," she remarked defensively, "I would have." Hearing this, Al responded, "Whatever she wants to do is O.K. with me." Now, with Al in the hospital again, she was four months pregnant and Margaret and Al Junior needed her at home. (Her family had been baby-sitters when Al had been working and could not do it.)

As before, Al was something of a problem in the hospital. He escaped several times, arriving home suddenly, wild-eyed and "scaring the children to death." One day he came home twice in a taxi, at a cost of $11, no joke at all to Kathleen who was feeding the family now on welfare funds. She had great faith in the hospital which had kept him for four months, two years before, and returned him to the community for twenty-one months, and she was determined to have him transferred there. When direct action failed, she shrewdly waited until just before a local election, then appealed to one of the candidates. So, after ten weeks, he was moved into the institution where he had spent the study hospitalization and, after five weeks in it, was sent home. He had been in the two institutions for a total of three and a half months. He emerged on August 14, 1959. He described his therapist as better than the one he had last time and had every intention, he said, of going to the weekly meetings of former patients that fall and winter; but night work intervened.

Late in September, a very few weeks after Al's return, the third child was born. He amazed his wife by taking good care of the two other children while she was away in the hospital. He had no work in August, but late in September, when the full import of having five mouths to feed began to dawn upon him, he heard through a neighbor of a ship-yard job. He applied himself and got it. He was to work as a pipefitter's helper on the construction of an atomic-powered cruiser. It would not be launched until April and Al was hopeful and happy. Neurotic as he was about dirt, it pleased him that work demanded absolute cleanliness. He drove the long distance to work with his neighbor who, like him, was on the 4:30 to 11:30 p.m. shift. To the Rossinis the salary was mag-nificent—from $125 to $140 a week, depending on overtime. In Decem-ber, however, he was making $100—which still was more than he had ever earned. The conditions of supervision suited him, for everyone was new at this type of work and there was constant but friendly oversee-ing. Al, indeed, grew expansive on the subject of the new and experi-mental construction: "They'll be building all ships like this pretty soon." All the same, both he and Kathleen realized that what he was learning was not applicable anywhere else, and Kathleen was fearful the job would not last, the more so because she was convinced the rail-road's market for labor was shrinking—the shipyard was full of former railroad men—and he might end with nothing at all to turn to.

Christmas of 1959 was naturally much brighter than it had been in the previous year. They had moved to a single-family house which Kathleen, again pulling strings, had contrived to get through the good offices of a politician, and which Al had painted and papered. When this account ended, the rent, $75, was due in a week. They thought it reason-able in the light of his wages, and, beside, they were waiting for be-tween $300 and $400 of back compensation from the railroad. And they could be proud of themselves that, despite repeated trials and setbacks, Al had bettered his standing in the world of work and his family was well housed and fed—at least for the time being.

DISCUSSION

Albert Rossini exemplifies the man who lived a sheltered life in the world of work. With his tenuous hold on mental well-being, he gives the impression for much of the time, even when holding a job, of being on the edge of illness. It is not worthy of note that when he was a

completely inexperienced high school graduate his first and second—
even his third—jobs should be found for him. But a decade after he had
entered the labor market, and had worked for six years for a single
employer, he still either asked or waited for some friend or relative to
bespeak a place for him. With this passive dependence went a number
of characteristics, to be discussed in what follows.

Career Pattern

For some seven of the nine years of his history covered by this
account, Al worked for one railroad in various unskilled capacities. He
held half-a-dozen other little jobs for short periods at the outset of his
career and then, following the study hospitalization, obtained in the
shipyard the nearest thing he had had to skilled work and certainly the
best paid. He seemed fairly well established in it when the record
ended.

If one looks for continuity, it is to be found in the fact that for the
greater part of his first seven years in the labor market he had one
employer. In effect, the employer was the union; here his lot resembles
Peter Stone's. But his career, nonetheless, was highly unstable: more
than once Al held a job for a matter of a day or two; yet it is also true
that he held the railroad job and the factory job, concurrently, for two
years at a stretch.

The union determined who among its members would work and at
what, and who would be laid off and its rules were apparently such
that a man could hardly move up into better work. Of course, in the
low level of physical work, which was all Al knew, there is no question
of capitalizing on experience and skill gained in one type of work in
order to advance into another. It was Kathleen's suggestion that he try
to get ahead by learning a trade in the railroad's shops; but it made no
impression upon him. In the railroad yards he was mobile, but only
horizontally. As a porter at the hospital he gained less money and probably not more status. His last post, the pipefitter's helper, may have
been one in which he did, at last, acquire a higher order of marketable
skill.

He is uniformly described as a good and conscientious worker, once
he knew what was expected of him. He lost many jobs but never, as
far as is known, from personal failure, with the possible exception of
the porter's job at the hospital. The reasons were seasonal or technolog-

ical; it was in one or two instances a job known from the first to be for a very short time, only. Al's fundmental tragedy was that he had depended on a dying industry, a fact which was borne in on him when he found himself in the company of a number of ex-railroad men, playing a part in a new type of enterprise in the shipyard.

Al went at job-hunting sporadically. Not even dire want, hunger itself, could drive him outdoors to seek work when he was in one of his wordless, tormented moods. His behavior in this respect is possibly to be explained if one defines him as an ambulatory sick man. Yet, no matter what his state of health, he defined job-hunting as finding someone to get work for him: to report openings or put in a good word. Although he had survived comparable ordeals in high school, he was incapable of facing tests and interviews, even the filling out of forms. But it is only fair to say that if he could not "sell himself" effectively, he had very little to sell beyond physical strength. Such a man was fortunate in that the union made the question, for most of the time, irrelevant: following union rules he was moved about in unskilled jobs. Put more accurately, he was lucky that his aunt got him work in the railroad, in the first place, and so early in his working life. When he did not have wages, he had compensation for unemployment which, to his mind, was sufficiently large to save him from the ordeal of job-seeking.

Qualifications for the Labor Market

A physical laborer, Al was by definition a man who lacked training for any occupation. His schooling apparently contributed nothing of value to this end just as was the case with Harold Lang. Had he served in the Army he might have acquired some skill which might have launched him at the level of a step or two higher on the occupational ladder. Unlike Peter Stone and David Field, who were tested and advised extensively, Al never received from the hospital or from the welfare agency which at one time supported the family any counsel in the matter of vocational training or retraining. His illness, however, already recurrent and threatening to be chronic by the time he was 22 years old, cast its shadow over all but the first three years of his working life. This is a version of his plight that finds validation in the therapist's statement that Al overworked in two jobs for two years in order to avoid human society. What he did, he did well, but no one ever inquired into what he might have done or gave him any guidance in finding his way about in the world of work. He depended on his aunt and other relatives and friends who fortunately were bolder and moved with more sophistication in the world of work than he.

Career Orientation

If consideration is given to Al's own words in order to learn his attitude toward work, it soon becomes evident from their inconsistency that this is a man whose sickness was with him almost continuously. Thus six months after the study hospitalization he complained, with sharp insight, that the pills kept him from being alert and that his personality was changed; yet he wanted to "get back into the swing of things." But at the same time he confessed he "liked loafing best," for it gave him "a happier feeling" to be able to come and go as he pleased. Clearly he thought of work as just a means to fill in time and support his family and on occasion the first purpose seemed to mean more than the second. Completely unlike the dedicated Arthur Jackson, he expressed no preferences, beyond remarking once, "I like physical work." Thus his choice, like David Field's, crystallized by default.

One suspects that Al liked the work at the yards, once his aunt had found it for him, largely because he had it and need not look further. But he also liked the easy supervision, the unhurried pace, and the long stretches of unfilled time. Admitting, in one of the many periods of unemployment, that he needed a job badly, he in the same breath insisted he would not take a job he did not like; but he added that he did not know what job he *would* like, beyond the general advantages of good pay and steady employment, and wound up with the characteristic wail, "But I don't know anybody to find me a job like that."

Several times he exercised choice by quitting, the grounds being hard hurried work, peremptory bossing, or dirty, unpleasant conditions. With the family in direst want, he left the job of truck-driving because he did not like to drive a large vehicle.

Although a railroad worker for years, he was weakly committed to the occupation. In the union which stood virtually in the place of employer, he took no interest until he belatedly realized there was some practical advantage to him in mastering its regulations. His expression of interest seemed no more than verbal, however, and in any case was too late. Thus for the most part he accepted the easy culture of the yards and showed no sign of passing judgment on it or on himself as a worker. His most trenchant criticism was that he could not count on having work at all times; however, there was always unemployment compensation to fall back on. It is hard to see how he and his family would have existed at all in a more competitive, less paternalistic environment.

Career Contingencies: The Hospital

Like David Field and Peter Stone, Al rejected the hospital's occupational therapy as childish and frittering but accepted hospital industry. As noted above, the hospital authorities gave him no guidance in returning to the community, but of course he could always count on the union to look after him. But when the hospitalization of 1959 came to an end and he could no longer expect anything of the union, the hospital gave him no help in re-establishing himself in the labor market. At the same time, he may have owed it to the medication and the psychotherapy which the institution continued to provide that he was able to survive at all in the community after the study hospitalization.

Al spoke appreciatively of the hospital interlude as a time so free from worry as to be almost happy. For him as for Frank Monaco it brought a reprieve from a burdened life. Certainly it is clear that he found comfort and support in the role of a sick man and fared best in a completely sheltered milieu.

Career Contingencies: The Family

The literature is convincing on the decisive role played by the demands and expectations of the family of the returned mental patient— of which Al's story contributes an almost classic demonstration. His family was given to coddling and consoling him as one in chronic need of special handling. Kathleen, although shrewder in her dealings with him, was endlessly patient and indulgent. Among the cases, only Arthur Jackson's family is comparable in its belief in the permanent patient. At the very end of the record, Kathleen had at last realized that what she had been accepting as excusable weakness might be nothing more than "bad acting," and declared she was going to demand better things of him; but what happened next is not known.

Al's one-time heavy drinking, thanks, no doubt, to the protecting union, seems not to have affected his employability. Nevertheless, it seems to have been his drinking which opened Kathleen's eyes to a new conception of his behavior. Her long-suffering tolerance, in the eyes of the interviewer, was to be explained by a psychological need to have a sick husband under her thumb, a diagnosis also offered in the case of Arthur Jackson's wife. But while the latter incontestably checkmated every effort her husband made to re-establish himself professionally, Kathleen Rossini gave no evidence of trying to circumvent her man's rehabilitation or take advantage of him to get ahead on her own.

Pattern of Career as Affected by Illness and Hospitalization

Stigma seems not to have handicapped Al at all in his return to work. The railroad workers' union assured Al employment after his illness, as the musicians' union did for Peter Stone. And when he sought work elsewhere he prudently said nothing of his history of mental breakdown. Indeed, when the record ended, he was apparently a steady employee of the shipyard, making better wages than ever before—and this was accomplished in spite of an additional three and a half months of institutionalization.

Nor was his social life affected: when he felt like going back to the boys on the corner, they accepted him. The stigma that was there was largely what Al himself imagined and anticipated; it was never borne out in experience. But in his attitude toward himself it was pervasive to a greater degree than in the other cases. He referred forlornly to his lost personality and wondered if he would ever again find the pleasure in work and play that he once did.

To the extent that this is true, it may be said that illness and hospitalization, while they barely changed him as a worker, went far toward ruining him as a man.

PART 4   CONCLUSIONS

10 COMPARISONS AND CONCLUSIONS

The point of departure for this study was the assumption that a mental patient's career at work can be understood in the same way as that of any other member of society and that it would be profitable, in attempting to understand the interrelation between illness, hospitalization, and career, to examine the patterning of the occupational career quite apart from mental illness, and then to show how it was broken into by illness and hospitalization. In the description of vicissitudes to which the occupational career is subject, the concepts of the sociology of work rather than those of psychiatry and social psychiatry have been drawn on, with the notion that they could yield new insight, and suggestions, as well, for programs of psychiatric rehabilitation. As Erikson remarks:

> In the treatment of young people . . . it is impossible to ignore what they are busy doing or not doing in their work life or in their unofficial avocations. . . . Decades of case histories have omitted the work histories of the patients or have treated their occupation as a seemingly irrelevant area of life in which data could be disguised with the greatest impunity. Yet, therapeutic experiments with the work life of hospitalized young patients indicate that patients in a climate of self-help, of planful work, and of communal association can display an adaptive resourcefulness which seemed absent only because our theories and beliefs decreed that it be absent. This is part of the wider problem, now being discussed in a large part of the psychiatric and sociological literature, of how much psychiatry has tended to make patienthood a self-defining, self-limiting role prison, within which the development of the patient's stunted capacities is as clearly prevented, by the mere absence of systematic stimulation and opportunity, as if it were professly [sic] forbidden.[1]

The individual case histories here presented may, it is hoped, open at least one window on the "role prison" of "patienthood," to reveal how patients live and act in the world of work, a world that may or may not be a part of their illness. Up to this point the focus has been on individual variations in the pattern of an occupational career, but these variations have been viewed from a common perspective which now permits systematic comparison through use of the concepts and issues employed in the analysis of work careers and the interrelations between work and mental disorders. As was said at the beginning of this book, such comparison cannot be expected to yield generalizations and indeed the cases were chosen for their variety and not their representativeness. For convenience, each of the eight cases will first be summarized.

CASE SUMMARIES

Victor Norton

Victor Norton (Worker to Worker) appears as a sort of paragon worker, exhibiting, despite mental illness and hospitalization, nearly the whole gamut of occupational virtues. The principal characteristics of his career are a remarkably continuous and stable history of work, true crystallization of choice at an early age, substantial satisfaction in work itself, and a set of values that matched the objective circumstances. He gave effective expression to the demands and expectations of the members of his family significant to him.

Although deflected by his illness from the career of his choice and the one in which all his experience lay, he suffered no loss in employability, although there may have been some loss in vertical mobility. Following a second stay in the hospital, he returned to his original occupation.

His decisions were stable and realistic. He was able to put them into effect through intelligent job-hunting and he left jobs, in every case, for reasons other than occupational failure. When necessary he acquired new skills, but he capitalized on those he already had, confident of his own ability to perform well and to bear his share of family expenses.

Harold Lang

Harold's (Nonworker to Nonworker) story exemplifies the man who is barely employable and, whether ill or not, is marginal in the world of work. He was an employee on so low a level that it seems incidental whether he was recovering from a psychotic episode or had been out of the hospital for months. As a matter of fact, he was hospitalized for so large a proportion of the years under study that one can hardly find an interlude when the hospital had receded into the background. Never anything but an occasional employee on humble jobs, he seemed to be dropping still further down when the study ended. There may be possibilities for one of his limited talents and tempo, but if so Harold never found them and no one helped him to look for them except for various members of his family, who made desultory attempts on his behalf. His history shows him to be a man who could be neither self-supporting nor self-reliant; indeed, one wonders whether the time might not come, and soon, when he would be a chronic hospital inmate, dependent on hospital services for his very survival.

Carl Duncan

Carl (Worker to Nonworker) represents the case of the man who, a worker at first, ended with no career. He entered the labor market with every promise of normal success. Dedicated to a profession early, he found his hopes dashed on the shoals of poverty and gave it up. He then sought to renounce the world entirely but was rejected by the monastery. Thereupon he took a number of small clerical jobs, drawing on skills learned in high school in the hope of making enough money to gain the training in his chosen field which he still lacked. His problems resolved themselves into dilemmas of personal and occupational identity. At every point where his plans had to be revised, he fell ill. His family was willing to put up with his bizarre behavior at home to an astonishing extent, but they had little to offer in the way of help in resolving his dilemmas.

Frank Monaco

In Frank (Student to Worker) is seen a young man who proved unable to stand the stresses of the prolonged education required to enter into the profession on which he had set his heart since childhood. Facing the disappointment he found his values shifting so that he began to seek extrinsic rewards: money, a car, and so on. A career in business attracted him as an alternative which would bring such rewards quickly and amply; he tried it and was repelled by it. Eventually, he found a compromise in teaching, a profession, at least, which required no further schooling. But he seemed to have looked for and found extrinsic rewards in work ordinarily appreciated for its intrinsic compensations. Other dilemmas were decisive in his life, however, notably his inability to declare his independence of the family and the family hearth. These unresolved conflicts and, as well, his uncertain relationships with girls, appear to have been centrally involved in his illness. Illness brought him to the hospital where, released for the moment from the pressure at home in the moratorium the hospital provided, he at last thought his way through his occupational puzzle.

Peter Stone

Peter's (Worker to Worker) professional career successfully survived at least two psychotic breaks and hospitalizations. In this array of cases he represents the man dedicated from youth to a specific pursuit, who recognized the limitations set by his psychosis, and made the compromises necessary if he were to stay well for relatively long periods, in preference to switching to less damaging work. Undeterred by illness, he did as well or better in his profession for a considerable time. He found satisfaction in the essential nature of his work as well as in the material gains, and was stubbornly and determinedly happy to be in it despite the frustration and stress it entailed.

David Field

David (Worker to Worker) was in his early thirties but still not well-established in an occupation when illness and hospitalization intervened. His parents taxed him emotionally but his wife bolstered his morale; yet her innumerable and costly illnesses and accidents would have put the household expenses at an impossible figure, had she not repeatedly succeeded in obtaining welfare funds. In this exhausting milieu David was almost continuously at work in the long intervals between his several short hospitalizations but he never made enough to support his family by himself. He hoped to do so by going into business for himself but always broke down when he was close to attaining his end. Three times he emerged into the community and launched on the catastrophic round of debt, overwork, and illness.

Arthur Jackson

Arthur (Worker to Marginal Worker), a physicist and, at times, a truck-driver for his brother-in-law's moving firm, is described as marginal for several reasons: he rarely found work in the competitive market but his jobs were likely to be in the nature of sheltered employment, cut down by considerate employers to suit his limited capacities; throughout his career he sought to be self-employed, which may be interpreted as a device for avoiding the open market altogether; and, finally, for long periods his family was supported by his wife's earnings. He had, in effect, two careers. The first, as a physicist, was blasted time and again by illness; the second, as a mover's helper and driver, not only was provided by relatives but also was one which seemed to satisfy their wishes for him. Growing restless in the unchallenging work of the second occupation, with returning health he would go back to the first, his dream being an independent consulting laboratory. The oscillation between high personal ambition and endeavor and the humble demands on him put by the family occurred repeatedly, always ending with Arthur back in the hospital.

Albert Rossini

Albert (Worker to Marginal Worker) provides the instance of a man whose sickness spread over into his working life. Since he was a union man, however, in an assured and sheltered job, he was able to remain employable after hospitalization and to resume work. Thus although handicapped by complete lack of skills and by timidity so great as at times to make job-hunting impossible to him, he contrived to stay in a position which would support his family either by wages or by compensation payments. Then when he became a victim of technological change, he got work only through the intercession of others.

EMPLOYABILITY AND PATTERN OF CAREER

As indicated in Chapter 1, the optimal characteristics of employability are: (1) high compatibility between occupational choice, satisfaction and desired rewards on the job, personal values, and occupational assets and qualifications; (2) effective mobilization to implement choice by obtaining appropriate jobs and performing adequately in them; (3) maintenance of independence and self-confidence in job-seeking and working; and (4) resilience and flexibility in modifying choice and in acquiring appropriate skills when requisite to insure employability.

Among the unmarried men it is clear that Victor Norton's career most nearly meets all these criteria. Throughout the period of his life portrayed in the case study he was consistently employable, even to the extent of seeking and finding work before his release on both the occasions when he was hospitalized. It is just as clear that Harold Lang's career constitutes the most dramatic contrast to Victor's. At his best he was no more than barely employable, and if ever he obtained a job it was unfailingly of short duration.

Although Carl Duncan and Harold Lang ended up as unemployable, there were notable differences in the earlier period of their careers. Of the two, Carl had more education, but more important is that his vocational choice crystallized early, as in the case of Victor, and, like Victor, he exhibited remarkable persistence in attempting to implement his occupational choice. Ironically, however, it was this persistence which contributed to his occupational deterioration. For a time he was employable and employed, holding low-level jobs by exploiting the skills he learned in high school. But these jobs never gave him intrinsic rewards; he worked in them as a means of financing his study of art. During his early career he was certainly flexible enough, first in turning to menial work when his way to art school was blocked, then in choosing a related alternative profession. When he realized that he would have to give up his professional career, he had little to sustain him and in the end lost both orientation and the capacity to work.

If anyone was resolute and unswerving in his occupational choice, it was Frank Monaco. From a relatively early age he was determined to become a physician, and it took repeated trials, each of which terminated in a psychotic break, to bring him to the point of giving up his goal. This is indeed an impressive instance of the weight, when crystallized and specified, that vocational choice carries in occupational orientation. Unlike Carl, however, who was unable to implement his choice, Frank went on to establish himself in a professional career: the initial commitment to a particular occupational goal worked *for* him but it had worked against Carl. He approximates, like Victor, the criteria of optimal employability, but, unlike Victor, the fit between his orientation and the available jobs was problematic, at least for a time. The discrepancy did not crush him, as it did Carl, but ultimately led to his finding in school teaching an acceptable alternative profession. Frank was clearly in a better position to retrieve his career than was Carl, since he had had more adequate preparation for the compromise on which he eventually settled. On the other hand, he derived little intrinsic satisfaction from the jobs he held even when he at last settled on school teaching, so that he could not quite attain the stability in employability achieved by Victor, to whom work itself was important and meaningful regardless of commitment to a particular occupational objective. Frank appeared to find his chief satisfaction in the things he was able to buy.

Of the married males in these case studies, Peter Stone and, in his early phases, Arthur Jackson came closest to exemplifying the criteria of employability if first consideration is given to early crystallization of occupational choice and its compatibility with the other components of the career; but Arthur, of course, ended as the least employable of all the married men. Similar to Victor, Peter left high school early but never floundered about in the transitional stages of finding his vocation. Music was clearly the only calling he would consider seriously and he began to work at it immediately after leaving school, deriving from it, again like Victor, both intrinsic and extrinsic rewards. He could not conceive of any other occupation that would give him as much satisfaction, given his particular assets and qualifications. In this respect he differed from Victor, who since his primary interest was in work itself was willing to make any compromise despite his strong investment in construction work as long as he could continue to work at all. In stability and continuity of working and in adequacy of performance, Peter and Victor clearly constitute the most impressive examples. They were both independent and self-confident in job-seeking and in working were firmly committed and could hold jobs for long periods of time. It is true that both were involved in considerable job-changing at certain phases of their careers, but neither ever left a job, as far as is known, because of occupational inadequacy (except that Peter was asked to leave a job just before his third hospitalization because of his bizarre behavior). In both cases, horizontal mobility can be accounted for by either the situation at the time or by opportunities for better jobs; never by personal instability. It may be pointed out that of all the cases presented these two men showed the greatest evidence of ultimate upward mobility over the total course of their careers.

In Arthur Jackson, too, choice crystallized early. He had far more education than Victor or Peter, and at the outset was an adequate performer who advanced more rapidly than any of the men studied. Just as his upward mobility was greater than that of the others, so his later downward mobility was the most rapid; it is true that he had the furthest to fall. Arthur had neither the confidence nor the independence of Victor and Peter, except when launched on his ventures to establish a consulting laboratory, and often, even from the beginning of his career, was dependent on friends and relatives for jobs and for support. Although Arthur was deeply committed to a specific choice and derived his principal satisfaction and rewards from the work itself, this was clearly not enough; ultimately he became as essentially unemployable as Harold and Carl.

David Field never voluntarily fixed on a vocational choice, whether early or late. Except for two brief interludes while in the community, he remained employable and employed throughout his career. Perhaps more than any of the others, he cherished aspirations to upward mobility coupled with substantial vitality in working at whatever job he had in hand, but his goals were either unrealistic, as yearning to become a mathematician, or too general, as his desire to become a businessman and make money while still not specific as to what or how. He had "big ideas" but did not know where to implement them, yet because of them he could never feel committed to cab-driving. And because his choice never crystallized he could not find an appropriate avenue through which to realize his aspirations. But he never gave up his conviction that he had to earn money and support his family, although it must be said that he at no time achieved this solely by his own efforts.

It might be said of Albert Rossini that in one sense he was as much a marginal worker in the early part of his career as in the later; he has been characterized as "worker to marginal worker" primarily to point up the greater irregularity and instability of his work career after illness and hospitalization began to take their toll. But when the optimal criteria of employability are applied to him, it is clear that he was always marginal in career orientation, occupational assets and qualifications, and independence and self-confidence in job-seeking and working. Even had he been firmly oriented and well equipped for a position his tortured shyness might have stood in the way of his being hired. Like Harold Lang and many other young men at the time of entry into the labor market, and frequently even after years of experience in the world of work, Albert not only had no training or skills to draw upon, but also no idea of what he wanted to do or of how to go about implementing his ideas, if he had any. He viewed work mainly as time-serving, although, unlike Harold Lang, for long periods he could perform adequately if he had a job; but he could never muster any intrinsic interest in the job itself. He preferred loafing to working, but this could become boring, and in any case, in addition to welcoming the distraction that work provided, he did entertain the notion that a man ought to support his family, although he was not particularly fastidious about whether this wherewithal came from his own efforts or from unemployment compensation. He was not socially mobile and expressed no ambition for a better position. Although the more fortunate may find intrinsic satisfaction in their work, it should be noted that in the lack of it Albert is no different from a substantial number of young men in the labor force; they too are employed in jobs which offer little reward in and of themselves.

Although his investment in the world of work was slight, his assets and qualifications minimal, and his dependence on others for job-hunting chronic, Albert did remain essentially employable throughout the period of his career here portrayed and was at work for the greater part of the time. But clearly his working was not attributable to any of the characteristics imputed here to employability; rather, it was external forces, such as relatives and friends and, most of all, the union, which permitted him to hold the job once he had one under its jurisdiction or, alternatively, obtained compensation for him. His story ended, however, in a phase of upward mobility when he was doing fairly skilled work, independent of the union.

This upward turn of Albert's career may or may not have persisted in the period subsequent to the study, but in any event if he was rising it might have been because, beginning in so lowly a berth as he was, chance might make any move an improvement. In the segment of their lives known through these studies, Victor Norton and Peter Stone were both vertically and horizontally mobile, and David Field was only horizontally mobile although he aspired to be upwardly mobile as well. Harold Lang, Carl Duncan, and Arthur Jackson were pursuing a downward course, while Frank Monaco showed vertical and horizontal mobility in his work career even though there was a loss downward if measured by his earlier aspirations to be first a physician and then a dentist, achieving ultimately a position as schoolteacher.

FAMILY AND CAREER

Among the unmarried males, Frank Monaco exemplifies best the observation that an individual's occupational horizon is set for him to a considerable extent by his family. Moreover, his father is a classic example of the parent who attempts to realize through his son the career he could not himself achieve. From childhood on, Frank never questioned his father's cherished desire for him that he become a physician and he took for granted not only that he be educated to that end but also that his family would provide him with the means to have the best possible training. Indeed his parents did everything they could to help him and at the same time apparently indoctrinated him with derogatory attitudes toward any other than a professional career, particularly if in business —in which, after all, his father had fair success. Beside, they were so effective in directing his ambitions that when it became clear to them and the boy that he could not continue toward the original goal, they nonetheless supported his continued attempts to persist, undeterred by repeated disaster. No son could have asked for more interest and support from his parents in his preparation for a career. But in Frank's case it was oppressive and overdone and he had to escape from the distractions and pressures before he could decide for himself on some alternative. His parents and brother, although models of thrift and industry, were in occupations he despised; it is true they supported him in his professional ambitions yet they somehow failed to transmit to him their heritage of personal qualities.

Carl Duncan's family was at least as middle-class as Frank's, and at an earlier point in the family's history it seems likely that the Duncans' aspirations for their sons were high and their efforts to realize them vigorous, for Carl's eldest brother was a teacher and the next two were engineers. There was even a carry-over beyond Carl to his younger brother, who was offered help by the older ones in getting through college. But Carl found no models of significance to him; contrasting with the example of his competent and self-reliant brothers and sisters was that of the father, whom they all regarded as a failure. Carl was not only passed over; he had the misfortune to be faced with the issues of his career at a time when his father was struggling with severe occupational problems of his own. Moreover, his choice of artist was not one that could mobilize the interest and support of his family, and he was left largely to his own devices to realize it. Like Victor, Carl began to work early at odd jobs and after finishing high school performed creditably in the Coast Guard and then for a time in a series of full-time jobs. So it seems probable that he acquired appropriate work attitudes and habits early in his life; but later, when he most needed support and recognition, his family failed him.

Neither Harold Lang's father nor his brothers could provide him with models of a stable and continuous occupational career, let alone equip him with the necessary habits and attitudes and the elementary information about the world of work. The family's need of the earnings of their children was great among all the single males except Frank Monaco, but in none was it more dire than in the Lang household. Financial pressure on Harold began early; indeed he attributed his leaving school prematurely in large part to the family's poverty. But this was all his family had to offer—the push to go to work and make money: they could not instruct or help him in acquiring the means and resources for becoming an adequate worker.

Victor provides an instance of the person who followed the orientation of an older brother and rejected that of the father whereas, as was just mentioned, Carl had no one for an example. Apart from the issue of role model, it is clear that in Victor's familial milieu it was taken for granted that children would go to work when they could and contribute to the family income; but in contrast to Harold's family, Victor's was able to provide him with basic motivation. Indeed his socialization into the world of work was so thorough that he left school early in his eagerness to get a job, despite the absence of familial pressure. In fact Victor was so well indoctrinated that he explained not respecting his father on the ground that the latter was easy-going and did not like to work.

The unmarried patients had to cope with only parents and siblings. But the four married men each returned to a personal world bounded by *three* families: the parental, the conjugal, and the in-laws; and as it chanced in each case the wife's family played an important part.

Like Victor, Peter Stone had powerful role models to encourage his attitudes and habits with respect to the world of work. Moreover, although the occupation he chose was very different from his father's, it was a tradition in his mother's family and none of his family regarded it as dubious or eccentric, as seems to have been the case in the Duncan family. Like Harold, he left school early because of the pressing financial need at home, but unlike Harold he immediately became a reliable breadwinner, contributing "good money" to the family, and his self-expectation of being a reliable breadwinner, presumably established as early as his choice of career, persisted when he moved into the roles of husband and father. Peter spoke of his father and the rest of his family as very close and affectionate and it seems clear that his familial experience was such as to facilitate his entry into the labor force with sufficient self-confidence and knowledge of the world of work for him to be adequate from the first.

Little is known of the background of Arthur Jackson, in part because his wife's family so much overshadowed his own and he married at the outset of his career. It is evident, however, that his parents must have had professional aspirations for their children, since Arthur's eldest brother also became a physicist and his other brother an accountant. His family, in fact, provides an instance of intergenerational mobility, for Arthur's father had held for most of his life a modest position with a railroad. Arthur largely financed his college education himself through scholarships and, later on, through veterans' benefits. His elder brother, the physicist, gave him his first job and launched him on his career. In any case, it seems clear that his socialization for the world of work was adequate and appropriate; when his education was interrupted by the war he returned to prepare for the career of his choice and went on to establish himself in it.

As a boy, David Field had little respect for the occupations his father followed, first a shoe factory worker and then a storekeeper; his own aspirations were much higher although not specific. His parents gave him little encouragement and less direction; indeed they tended to dampen his enthusiasm and had no confidence in his ability to get ahead in any of his several ventures. Their discouraging attitudes persisted relatively unchanged when he was a grown man and his many vicissitudes strengthened them in their conviction that he would not make much out of his life. Nevertheless they provided financial support when he attempted to change his career by moving to California and again when he tried to buy his own cab.

Albert Rossini's father died when he was an infant, and the stepfather whom he had for five years when he was a young boy is described as strict and unloving. Permissive and indulgent, his mother throughout his youth provided Albert and his brother with money for their various diversions. Thus the boys could acquire little knowledge of the realities of the world of work and there was no one to signalize the appropriate attitudes and habits. When facing the torments, to him, of job-hunting, Albert moaned, "If only I had a father, he would tell me what to do!" There is no indication that Albert worked at all until after he finished high school, and when he did seek a job he had no notion of what he wanted to do. He may have obtained his first job on his own, but afterward it was his aunt, some other person, or the union that obtained his jobs for him, and when he was in financial straits it was always his mother or aunt who came to his aid.

While, as these cases show, socialization into the world of work bears significantly on successful entry into the labor market and employability, there is no one-to-one relationship between socialization and continued employability. Victor, Carl, Frank, Peter, and Arthur were all presumably relatively well equipped to embark upon stable work careers but Carl and Arthur eventually became unemployable. Conversely, among Harold, David, and Albert, who did not enjoy the benefits of appropriate occupational socialization, only Harold ended up virtually a failure. The important difference is that the choice of career crystallized among those of the first group early but not at all in the second group. An element which seems largely a matter of uncontrollable chance, and one whose consequences may be fateful, is timing. The careers of Peter Stone and David Field were gravely threatened by illness but each was already firmly established at work before he succumbed, as was true of the younger Victor Norton. Even the fragile Albert Rossìni had been a railroad worker and, *more* important, a union member, for two years before he was first hospitalized. Consequently each of these men had some place in the world of work to fall back on, such as an employer who knew them; two of them belonged to a union with obligations to them. The lot of Arthur Jackson was very different, as he had just come to the point at which he ceased to be a full-time university student and began to earn his living; and Frank Monaco, Carl Duncan, and Harold Lang never made a real start as workers. Most notably, Arthur Jackson's early illness and hospitalization may have offset the advantages of firm crystallization, sound socialization, and commitment.

Several recent studies of former mental patients show that if the expectations of their relatives are high, their performance is better.[2] These case studies also show that the relationship between expectations and performance (quite apart, for the moment, from the issue of illness and hospitalization), is in the direction indicated by the large-scale surveys. But in the individual case, whether familial expectations are fulfilled is complicated by several circumstances which were not apparent in the findings of the surveys. One is early socialization, which has just been discussed; a second is the support and recognition provided by the family; and a third is the patient's self-expectations.

Harold Lang's mother repeatedly expressed her concern about her son's need for work, and she and other members of the family made a number of attempts to push him into job-seeking and to find employment for him. But the boy had never acquired the requisite qualities for employability and thus had no resources with which to respond to their demands. Mrs. Duncan, too, came to the conclusion that the solution to her son's problems was a job; but the Duncans neither supported nor recognized Carl's artistic ambitions nor did they express any confidence in his ability to obtain and hold a job. Carl himself, although his earlier socialization for work seems to have been appropriate, entertained relatively low expectations for himself by the time of the study and this was matched by his parents' lack of confidence in him. These two cases demonstrate that the familial expectation that the patient go to work is not enough; Harold simply had no resources with which to respond to expectations, while Carl could not overcome his family's indifference and lack of support.

Expectations of Victor as a worker were high; indeed it was taken for granted that he would work. Actually, by self-propulsion, he exceeded whatever the Norton family expected of him, and his adequate early socialization for work converged with his family's continued support and recognition of him in adult life.

The Monaco case provides an instance where familial support was overwhelming. Both Frank and his parents held high expectations of him; but where Frank desperately wanted to find his own way, his parents refused, in effect, to let him loose. Here there is a curious incompatibility: the elder Monacos expected high achievement from Frank, but demanded nothing of him in the way of financial contribution to the family, and indeed indulged him in every way even when he was earning money regularly and could have borne his share.

Peter Stone's wife gave an impressive display of indulgence, support, and permissiveness, but this was tempered by her faith and confidence in his ability to work and bring home his earnings. Mrs. Stone never put pressure on Peter to go to work, as was true, too, of Mrs. Norton and Victor, and in the case of each there was no need of it. Both men had high self-expectations and returning to work was no more an issue for Peter than for Victor, although it took Peter some time to do it.

Like Joan Stone, Nelly Field gave her husband strong and loving support and rarely put pressure on him. Although she expected him to work—it will be recalled that she left him in protest on one of the occasions when he refused to seek a job—she was more lenient and indulgent than Joan Stone and took the initiative in seeking out agencies to help supplement the family income. Joan Stone was willing to exercise her ingenuity in making Peter's income stretch to satisfy his particular needs as well as those of the family, but, unlike Nelly Field, she did expect her husband to assume his full burden as husband and father. David, like Peter, expected to be the breadwinner and to support his family but, unlike Peter, he was not averse to accepting help from his family and the agencies; so little averse that his wife had ADC help stopped when she realized that he was counting on it.

Hannah Jackson also loved and gave support to her husband, but as she took over the breadwinner's role and developed her own investment in it, she exacted an increasingly greater price for her efforts on Arthur's behalf. Alone among the wives in these studies she discouraged her husband's return to his principal occupation; indeed she perceived his persistence as a threat to her own emerging career. Arthur's self-expectations were high, although he was willing to compromise on manual work as a temporary measure, and one is impressed with his repeated attempts to return to physics in the face of the imposing opposition of Hannah and her family. When he finally succeeded in setting up his own laboratory Hannah responded by leaving him, and dropped divorce proceedings only when he became disturbed again. High self-expectations alone are not enough; Arthur eventually conformed to the low expectations which his wife so tenaciously held for him.

Albert Rossini's story also illustrates the effect of familial expectations on performance. Indulgent and protective toward him while he was growing up, his family continued to be so when he was an adult, by which time his wife joined in by making excuses for him. His career reflects the fact that when he was employed it was due primarily to the efforts of others.

ILLNESS, HOSPITALIZATION AND CAREER

The families of six of the eight patients—Harold Lang, Carl Duncan, Frank Monaco, David Field, Arthur Jackson, and Albert Rossini—at one time or another treated their former patients as invalids, expecting and indeed sometimes welcoming their playing the role of sick men. Where psychiatric disability seems to have been the most severe and pervasive, affecting several areas of life functioning—Harold Lang, Carl Duncan, and Arthur Jackson—the family still expected the patient to go to work but their standards were low, based on the premise that he needed a "special" job, appropriate to the convalescent. Thus the Langs believed that Harold should not be expected to take and hold a job he did not like, and Mrs. Lang declared that it was the hospital's responsibility to find work for him. Carl Duncan's mother hoped that he would find a "labor job, something that would place no strain on his mind," and, like Mrs. Lang, she thought that the hospital should have a place "where fellows like him could go to get jobs: something special for them." Arthur's wife and her family not only believed that he should accept manual work protected from the normal strains of the competitive world, but also they succeeded in relegating him to just such a job and did their best to keep him from returning to his original career.

Frank Monaco's parents, David Field's wife, and Albert Rossini's mother, aunt, and wife, whether they actually viewed themselves as responsible for the rehabilitation of the former patient, certainly behaved as though they did. The Monacos and the Rossini clan constantly intervened in Frank's and Albert's affairs, respectively (Frank opposed and Albert welcomed it), and indulged them when they were not working; and Nelly Field did all she could, up to a certain point, to supplement David's capacity as a breadwinner and to defend him from their relatives' complaints.

Peter Stone's wife was also inclined to treat him permissively. She wondered whether he might not seek daytime work that would be less strenuous, but once he returned to his regular occupation she fostered his independence and behaved as though he did not need special consideration. When Peter returned to work, the illness and hospitalization were sealed off and compartmentalized from the working career itself. But Victor Norton's case exemplifies most clearly the policy of relatives to treat illness and hospitalization as irrelevant circumstances. Mrs. Norton, from the time Victor returned home, simply assumed his recovery, and she took it for granted that he had to return to work, preferably to his former job.

In some of the cases, the question arises as to whether the family's attitudes and actions were strategically influenced by the intrusion of illness and hospitalization or whether they would have acted as they did, anyway; but this question cannot be answered from the data at hand. In any case, the concern of the present study is with consequences, not causes.

A number of the men exhibited considerable dependence on their families, a characteristic that has been mentioned frequently in the literature on schizophrenia. When a strong supporting figure fails the patient, he, too, may fail. All too well-known is the crisis precipitated by the departure or illness of the patient's therapist. And the emergency is perhaps even more severe when it involves a member of the family in whom the individual has a significant emotional investment. When their wives became pregnant, Arthur Jackson, Peter Stone, David Field, and Albert Rossini were seriously disturbed. The threats they spoke of were illness and death and competition for their wives' time and attention: although all were desperately pressed for money, not one mentioned the burden of an extra mouth to feed.

Of the wives of Arthur Jackson, David Field, and Albert Rossini, the social workers offered the comment that each stood in psychological need of a sick husband. Hannah Jackson, although she seemed affectionate and uncalculating, found her opportunity in Arthur's affliction, and the time came when his recovery stood in her way and her projects stood in his. The wives of David Field and Albert Rossini, who had no personal ambitions, devoted their talents to the crushing problems of simply coping. One is led to speculate on what kind of woman can or will tolerate and stand by a psychotic man and whether a woman in psychological need of a sick partner may not perhaps prove a very good risk as his wife. Moreover, although the three wives at times did cater to their husbands' dispositions to be dependent and thereby perhaps fostered it, Nelly Field and Kathleen Rossini became aware on their own of the importance of setting limits. Nelly saw that the ADC payments were brought to an end and Kathleen ultimately recognized the dilemma, how to distinguish sickness from "normal" irresponsible behavior. When she reached this moment of truth she resolved to make no more allowances but instead to demand that Albert resume his obligations.

Nevertheless, these cases demonstrate that where there are no available outside resources to induce responsibility in the patient and no internal resources to help him maintain occupational and financial self-sufficiency, the patient and his family will pay an awesome price. More-over, when the family provides no adequate socialization for the career by failure to inculcate ambitions and standards in children and adoles-cents or to insist on them in adults, the price will be even greater. Apart from the all-too-evident suffering which is inflicted on a sick man, there is a heavy cost to those about him. To cite just a few examples: A psy-chotic relative may drain the family financially, as happened to the Monacos, Stones, Jacksons, and Rossinis; he may severely disrupt domes-tic life if the family keeps him home during psychotic interludes, as was true of the Langs and Duncans; and if the family believes he is threat-ened by the handicap of stigma, the deceit and connivance necessary to conceal his hospitalization may impose considerable strain on them all, as seemed to have been the case with the Monacos. No matter how the family meets the crisis, it pays a formidable price in time and emotional stress.

The present case studies indicate that pernicious and pervasive stigma is more imaginary than real. Many of the patients and their relatives were convinced that they were harassed or rejected and for the most part they sought to conceal the illness and hospitalization and never experienced what might have happened if their neighbors and other associates had actually known the truth. In Arthur Jackson's commu-nity, people mobilized to help the family and the school superintendent voluntarily appointed Arthur's wife as a teacher. David Field's boss offered to use political influence to help him recover his driver's li-cense and in fact let him drive illegally. Albert Rossini believed himself handicapped and did not divulge his hospitalization when applying for jobs outside of those covered by his union. And Peter Stone's work associates made up a purse to help the family and took him back will-ingly when he was released. In the experience of both these men, the union does not stigmatize.

Compared with most parts of the country, the Boston area has rela-tively good psychiatric facilities and services and considerable local effort goes into programs of mental health education. It is evident in these cases, however, that few of the patients and their families were well informed about the nature of mental illness and resources for its treatment beyond the state hospital. Virtually all of the patients were exhibiting severe symptoms and had become essentially unmanageable. It may be to their credit that the families were willing to tolerate a great deal before they decided to send the patient away, but on the other hand this way of proceeding makes any preventive measures or other timely strategic intervention unlikely. Left for the most part to their own resources, the relatives rarely knew where to turn for appropriate help. Nelly Field, it is true, knew very well where to go for financial and medical support and aid for her family, but a familiarity with agencies did little to help directly with her psychotic husband; indeed the kind of help offered at one point by the workers was actually exacerbating.

Most of the patients either rejected or cooperated minimally in the therapy offered them when in the hospital, whether it was psychotherapy, group or occupational therapy. Only in one or two instances did a patient, after several hospitalizations, begin to show any interest in therapy at all. This may or may not have been due to the fact that virtually all the patients either refused to admit they were mentally ill or were unable to recognize that they were. Notable exceptions were Victor Norton, who readily admitted that he had been ill and might become so again; and Albert Rossini, who lamented his "lost personality." Characteristically, Victor handled this by "watching" himself, and by planning what steps he would take if he found himself getting ill again. Victor was not the only one, however, who could be pragmatic about issues of work and illness: Peter Stone, and also David Field (whether or not he had insight into his illness), both took measures progressively to limit their work without, however, giving up their original occupations; although they identified them as somehow conducive to the recurrence of their difficulties. Illness and hospitalization did little to change Victor's, Peter's, and David's careers or their employability, perhaps because of the substantial investment and experience in work they had already acquired (although in the case of David, the commitment to his occupation was more involuntary than voluntary), and because of the support and recognition they received at home. These three seem not to have felt that the experience of mental illness and hospitalization had altered their personalities in any way.

Carl Duncan, on the other hand, was one whose pattern of career was changed drastically during the period covered by the study. He, too, had had some previous experience in the world of work but illness came at a time when he was wrestling with the dilemma of how to realize his ambitions, a dilemma that proved insuperable because he had no resources, either of his own or from his family. Then illness compounded the issue and essentially sealed his fate. Carl, like a number of other men in these studies, was beset by problems of identity. (There are many indications in the sociological and psychological literature that problems of identity are ubiquitous in our society, and hardly an exclusive characteristic of schizophrenics.) [3] There may be a circular reaction: placement in an occupational role provides a means of establishing ego-identity and opportunities for action whereby further definition and stabilization can take place, and a stabilized identity no doubt facilitates the building of a career.[4] Carl was able to make an occupational choice but never to establish an occupational identity which could have helped him to find himself.

A stable occupational identity was no more achieved by Albert Rossini than by Carl. If Albert held to an occupation, it was, as in the case of David Field, by default, and his hold was precarious indeed. Despite it, illness and hospitalization had hardly a discernible effect on the pattern of his career. In part this must have been because the union assured him of employment and in part because his relatives interceded in his behalf as vigorously after hospitalization as before. Having little investment in work itself, and even less confidence in his ability to make his own way in the world of work, Albert had little to lose in either respect as a consequence of illness. Nevertheless, he believed that he had suffered from his illness as a man if not as a worker, complaining that he "lost" his personality and wondering if he would regain his pleasure in work and play; but whether he had ever found much pleasure in work is doubtful. The record ends, however, on a hopeful note: he had held the best job he had ever had for three months.

Harold Lang's first hospitalization occurred only a year after he entered the labor market but there was no indication that he could have found a place for himself in the world of work by then. And, as has been indicated, there is no evidence that his illness was the principal cause of his unemployability. Even when he was well, he rarely was employed, and at times he worked, in his sporadic way, when he was ill. Whether Harold ever perceived illness and hospitalization as deterring him from making his way as a worker must remain an open question, but in view of his haphazard approach to it, it does not seem likely. Yet it is clear that hospitalization itself severely limited whatever may have been his chances of ultimately becoming a worker; he was taken out of the community before he could acquire any real experience and thereafter was hospitalized frequently and for long periods.

For both Frank Monaco and Arthur Jackson illness and hospitalization led to dramatic changes in career pattern, and in their cases the eruption of illness was most nearly tied in with occupational issues, although at different points. Frank's earlier psychotic breaks each followed his attempts to train for a professional career. Despite his tendency to deny his illness, the disasters recurring each time he returned to school clearly showed him that he was incapable of becoming a physician, or even a dentist. In the end he was convinced that he would "crack up again" if he tried any more, and later he voiced the apprehension that even if he could have become a dentist the fine work and concentration might have been "too much for him." Even after he had abandoned the notion of going back to school and was looking for a job, he lamented, "Look where I've ended! How am I to know that I won't break again? It's your self-respect that goes." Certainly his illness and hospitalizations were decisive in ending his educational career, in altering his choice of occupation, and in deflecting him into a career rather different from the one he had originally envisioned.

Arthur Jackson's emotional difficulties began after he had acquired a substantial education and had launched upon his professional career; yet he ultimately descended much lower in the occupational hierarchy than did Frank and had more severe problems of employability, at least during as much of their lives as these stories cover. Seven years passed between his first psychotic break at the age of 22 and his second illness, an indication of his persistence and durability in his profession, and even after his psychotic episodes grew more frequent with concomitant hospitalizations, he was still able to obtain a substantial job in physics and hold it for five months. But his recurrent illness became tied up with his repeated struggles to set up a consulting laboratory of his own, and it apparently became so pervasive that at times he could not even perform the simple duties of his alternative career in the moving business.

CONCLUSIONS

The hospital appears to set out with the conception of a sick man who cannot be expected to go right into a serious job when he is released. It then becomes a question of: when does *real* life begin for a patient?

These studies reveal that for the most part the patient seems to learn little or nothing from hospitalization. It may be said without further elaboration that occupational therapy, as seen in these case studies, is pointless, childish, and humiliating—even humorless: when Peter Stone, a professional musician, could not be given music therapy because there was no music therapist on the staff, he independently found a patient to whom he taught trumpet and he organized the patients in giving concerts. The patient may learn certain behavior which is adaptive in the hospital, but what he learns is likely to be useless or to bring down punishment on him when he is in the community. It may well be that the hospital is to some extent creating conditions which contribute to relapse and lead to rehospitalization. The hospital seems to be at its best when it serves as a moratorium, an oasis from life, as it did most notably for Frank Monaco. There, tranquillized and rescued from his invasive parents, he recast his career to match his capacity. To the tortured Albert Rossini, the hospital gave a happy release, "free from worries," as he said. Here, then, is a question of balance: a sick man must be eased; yet before he is returned to the community, surely he should be prepared to assume an acceptable amount of responsibility.

The hospital and various social welfare agencies make gestures in the direction of rehabilitating patients occupationally, but these case studies offer no instance of hospital personnel having actually taught patients trades and skills nor of other agencies having delivered such services. Had the proposition to retrain Peter Stone or David Field for less wearing occupations been firm and realistic, their posthospital fates and their families' situations might have been happier. The hospital staff did, at least in the case of Harold Lang, insist on his having a job to go to before releasing him, although in the end they relented and released him without one; and they found work for Carl Duncan of a sheltered nature within the institution. But Harold Lang, who has been defined as an unemployable youth who was sometimes psychotic, might have been given his first real training in a trade.

To quote from the analysis of Harold Lang's case: "It is as if the hospital, while attending to him as a patient, never took him seriously as a potential worker." But the Air Force did.

The armed services, like a surrogate family, offer the fragile pre-psychotic or even the former patient authoritarian support based on forthright, unequivocal tradition and example.[5] Thus it should not be surprising that this array of cases offers instances of men who made satisfactory servicemen although they were not successful workers in civilian life. To Carl Duncan, for example, the Coast Guard supplied a strongly structured milieu where he had no choices to make, was told exactly *what* and *when*, and was surrounded by others doing just exactly what he, too, was expected to do. He served three years and was honorably discharged, a record he hardly equalled in civilian life. The ineffectual Harold Lang, too, was at his best in the Air Force. It is likely that the armed services would have been a stabilizing milieu for the shy and frightened Albert Rossini, although he, of course, found another surrogate for the family in the union. When Frank Monaco at last entered into his military service, and did it well, it was one of the few enterprises that he could boast of as having brought to a successful finish and no doubt the reward was some measure of renewed confidence and sense of personal worth. It is not necessary to enlarge on the obvious usefulness of the skills acquired in the armed services when the serviceman returns to civilian life. Arthur Jackson, for one, was helped tremendously by having been in the Navy's V-12 program.

In Frank Monaco and Peter Stone we have instances of men rejected by the draft on grounds of their histories of psychosis. Peter Stone soon afterward went into the USO and served nine months there, sometimes under fire. Not until three years later was he hospitalized. And Frank Monaco, in the end, served his full term of six months in the Army Signal Corps, yet had five hospital sojourns behind him. On the other hand, Carl Duncan served honorably in the Coast Guard for three years and not until three years later did he become a mental patient. Sometimes the illness precedes, sometimes it follows, the day when a man reports to his draft board. This study offers the argument that some who were rejected because their hospitalization came first would have served as adequately as some whose hospitalization happened to come later.

In his union, the union man has the advantage of an environment which, like the armed services, appropriates to itself some of the functions of a masterful family. The union saved Peter Stone and, when possible, Albert Rossini, from job-seeking and to each man held out a secure berth when he came out of a hospital and re-entered the labor market. The railroad culture set low standards, it is true, but the perspective in this study is through Albert Rossini, who moved at the lowest level of work; no doubt Peter Stone had to prove himself qualified to get into the musicians' union and remain in it. Mental illness and hospitalization appear not to stigmatize a man in his union; when he is not paid wages, he is granted unemployment compensation and his hospital expenses are met. The union offered Albert Rossini almost sheltered conditions of employment.

The paramount fact of the mental patient's predicament that is incontestably demonstrated by these cases—the fact often noted but not always taken seriously—is that the course of his occupational career cannot be understood without reference to the social world in which he lives. He is surrounded by figures immensely important to him— parents, siblings, neighbors, employers, work-mates, and perhaps a spouse and children. They pose contingencies to his fate as a worker which are as decisive in the career of the sick man as his affliction itself. Indeed, in some cases illness may be almost incidental, while childhood and later socialization for the world of work and familial expectations of him as an adult may be the most powerful of all influences upon his career. Thus the Simmons-Freeman studies and those of Dinitz, Pasamanick, and their associates suggest that psychiatric and other medical aspects are less important in determining outcome than are the attitudes of relatives to whom the patient is sent back.[6] Brown has found that the type of living arrangement to which patients are returned is the most significant element in their success or failure.[7]

Most recent studies indicate that the hospital has little influence on the outcome of a patient's posthospital experience whether with regard to occupational performance or to rehospitalization. It seems apparent that integration into the work role has, for most people, preventive effects with respect to personal disorganization and emotional disturbance, and that helping the patient to acquire the qualifications and assets necessary for such integration should be a proper object of hospital treatment. Indeed, the finding of a lack of relationship between receipt of conventional therapies and the outcome of posthospital experience must be in part a consequence of the neglect in hospital treatment programs of the work role and its potentialities as a preventive measure. But it should also be observed in all fairness that responsibility for the outcome of a case can hardly be considered completely the hospital's, since at least two major determinants of outcome, namely, the attitudes of the patient, and others' attitudes toward him, are as a rule only peripherally under the influence of the institution.

As pointed out in Chapter 1, work is of central concern in our American society, and the great majority of American men look to work as the area within which to validate themselves.[8] The high value attached to work is documented in all of these cases; with one exception, both patient and family expressed genuine concern with the question of work, whether their patient was a worker or nonworker. The one exception is Harold Lang, but even his family in its ineffectual way exerted considerable pressure on him to find and hold a job. Despite this concern, six out of the eight families at one time or another persisted in treating their former patients as sick men. In like fashion, hospital and community programs of aftercare continue to place the principal emphasis on maintenance therapy and on increasing understanding of the illness by the family and other associates.

One important lesson to be learned from the intervention of the armed services and the unions by both families and mental health practitioners is, as some of these cases have illustrated, that the former patient is not to be treated as a sick man if he is to become an effective worker. Indeed, if posthospital programs are to bring about acceptable occupational performance, there must be a shift away from exclusive preoccupation with the *patient* toward focusing on the *worker* as well. The practitioner has, of course, the responsibility for treating the pathology constituted by illness, but in view of the value attached to work, it is also his proper responsibility to apply his therapeutic efforts to the problems of work attitudes and behavior as well; and these are two quite different tasks.

All of the patients in these case studies were diagnosed as psychotic; yet some were successful workers while others were not. Many of the problems of work behavior, as these cases illustrate, are not illness-connected but stem from the complexities and strains inherent in the development of the career itself. To explain the success of former patients like Victor Norton with his work ethic, or Peter Stone and David Field, who returned doggedly to jobs which they believed were hurtful to them, one must turn not to psychiatry but to the world of work, itself, where appropriate preparation, expectations, skills, work habits, early and powerful motivation, firm crystallization of choice—in short, each of the components of the occupational career that have been conceptualized for the analysis of these cases—may be regarded as a station along a route. While some workers go directly to a destination of their own choosing (and sometimes they are former mental patients) others break down at one or several of the stops, or stray off the course and lose their way entirely. If more are to find their way, some effort must be made, even if belated, to socialize them effectively into the world of work. Socialization alone is not enough, of course; opportunities to obtain jobs and to keep them must also be made available.

If help of this sort were to materialize, the predominant emphasis should be on teaching the former patient how to look for a job, on inculcating appropriate habits of work so as to get him into, or back into, the world of work as soon as possible, and on providing job opportunities. If he does not return to work early he may end by adjusting himself permanently to failure.[9] If he is treated as a special case because of his illness, it is likely to reinforce his notion that he cannot take his place as a worker just like anyone else and it may suggest to him additional justification of his failure. The greater the preoccupation with remission of symptoms and with staving off rehospitalization on this basis alone, the greater will be the tendency to attribute a patient's inadequacies as a worker to illness rather than to his lack of occupational skills, acceptable habits, and commitment to work. The problems of matching whatever skills and experience he may have to a job, or of helping him to acquire specific skills and knowledge are sufficiently complex and difficult and not likely to be resolved by focusing attention and effort on his illness.

Success in the world of work in contemporary American society is not, of course, given to all. There are permanent failures—the chronically unemployed—only some of whom are mental patients. A man may become permanently unemployable because he cannot overcome his mental illness, but also he may become so because he was cheated by bad luck, bad management, ethnic discrimination, or perhaps only by bad timing, or the state of the labor market. There is some question as to whether socialization delayed until adulthood can in fact generate suitable beliefs, attitudes, and motivation for certain types of work.[10] It may be that in some cases attempts at resocialization may be too costly from society's point of view.

To arrive at realistic programs of effective habilitation and rehabilitation for work, there must be reliable knowledge of how successful workers are produced; the process, which should be essentially the same for the psychotic or prepsychotic as for the sound and whole, can be discovered in the family life of successful workers. Thus Brim notes three requirements of performing satisfactorily in a social role: one must know what is expected of him, both in behavior and values, must be able to meet the requirements of the role, and must desire to practice it and pursue the appropriate ends.[11] One may be sure it will be considerably more fruitful to pursue, in further inquiry into the relationships between work and mental illness, the socially structured differences in access to opportunities for learning and for development of a career between families which turn out successful workers and those which do not, than to seek the explanation of persistence and change in employability by reference to the history of illness. The conceptual framework formulated in the present study has been useful in identifying the problems to be investigated in such research, as is demonstrated by these case studies. But this conceptualization was developed *ex post facto*, and the extent of its applicability can be tested only in further empirical research.

NOTES

1. Erik H. Erikson, *Young Man Luther*, New York: W. W. Norton and Co., 1962, 17–18.

2. Ozzie G. Simmons and Howard E. Freeman, "Familial Expectations and Posthospital Performance of Mental Patients," *Human Relations*, 12 (August 1959), 233–243; Howard E. Freeman and Ozzie G. Simmons, *The Mental Patient Comes Home*, New York: John Wiley and Sons, 1963; Simon Dinitz, Mark Lefton, Shirley Angrist, and Benjamin Pasamanick, "Psychiatric and Social Attributes as Predictors of Case Outcome in Mental Hospitalization," *Social Problems*, 8 (Spring 1961), 322–328, and "Instrumental Role Expectations and Posthospital Performance of Female Mental Patients," *Social Forces*, 40 (March 1962), 248–254.

3. See, for example, Milton Rokeach, *The Three Christs of Ypsilanti*, New York: Alfred A. Knopf, 1964, 310–329.

4. Robert W. White, *Lives in Progress*, New York: The Dryden Press, 1952.

5. For some, of course, the Army milieu has been far from salutary. Many apparently could not take the 24-hour-a-day control and found the restrictions on their freedom so crippling that they were unable to perform effectively. But for some of the men in these case studies this milieu appeared to be the only one in which they could perform effectively. See Eli Ginzberg, John B. Miner, James K. Anderson, Sol W. Ginsburg, and John L. Herma, *The Ineffective Soldier: Breakdown and Recovery*, New York: Columbia University Press, 1959, Vol. 2. The studies of Ginzberg and his associates also show that many psychotics were able to perform more or less satisfactorily for long periods of time while in the Army. See Eli Ginzberg, James K. Anderson, Sol W. Ginsburg, and John L. Herma, *The Ineffective Soldier: The Lost Divisions*, New York: Columbia University Press, 1959, Vol. 1.

6. See Note 2.

7. George W. Brown, "Experiences of Discharged Chronic Schizophrenic Patients in Various Types of Living Group," *The Milbank Memorial Fund Quarterly*, 37 (April 1959), 105–131.

8. See Robert S. Weiss and David Riesman, "Social Problems and Disorganization in the World of Work," in Robert K. Merton and Robert A. Nisbet (editors), *Contemporary Social Problems*, New York: Harcourt, Brace and World, 1961.

9. See Eli Ginzberg, James K. Anderson, Sol W. Ginsburg, and John L. Herma, *The Ineffective Soldier: Patterns of Performance*, New York: Columbia University Press, 1959, Vol. 3.

10. Orville G. Brim, Jr., "Socialization through the Life Cycle," *Items* (published by the Social Science Research Council), 18 (March 1964), 1–5.

11. *Op. cit.*

APPENDIX

The Community Health Project, of which the longitudinal case study program is a part, was initiated in 1953 at the Harvard School of Public Health. The author was director of the Project from its inception. At the outset the Project was small and exploratory but by the end of 1954 the staff had been expanded to include representatives of sociology, anthropology, psychology, psychiatric social work, and psychiatry. The strategy of research, as it finally evolved, included two principal types of studies, combining the rich detail and depth of qualitative analysis with quantitative precision. The first approach resulted in the longitudinal case study program, and the second eventuated in a series of surveys testing hypotheses concerning correlates of patients' posthospital performance. Reports of all the surveys have been published. The last and largest one, which included 649 cases, inquired into the success and failure of patients in remaining in the community, as well as into the levels of their work and social performance subsequent to hospitalization; the results were reported in *The Mental Patient Comes Home*, written by Howard E. Freeman and the present author.[1]

In the longitudinal case study program, a panel of thirty-two former patients and one or more members of their immediate families were interviewed for periods of time lasting in some cases as long as four years. This research was envisioned from the outset as exploratory, and because of this and the limited size of the study group the emphasis was

1. Published by John Wiley and Sons, New York, 1963.

placed throughout on collection of a broad range of empirical data and on analysis of them as a means of delineating types and patterns of posthospital experience rather than on the testing of specific hypotheses.

A number of considerations led to the adoption of longitudinal case studies:

1. The paucity of research on the posthospital experience of mental patients called for an effort to collect data that would yield "phenomenological" knowledge of it. Since no data were then available on which to formulate a hypothetical-deductive model, it seemed the wiser course to choose a flexible inductive procedure which held out the promise of bringing to light significant circumstances and relationships in a largely uncharted area of research.

2. The general aim was to obtain a dynamic, that is, a processual, picture of posthospital experience while it was actually taking place, in contrast to the relatively static picture which would be obtained by collecting retrospective data at particular points in time. This called for a longitudinal study in which repeated periodic observations of persons and events would, as time went on, permit comparisons of attitudinal and behavioral changes, if any, and identification of linkages between events.

3. If significant circumstances and relationships in posthospital experience were to be systematically identified, the collection and analysis of data would have to be organized with reference to the basic unit of investigation, whether it be just the patient or the patient and his family, friends, or work associates, so that the unit would not be lost from view and the analysis become one of simply cross-tabulating distributions of traits or characteristics. The case study appeared to be the most appropriate way of keeping together the identity of the unit and the relevant characteristics. Moreover, the case study method, since it imposed no inherent restrictions on the content, amount and levels of data, seemed most likely to yield material about the posthospital experience of patients that would point up the significant patterns.

4. The cooperation and support of mental health practitioners in assembling a study group of former patients and their families was a necessity and one which seemed to call for the adoption of the case study method. Despite the substantial differences between use of the case study in social research and in clinical practice, the similarities are sufficient to facilitate a more ready understanding and acceptance on

the part of practitioners than if other methods, particularly quantitative ones, had been used. Moreover, the Project was committed to undertake research bearing upon the practical concerns of rehabilitation and to this end the case study seemed the most promising; at least it entailed descriptions of empirical situations and statements of substantive findings of an order most congenial to the practitioners' professional orientation and experience.

In view of all these considerations, the longitudinal case study program was explicitly designed to permit an intensive examination of a small number of cases over as long a time as possible, beginning with the collection of data on the patient and his family before he was released from the hospital. The first series of cases was initiated in 1954 as a pilot study; regular interviewing in this group was terminated in 1955. Some contact was maintained subsequently with eight of them and when the second series was begun in 1957, the eight were brought back into the study for intensive interviewing. In all cases in both series interviewing was finally brought to an end in July 1959. Thus eight cases were followed by direct interviewing for periods up to four years, while the twenty-four cases comprising the second series were interviewed for a minimum of seven months and a maximum of over two years, depending on the date of their introduction into the study.

At the time of their entry into the study, all the patients were hospitalized at one or the other of the two state hospitals serving Boston and its immediate environs. One is quite typical of state hospitals and then had 3000 beds; the other is a teaching hospital of 200 beds. The total study group consisted of eight married males, seven single males, ten married females, five single females, a male separated from his wife, and a female who was divorced. The criteria of selection were that they be between 18 and 50 years of age, reside in Boston or a contiguous suburb, and be diagnosed by the hospital as schizophrenic, without concurrent diagnosis of alcoholism, organic disorder, or mental deficiency. The length of the study hospitalization had to be at least forty days unless there had been a previous hospitalization of at least that extent. The study called for thirty-two cases evenly divided between male and female, between patients who returned to conjugal and to parental families, and those with "long" (over two years) and "short" (less than two years) histories of hospitalization. As can be seen from the description of the composition of the study group, these distributions were not actually realized. Of the eight cases included here, one (David Field) was selected from the first series and seven from the second. All eight patients and their relatives have, of course, been given fictitious names.

A single interviewer, either a sociologist, anthropologist, psychologist, or psychiatric social worker, was responsible for the collection of all the data in a given case—from patients and relatives, hospital personnel, and hospital records. In a few cases, where it seemed advisable to have different interviews for the patient and relative, a second worker was assigned to interview the relative. Interviews were usually conducted in the home of the patient and although every effort was made to interview patients and relatives separately, occasionally there was no alternative but to see them together. In keeping with an exploratory study, it seemed inappropriate, in the beginning, to conduct the interviews according to structured schedules or even focused guides. "Nondirective," open-ended interviewing of patients and relatives was preferred as best suited to drawing out information about them and about aspects of their posthospital experience which might prove important in the research but which were unknown to the investigators at the outset.

It was clear from the beginning, however, that content areas must be specified which would have to be covered in all cases to make it possible to compare them. One device for insuring uniform coverage was the holding of frequent staff conferences in which all the interviewers participated; another was the scheduling of regular individual sessions of the interviewer with the study director. Eventually, however, it became necessary to develop interview guides covering each of the content areas of interest to the study—such areas as family composition, living arrangements and division of labor, occupation and employment, financial arrangements, education and vocation, interpersonal relations within the family, ethnicity and class, modes of participation of patient and family in everyday activities, in friendship and neighbor networks, and in recreational activities and voluntary associations, specific aspects of hospital experience, posthospital contact with the hospital, use of community resources, and conceptions of and attitudes toward mental illness and hospitalization.

The interests pursued by the longitudinal case study program remained very broad throughout its duration. The decision to focus on occupational career in the preparation of this volume was made after all field work in the study had been completed; the reasons for it are reported in Chapter 1. The conceptualization and mode of analysis adopted for presentation of the cases were thus developed *ex post facto;* they provide a particular perspective considerably more limited than that embodied in the broad conceptualization which guided the data collection.

AUTHOR INDEX

SUBJECT INDEX

Career, as affected by illness and hospitalization, Norton, 43–44, 47
   Rossini, 223–224
   Stone, 142–144
Choice, occupational, 10, 11, 12–15, 235
  crystallization of, 12–13, 15, 16, 243, 256
      Duncan, 89, 90, 236
      Field, 169, 238
      Jackson, 194, 195, 237, 238, 243
      Lang, 68
      Monaco, 114, 116, 121, 236
      Norton, 45–46, 47, 49, 232
      Rossini, 225
      Stone, 140, 237
      Field, 238
      Monaco, 236
      Norton, 46
      Rossini, 225
      Stone, 242
Commitment, 10, 11, 13, 16, 256
  Duncan, 90, 236
  Field, 165, 238, 249
  Jackson, 195, 238, 243
  Monaco, 111, 236
  Norton, 237
  Rossini, 225
  Stone, 237
"Corner" boys, 205, 211, 212, 213, 227

Doctor, see Therapist
Dream, see Goal

Education, 6, 8, 10, 12; see also Assets; Qualifications for the labor market; Skills
  Duncan, 79–80, 88, 89, 94
  Field, 152–153, 161
  Jackson, 177, 194, 237, 242, 251
  Lang, 64
  Monaco, 101–102, 118, 233
  Norton, 34
  Rossini, 204, 224
  Stone, 129
Employability, as career pattern, 6–7, 235–239, 257
  Field, 238, 249
  Jackson, 251
  Lang, 72, 73, 232, 244, 249

Employability, Monaco, 115, 236
  Norton, 44, 47, 236, 237
  Rossini, 226, 238, 239
  Stone, 126, 237, 249
Employment, sheltered, Duncan, 252
  Jackson, 192, 193, 235, 246
  Rossini, 222, 226, 235, 254
Employment agency, 8
  Duncan, 85, 87
  Lang, 53, 58, 60, 61, 63, 66, 68, 69, 71
  Norton, 37, 38, 39, 40
  Rossini, 213, 217
  Stone, 144
Expectations, 12, 22, 252, 256, 257
  familial, 19, 20, 21, 243–248, 254
    Duncan, 244
    Field, 242
    Jackson, 235
    Monaco, 244
    Norton, 48, 232
    Rossini, 226, 245
    Stone, 140
  Lang, 66
  Rossini, 223
  self, 244
    Duncan, 244
    Field, 245
    Jackson, 245
    Monaco, 244
    Norton, 245
    Stone, 245

Family, see Carrier, occupational, as contingency of; Expectations, familial

Goal, see also Rewards; Satisfactions; Values
  Duncan, 83
  Field, 161, 163–166, 169, 172
  Jackson, 179, 191, 192, 195, 196, 198, 235
  Monaco, 104–105, 236, 240
  Norton, 41
  Rossini, 207, 225